WINNACUNNET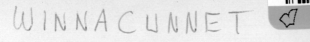

HIGH

SCHOOL

MATHEMATICS

DEPARTMENT

INTRODUCTION
TO
A Programmed Unit
in Modern Mathematics
PROBABILITY

BOYD EARL
Wilkes College
Wilkes Barre, Pennsylvania

and Program Editors

J. William Moore
Department of Education
Bucknell University
Lewisburg, Pennsylvania

Wendell I. Smith
Department of Psychology
Bucknell University
Lewisburg, Pennsylvania

McGRAW-HILL BOOK COMPANY, INC.
New York   San Francisco   Toronto   London

INTRODUCTION
TO
A Programmed Unit
in Modern Mathematics
PROBABILITY

Introduction to Probability

Library of Congress Catalog Card Number 63-14577

PREFACE

The discipline of probability theory originated in the seventeenth century, but it was not until the early nineteenth century that it was stated in a rigorous form. The science of probability seems to have developed rapidly only since 1920. It now occupies a prominent role in mathematics, and the uses of probability theory in areas of knowledge other than mathematics are increasing each year. A working knowledge of probability theory now is highly desirable for such diverse fields as biology, government, physics, sociology, economics, psychology, engineering, astronomy, and business administration.

This program is intended to introduce the student to the elementary concepts of probability, an important branch of mathematics. Further, because of some of its characteristics the subject matter of probability provides an excellent example of the use of sets and operations on sets; hence, this programmed unit of mathematics provides an excellent follow-up of an introduction to sets, e.g., McFadden's "Sets, Relations and Functions."[1]

In our treatment, the underlying ideas, the terminology, and the symbols used are in agreement with current practice, thus enabling the reader to continue a study of more advanced topics in probability. The probability of an event is defined in this text as an "ideal" relative frequency, enabling the discussion to include experiments for which the associated probabilities are not all equal. An informal dis-

[1]McGraw-Hill Book Company, Inc., New York, 1963.

cussion of simple experiments and events is used to lead to a definition
of a finite sample space and an event as a subset of the sample space.
In the discussion of events, complement of an event, conditioned
probability, independent events, mutually exclusive events, and
unions and intersections of events, (1) many simple examples with
the sample space constructed in detail are used, (2) theorems are
motivated by considering the events in terms of points in a sample
space and drawings are used extensively and (3), examples and problems are drawn from industry and several fields of knowledge.

The prerequisites for undertaking the study of probability as presented in this text are (1) two years of high school algebra and (2) a
knowledge of elementary set notation. For those who need a review
of elementary set theory, the concepts and results of set theory
requisite for this program are presented in Appendix A. A student,
upon completion of this unit, should have a clear idea of what can
be done with the techniques of probability and how to use these techniques on elementary problems. In short, he should be ready for a
course in nonmathematical statistics.

How to Use This Text

The material presented to you in this book is in the form of a program
for self-instruction. The subject matter covered in this program has
been broken into items or frames which permit you to learn efficiently
by studying and answering each step or frame separately.

The material in this text will be arranged in this manner:

---

1   To assist the student to learn mathematics more efficiently, a self-
instruction program provides units of new information in separate
frames. The information is broken down into separate question-
and-answer frames to make it easier for you to _____.

learn

2   Thus, each program item or ——————— provides new information which you will read carefully and for which you provide an
answer in writing. You will then be able to compare your answer
with the correct one given below each question frame.

frame

Usually, a student will find that the most effective way to study a
program for self-instruction is to read and study each frame carefully,
covering with a sheet of paper or an index card all the material on
the page below the frame which he is studying. It is best to study
definitions and formulas thoroughly as you go along so that you will
be able to acquire new information, step by step, as you go through
this self-instruction course.

After you have studied a question frame, write out your answer fully
on a separate piece of paper. Then, move the sheet of paper down
the page until you uncover the correct answer below the question
frame. Compare your answer with the answer given in the book. Later
topics in the program build on the material covered in earlier sections;
hence, you will find it desirable to study again each question on which
you make an error and to correct your first answer to that question.

Important Things to Remember

1. Always read the question frame first.
2. Write your answer out in complete form.
3. Compare your answer with the answer given in the answer frame
    of the text.
4. If you make an error, correct your answer before going on to the
    next question frame.
5. Learning is an *active* process. You must *do* something, i.e., you must
    respond to each question by writing your answer before you read
    the answer provided.

Review

To enable you to review the material in a programmed text, the author has made three provisions: (1) At regular intervals, *review frames* have been prepared. Each of these will be recognized by the symbol ● If you are unable to answer a review frame correctly, you should reread the teaching frames immediately preceding it to be certain that you have acquired the information before proceeding to the next set of teaching frames. (2) Self-test frames have been provided at the end of each part of the program. The answers to these test frames are given in Appendix B at the back of the book. It is advisable to work through each test frame before proceeding to the next part of the program. If you find that you are not able to answer most of the questions correctly, you should reread the teaching frames which contain the information needed to answer correctly any question upon which you have not succeeded. (3) An index to the teaching frames in which key concepts are presented is provided at the back of the book.

The Development and Testing
of a Self-instructional Program

Unlike nearly all textbooks, a self-instructional program is developed in a manner which maximizes its ability to teach. If the program has been properly constructed, the reader who *follows the directions* for its use carefully will be able to learn its contents with no other help.

Probability has been tested during its development on approximately two hundred students enrolled in high school and college courses in mathematics. In a sense, a programmed text is written by students— or, what is written in the final form is determined largely by the students upon whom the program was tested. Our "student authors" were drawn from several sources:

1. High school teachers of mathematics, enrolled in summer institute in modern mathematics

2. High school students enrolled in college preparatory programs
3. High school students enrolled in an enrichment program in which two hours were devoted to work with programmed mathematics once each week.
4. College students enrolled in a course in general mathematics

The mean gain in achievement for the total population upon whom the program was tested was 78 per cent. Approximately three-quarters of the students achieved scores above 80 per cent on the final examination. If the programmed unit is used as a supplement to regular classwork with a teacher, it is expected that the mean gain in achievement would be somewhat higher, since our testing program requires that the student learn the material without assistance from a teacher.

How much time will be required for a student to complete the total program? Our average students required approximately twenty hours; the above-average students required fourteen hours; the slower students required approximately thirty-two hours. These times include the completion of all review questions.

Acknowledgments

The original draft of the program was written by Boyd Earl; each of the succeeding revisions was prepared by Mary Haupt Smith with the assistance of William Hauck. Without their contribution, publication of the program would not have been possible.

We, also, are indebted to all the students and teachers around the country who volunteered to work through the program to improve its instructional value and to the McGraw-Hill Book Company, Inc. for its sincere efforts to test the program widely before its publication.

J. William Moore
Wendell I. Smith

References

Borel, Emile, "Probabilities and Life," Dover Publications, Inc., New York, 1962.

Clark, J. F., "Programmed Learning: My First Six Months," The Mathematics Teacher, vol. 55, pp. 579-581, 1962. Student achievement, teacher role, suggestions for use (very favorable).

Cohen, John, "Chance, Skill and Luck," Penguin Books, Inc., Baltimore, 1960.

Commission on Mathematics, "Introductory Probability and Statistical Inference," College Entrance Examination Board, New York, 1959, pp. 43-59, 71-87, 91-99, 103-104.

Dartmouth College Writing Group, "Modern Mathematical Methods and Models," vol. II, Mathematical Association of America, Ann Arbor, Mich., 1958, pp. 1-109.

Gnedenko, B. V., and A. Ya. Khinchin, "An Elementary Introduction to the Theory of Probability," 5th ed., Dover Publications, Inc., New York, 1962.

Hammond, K. R., and J. E. Householder, "Introduction to the Statistical Method," Alfred A. Knopf, Inc., New York, 1962, chap. 7.

Kemeny, J. G., J. L. Snell, and G. L. Thompson, "Introduction to Finite Mathematics," Prentice-Hall, Inc., Englewood Cliffs, N.J., 1957, chap. 4.

McGarvey, Paul, "Programmed Instruction in Ninth-grade Algebra," The Mathematics Teacher, vol. 55, pp. 576-578, 1962. Student reactions, suggestions for use teacher role (very favorable).

von Mises, Richard, "Probability, Statistics and Truth," rev. ed., The Macmillan Company, New York, 1957.

Mosteller, Frederick, R. E. K. Rourke, and G. B. Thomas, Jr., "Probability: A First Course," Addison-Wesley Publishing Company, Inc., Reading, Mass., 1961.

CONTENTS

INTRODUCTION
TO
PROBABILITY

A Programmed Unit
in Modern Mathematics

part i FREQUENCY AND RELATIVE FREQUENCY

In order to understand the concept of the "probability of an event," to be discussed later in this program, we introduce the concept of the "relative frequency of an event." Fortunately, relative frequency is not a new idea for you, since you have used it in a variety of places, possibly without calling it relative frequency. For example, the fact that team A has won four games while team B has won only two games during the current basketball season is subject to a different interpretation when we add that team B has played only three games while team A has played eight games. You could describe this situation by saying that team A has won $\frac{1}{2}$ of its games and team B has won $\frac{2}{3}$ of its games. These two numbers $\frac{1}{2}$ and $\frac{2}{3}$ are relative frequencies, the former being the relative frequency of winning for team A and the latter being the relative frequency of winning for team B.

In other situations you have seen and used relative frequencies. We shall introduce some new terminology and notation in order to discuss the concept with ease.

1 A light-bulb manufacturer performs the following experiment: From a set of new bulbs, one bulb is selected and inserted in a light socket which is turned on. If the bulb lights, a G (for good) is recorded. If the bulb does not light, a D (for defective) is recorded. Suppose this experiment has been performed for 10 different bulbs and the following results have been recorded: $GGGDGGGGGD$.
If $n(G)$ (read n of G) represents the number of good bulbs among the 10, $n(G) = 8$.
If $n(D)$ (read _____) represents the number of defective bulbs among the 10, $n(D) = \_\_$.

n of D,   2

2 A biologist performs the following experiment: A healthy mouse is injected with a vaccine and then exposed to disease X. If the mouse does not contract disease X, a W (for well) is recorded. If the mouse does contract disease X, an S (for sick) is recorded. Suppose this experiment has been performed in the same manner on 10 mice and the following results have been recorded: $SWWWSSWWWW$.
   (1) If $n(S)$ represents the number of mice of the 10 contracting disease X, $n(S) = $ ___.
   (2) If $n(W)$ represents the number of mice of the 10 not contracting the disease, $n(W) = $ ___.

   (1) 3   (2) 7

3 Consider the following experiment: A hat contains a number of balls: some red, some white, some blue, some yellow. A single ball is drawn from the hat, its color is observed, and the ball is replaced. Let R, W, B, and Y represent the colors. Suppose this experiment has been performed 12 times and the following recorded: $RRYRWWRWWYRR$.
   If $n(K)$ is the number of balls of the 12 drawn having color K, then
   (1) $n(R) = $ ___, (2) $n(W) = $ ___, (3) $n(B) = $ ___, (4) $n(Y) = $ ___.

   (1) 6   (2) 4   (3) 0   (4) 2

4 Consider the following experiment: A coin is tossed in the air and allowed to come to rest. It is observed whether a head H or a tail T has appeared. Suppose that this experiment has been performed 10 times with the following results: $HHTHTTHTHH$.
   (1) $n(H)$ represents _____, then $n(H) = 6$.
   (2) $n(T)$ represents _____, then $n(T) = 4$.

   (1) the number of times out of the 10 tosses which a head has appeared
   (2) the number of times out of the 10 tosses which a tail has appeared

5 Suppose a coin has been tossed 10 times and the following recorded: $TTHTHTTTTH$. Then (1) _____ = 3, (2) _____ = 7.

   (1) $n(H)$ (2) $n(T)$

6 Consider the following experiment: Joe Zilch runs the hundred-yard dash and his time (in seconds) is recorded. Suppose, during the last week, this experiment has been performed seven times with the following results: 10.7, 10.3, 11.0, 11.1, 10.2, 10.0, 10.3.

▼

Let A be the event that Joe's time for the hundred-yard dash is less than 11 seconds.
(1) If $n(A)$ is the number of times (out of the seven trials) which event A occurred, then $n(A) =$ ___.
(2) If B is the event that Joe's time is less than 10.8 seconds but greater than 10.1 seconds and $n(B)$ is the number of times in which event B has happened, $n(B) =$ ___.

---

(1) 5   (2) 4

---

7 In frames 1 to 6, we considered a certain experiment. The experiment was performed N times, and the results were observed and recorded. We then singled out some event A and counted the number of times event A occurred and indicated this number by $n(A)$. For example, a coin is tossed 11 times with the following results: *HHTHHHHTTHTH*. (1) $N =$ ___, (2) $n(H) =$ ___, (3) $n(T) =$ ___.

---

(1) 11   (2) 7   (3) 4

●8 Suppose an experiment has been performed N times and the results have been recorded. Let A be some specified event. Then out of the N trials of the experiment, A has occurred a certain number of times. Note that the number of times which A has occurred is indicated by $n(A)$ (read n of A). $n(A)$ does not indicate any sort of multiplication. The following is the result of tossing a coin eight times: *HTTHTTTH*. (1) $N =$ ___, (2) $n(H) =$ ___, (3) $n(T) =$ ___.

---

(1) 8   (2) 3   (3) 5

---

9 *Definition:* If an experiment is performed N times and out of these N results event A has occurred $n(A)$ times, the *relative frequency of event A* $= n(A)/N$.
For example, of the 10 babies born in the local hospital yesterday, the following results were recorded, where G represents girl and B represents boy: *BBGGBGGGBG*.
(1) If G is the event that a girl is born, $n(G) =$ ___.
(2) The relative frequency of event $G = n(G)/N =$ _____.

---

(1) 6   (2) $\frac{6}{10}$ (or 0.6 or $\frac{3}{5}$)

---

10 If an experiment is performed N times and event A occurs $n(A)$ times, then the relative frequency of event $A = n(A)/N$. The relative frequency of event A, then, is the ratio of the number of times event A occurs to the number of times event A is given the opportunity to occur.
Suppose the weights of 10 girl students from your school are as follows: 110, 150, 96, 112, 138, 116, 120, 100, 110, 115. If A

▼

is the event that a weight is less than 120, then for this experiment,
(1) $N = $___, **(2)** $n(A) = $___, **(3)** relative frequency of $A = n(A)/N = $___.

(1)   10   **(2)**   7   **(3)** $\frac{7}{10}$

●**11** The notation we have been using is as follows:
   (1)   The number of times an experiment has been performed is in-
          dicated by ___.
   (2)   The number of times event A has occurred is indicated by ___.
   (3)   The relative frequency of event A is given by _____.

(1) N **(2)** $n(A)$ **(3)** $n(A)/N$

12 One hundred overweight people were placed on a special diet for
   one month and their weights recorded before and after the month.
   If a person lost 7 pounds or more, an S was recorded, and if a person did not lose 7 pounds or more, an F was recorded. Out of the
   hundred people in the experiment, 63 S's occurred and 37 F's
   occurred.
   (1) ___ = 100   **(2)** ___ = 63   **(3)** ___ = 37
   (4) The _____ of event $S = \frac{63}{100}$
   (5) The _____ of event $F = \frac{37}{100}$

(1) N **(2)** $n(S)$ **(3)** $n(F)$ **(4)** relative frequency
(5) relative frequency

13 A coin is tossed five times with the following results: *HHTHH*.
   (1) $N = $___,   **(2)** $n(H) = $___,   **(3)** relative frequency of $H = $___.

(1) 5   **(2)** 4   **(3)** $\frac{4}{5}$

14 A radio manufacturer tests the radios coming out of the factory.
   If the radio works, an S is recorded; if the radio fails to work, an
   F is recorded. During the last hour, the following results were
   obtained: *SSSSSSSSSSSSSSSSS*.
   (1) $N = $___   **(2)** $n(S) = $___   **(3)** $n(F) = $___
   (4) Relative frequency of $S = $___
   (5) Relative frequency of $F = $___

(1) 17   **(2)** 17   **(3)** 0   **(4)** $\frac{17}{17} = 1$ **(5)** $\frac{0}{17} = 0$

15 A coin was tossed 60 times, and the relative frequency of H was $\frac{5}{12}$.
   To find the number of times H appeared,
   Relative frequency of $H = \frac{n(H)}{N}$ $\frac{5}{12} = \frac{n(H)}{60}$ $\therefore$ $n(H) = $___.

25   *Note:* $\frac{5}{12} = \frac{n(H)}{60}$
      $\frac{5}{12} \times 60 = n(H)$
      $n(H) = 25$

●**16** A coin was tossed 150 times and the relative frequency of H was $\frac{8}{15}$. Relative frequency of $H = n(H)/N$. Find $n(H)$.

80   *Note:* Relative frequency of $H = \frac{n(H)}{N}$

$$\frac{8}{15} = \frac{n(H)}{150}$$

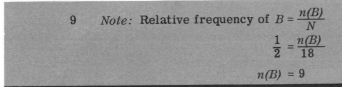

$$\cancel{1,200 = 15n(H)}$$ leave, it's correct

$$n(H) = 80$$

17 There were 18 births at the local hospital yesterday. B is the event of the birth of a boy. The relative frequency of event B was $\frac{1}{2}$. How many of the 18 babies were boys?

9   *Note:* Relative frequency of $B = \frac{n(B)}{N}$

$$\frac{1}{2} = \frac{n(B)}{18}$$

$$n(B) = 9$$

18 A biologist tested a vaccine on 60 mice. After exposure to the disease, if a mouse did not get the disease, an S (for success) was recorded, and if the mouse did get the disease, an F (for failure) was recorded. The relative frequency of S was 0.3 $\left(\frac{3}{10}\right)$. How many of the 60 mice did not get the disease?

Relative frequency of $S = \frac{n(S)}{N}$ $0.3 = \frac{n(S)}{60}$ $n(S) = 18$

19 A coin was tossed five times, and the *relative frequency* of H was 1. How many times did a head appear?

five times   *Note:* Relative frequency of $H = \frac{n(H)}{N}$

$$1 = \frac{n(H)}{5}$$

$$\therefore\ n(H) = 5$$

20 In doing this section of the program, student A has kept a record of his errors. If E represents the event of making an error, the relative frequency of E for the first 10 frames was 0. How many errors did student A make in the first 10 frames?

0   *Note:* Relative frequency of $E = \frac{n(E)}{N}$

$$0 = \frac{n(E)}{10}$$

$$n(E) = 0$$

21 Suppose an experiment has been performed N times and the relative frequency of event A is 0.6. Roughly speaking, this means that event A has occurred $\frac{6}{10}$ of the time.

▼

If the relative frequency of H is 0.48 when a coin has been tossed in an experiment, we know that H has appeared $\frac{48}{100}$ of the time. Thus, if, in this experiment, the coin was tossed 500 times, $n(H) =$ ___.

240   *Note:* Relative frequency of $H = \dfrac{n(H)}{N}$

$$0.48 = \dfrac{n(H)}{500}$$
$$n(H) = 240$$

22 If a coin is tossed 100 times, the *greatest* number of times a head could possibly occur is ___.

100

●**23** If an experiment is performed N times, the greatest number of times event A could occur would be ___.

N

24 In an experiment testing light bulbs, 10 bulbs were tested with the following results (recall, G means good, and D means defective): *GGGGGGGGGG.* In this experiment, (1) $N =$ ___,   (2) $n(G) =$ ___, (3) relative frequency of $G =$ _____.

(1) 10   (2) 10   (3) $\frac{10}{10} = 1$

25 (1) If an experiment is performed N times, the greatest possible value of $n(A)$ for any event A is ___.
(2) In this case, the relative frequency of event $A =$ ___.

(1) N (2) 1

26 If the relative frequency of event A is 1, we know that event A occurred every time the experiment was performed. Thus, if a coin was tossed seven times and the relative frequency of event H was 1, (1) H appeared _____ times; that is, (2) $n(H) =$ ___.

(1) seven   (2) 7

●**27** The largest possible value for the relative frequency of event A is ___. In this case, we know that the event A occurred every time that the experiment was performed.

1

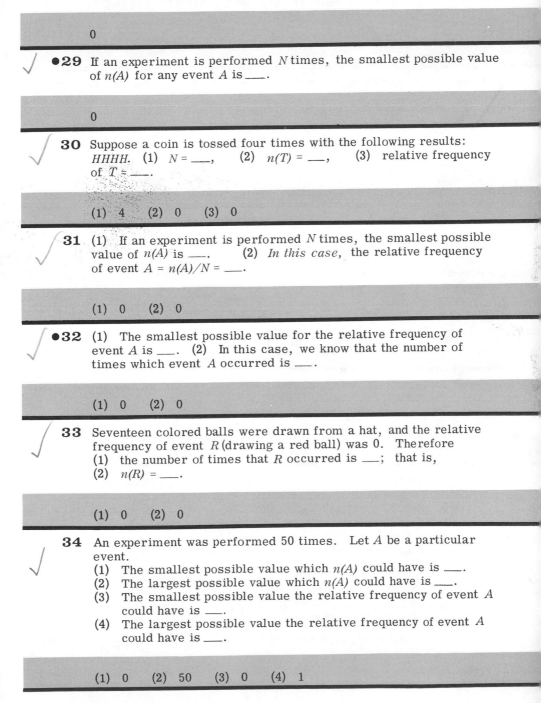

28 If a coin is tossed 10 times, and A is the occurrence of a head, the *smallest* possible value of $n(A)$ is ___.

0

●29 If an experiment is performed N times, the smallest possible value of $n(A)$ for any event A is ___.

0

30 Suppose a coin is tossed four times with the following results: $HHHH$. (1) $N =$ ___,   (2) $n(T) =$ ___,   (3) relative frequency of $T =$ ___.

(1) 4   (2) 0   (3) 0

31 (1) If an experiment is performed N times, the smallest possible value of $n(A)$ is ___.   (2) *In this case,* the relative frequency of event $A = n(A)/N =$ ___.

(1) 0   (2) 0

●32 (1) The smallest possible value for the relative frequency of event A is ___.   (2) In this case, we know that the number of times which event A occurred is ___.

(1) 0   (2) 0

33 Seventeen colored balls were drawn from a hat, and the relative frequency of event R (drawing a red ball) was 0. Therefore (1) the number of times that R occurred is ___; that is, (2) $n(R) =$ ___.

(1) 0   (2) 0

34 An experiment was performed 50 times. Let A be a particular event.
(1) The smallest possible value which $n(A)$ could have is ___.
(2) The largest possible value which $n(A)$ could have is ___.
(3) The smallest possible value the relative frequency of event A could have is ___.
(4) The largest possible value the relative frequency of event A could have is ___.

(1) 0   (2) 50   (3) 0   (4) 1

35 As a result of frames 22 to 34, we see that when an experiment is performed N times there are restrictions for $n(A)$ and consequently for the relative frequency of A. In fact (1) ___ $\leq n(A) \leq$ ___, and (2) ___ $\leq$ relative frequency of $A \leq$ ___.

(1) 0, N (2) 0,   1

36 If an experiment is performed 100 times and the relative frequency of event A is 1,

Relative frequency of $A = \dfrac{n(A)}{N}$

$$\therefore 1 = \frac{n(A)}{100}$$

$$\therefore n(A) = \underline{\quad}$$

100

37 If an experiment is performed 50 times and the relative frequency of event A is 0, then $n(A) =$ ___.

0

38 If an experiment was performed 50 times and the relative frequency of event A is $\frac{1}{5}$, then $n(A) =$ ___.

10

39 An experiment was performed N times.
The relative frequency of event $A = 0$. $n(A) =$ ___
The relative frequency of event $D = 1$. $n(D) =$ ___

0, N

40 A pair of dice is rolled, and the sum of the dots is recorded. This experiment is performed 10 times with the following results:
5, 7, 2, 6, 7, 11, 10, 5, 8, 8.
Let A be the event the sum of the dots is 6.
Let B be the event the sum of the dots is 4.
Let C be the event the sum of the dots is an odd number.
$N = 10$
Then: (1) $n(A) =$ ___ (2) $n(B) =$ ___ (3) $n(C) =$ ___
(4) Relative frequency of $A =$ ___
(5) Relative frequency of $B =$ ___
(6) Relative frequency of $C =$ ___

(1) 1,   (2) 0,   (3) 5,   (4) $\frac{1}{10}$,   (5) $\frac{0}{10}$ or 0,
(6) $\frac{5}{10}$ or $\frac{1}{2}$

41 Mrs. Zilch has kept a record of the last 10 days, recording if Jill Zilch has had a date D or not N. The following resulted: *DDDNDDDDDD*. Then, if D is that Jill had a date, the relative frequency of D = ___.

Jill is a tramp!

$\frac{9}{10}$

42 Mrs. Zilch has also kept a record of Joe's dating. If Mrs. Zilch says, "During the past 25 days, if D is the event that Joe has had a date, then the relative frequency of D is $\frac{3}{5}$." How many nights out of the last 25 has Joe had a date?

Take a cold shower, Joe!

15

43 If an experiment is performed N times and the relative frequency of event Y is 0, then $n(Y)$ = ___.

0

44 If an experiment was performed N times and the relative frequency of event X is 1, then $n(X)$ = ___.

N

45 A die is rolled 12 times, and the following results are recorded: 3, 5, 1, 3, 4, 2, 1, 5, 6, 5, 1, 2.
(1) N = ___.
(2) If A is the event that an odd number appears, $n(A)$ = ___.
(3) The relative frequency of A = ___.

(1) 12   (2) 8   (3) $\frac{8}{12}$ or $\frac{2}{3}$

46 A die is rolled and the dots on the upper face are counted. This experiment is performed 10 times with the following results: 3, 5, 6, 5, 2, 4, 2, 4, 6, 2.
(1) N = ___   (2) $n(2)$ = ___   (3) $n(3)$ = ___
(4) Relative frequency of a 2 = ___
(5) Relative frequency of a 3 = ___

(1) 10
(2) 3
(3) 1
(4) $\frac{3}{10}$
(5) $\frac{1}{10}$

47 An experiment was performed 150 times and event A occurred 37 times. For this experiment, supply the correct notation:
(1) ___ = 150   (2) ___ = 37   (3) _____ of $A = \frac{37}{150}$

(1) N (2) $n(A)$ (3) relative frequency

48 The local basketball team has played 15 games. Of the 15, they have won 6 and lost 9. If W is the event of winning a game and L is the event of losing a game,
(1) $n(W) =$___   (2) $n(L) =$___   (3) $N =$___
(4) Relative frequency of $W =$ _____
(5) Relative frequency of $L =$ _____

(1) 6   (2) 9   (3) 15   (4) $\frac{6}{15}$ or $\frac{2}{5}$ or 0.4
(5) $\frac{9}{15}$ or $\frac{3}{5}$ or 0.6

49 In a botany class, 20 seeds of a certain type were planted and tested under the same conditions. If a seed grew, an S (for success) was recorded. If a seed failed to grow, an F (for failure) was recorded. The following results were tabulated:
$SSFSSSSSSSFSSSFSFSSSS$.
Then: (1) relative frequency of $S =$ ___
      (2) relative frequency of $F =$ ___

(1) $\frac{16}{20}$ (or $\frac{4}{5}$)   (2) $\frac{4}{20}$ (or $\frac{1}{5}$)

50 A botanist performed the following experiment. Three seeds of a certain type were planted, and the number of seeds which grew were recorded. This experiment was performed 20 times under the same conditions with the following results (actually he planted 20 rows with three seeds in each, and did the 20 experiments at once): 3, 3, 0, 2, 3, 3, 1, 2, 3, 3, 3, 2, 2, 3, 2, 1, 2, 3, 3, 3
Let A be the event that exactly 3 seeds of the 3 planted grew.
Let B be the event that exactly 2 seeds of the 3 planted grew.
Let C be the event that exactly 1 seed of the 3 planted grew.
Let D be the event that exactly 0 seeds of the 3 planted grew.
Then: (1) relative frequency of $A =$ ___
      (2) relative frequency of $B =$ ___
      (3) relative frequency of $C =$ ___
      (4) relative frequency of $D =$ ___

(1) $\frac{11}{20}$ (2) $\frac{6}{20}$ or $\frac{3}{10}$ (3) $\frac{2}{20}$ or $\frac{1}{10}$ (4) $\frac{1}{20}$

51 A die is tossed and the number of dots are recorded. This experiment is performed 15 times with the following results:
2, 3, 6, 6, 5, 1, 3, 4, 2, 1, 6, 5, 1, 4, 3
Let A be the event that an even number appeared.
Let B be the event that a 3 appeared.

▼

(1) The relative frequency of A = ___
(2) The relative frequency of B = ___

---

(1) $\frac{7}{15}$ (2) $\frac{3}{15}$ or $\frac{1}{5}$

---

52 A hat contains some red balls, some white balls, and some blue balls. *Two* balls are drawn from the hat, their color is noted, and they are then returned to the hat. This experiment is performed 10 times with the following results:
RW, WW, BR, WB, WW, RR, RW, BR, RW, BB
Let A be the event that both balls were white.
Let B be the event that at least one ball is blue.
(1) The relative frequency of A = ___
(2) The relative frequency of B = ___

---

(1) $\frac{2}{10}$ or $\frac{1}{5}$ (2) $\frac{4}{10}$ or $\frac{2}{5}$

---

53 Suppose a die is rolled six times with these results:
3, 5, 6, 1, 4, 2
(1) If event A is that an odd number appears,

   x x   x
   3, 5, 6, 1, 4, 2, then $n(A)$ = ___.

(2) If event B is that a number less than 4 appears,
   3, 5, 6, 1, 4, 2, then $n(B)$ = ___.
   x   x   x

To find $n(A$ or $B)$ we want to find the number of times event A *only* occurred, the number of times event B *only* occurred, and also the number of times in which both A and B occurred *together*. In other words, *or* will mean or/and.

  [x] [x]   [x]   [ ] Event A
  3 , 5 , 6 , 1 , 4 , 2
  [x] [ ]   [x]   [x] Event B
(3) Then $n(A$ or $B)$ = ___

---

(1) 3
(2) 3
(3) 4

---

54 A die is tossed eight times with the following results:
5, 1, 6, 6, 4, 2, 1, 2,
(1) Let A be the event that an even number appears. $n(A)$ = _5_.
(2) Let B be the event that a number less than 3 appears.
  $n(B)$ = _4_.
(3) Let A or B be the event that either A and/or B appear.

▼

5, | 1 | , | x 6 | , | x 6 | , | x 4 | , | x 2 | , | 1 | , | x 2 | Event A / Event B

$n(A \text{ or } B) = 7$

(1) 5   (2) 4   (3) 7

55 A die is tossed 10 times with the following results:
6, 1, 1, 2, 5, 3, 5, 1, 2, 4
(1) Let A be the event that an even number appears. $n(A) =$ ___
(2) Let B be the event that a number greater than 4 appears. $n(B) =$ ___
(3) Let A or B be the event that either A and/or B appear.

| x 6 | , 1 , 1 , | x 2 | , | 5 | , 3 , | 5 | , 1 , | x 2 | , | x 4 | Event A / Event B

$n(A \text{ or } B) =$ ___
(4) Let A and B be the event that both A and B appear.
6, 1, 1, 2, 5, 3, 5, 1, 2, 4 Event A / Event B
$n(A \text{ and } B) =$ ___

(1) 4   (2) 3   (3) 6   (4) 1

●**56** In rolling a die, event A is that an odd number appears; event B is that a number less than 4 appears. If a die is rolled 10 times with the following results: 2, 4, 2, 3, 1, 6, 5, 5, 1, 4
(1) $n(A) =$ ___ (2) $n(B) =$ ___ (3) $n(A \text{ or } B) =$ ___ (4) $n(A \text{ and } B) =$

(1) 5   (2) 5   (3) 7   (4) 3

57 The following is a record of the births at the local hospital last week, where B represents a boy and G represents a girl:
BBGGGBGGBGGBGBBG
(1) $n(B) =$ ___ (2) $n(G) =$ ___ (3) $n(B \text{ or } G) = N$ (4) $N = 16$
(5) Relative frequency of B = ___
(6) Relative frequency of G = ___
(7) Relative frequency of (B or G) = ___

(1) 7   (2) 9   (3) 16   (4) 16   (5) $\frac{7}{16}$ (6) $\frac{9}{16}$ (7) $\frac{16}{16}$

58 If an experiment is performed N times, (1) the number of times which event A occurs is indicated by ___. (2) The relative frequency of event A is indicated by ___.

(1) $n(A)$ (2) $\frac{n(A)}{N}$

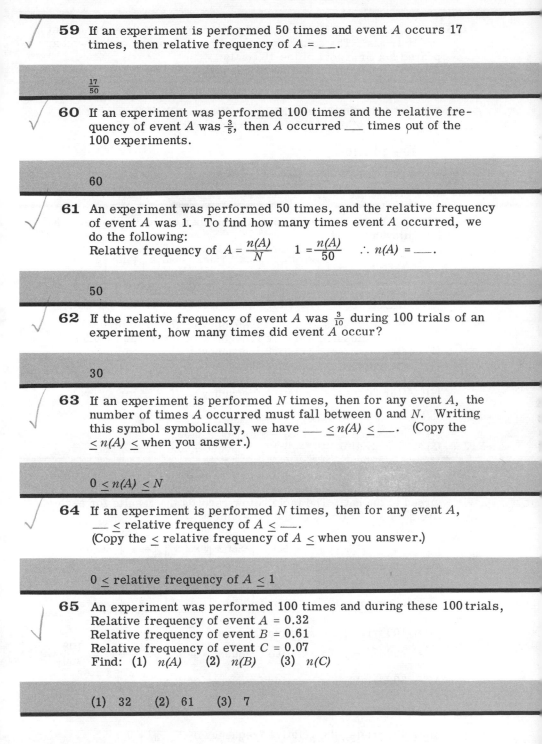

59 If an experiment is performed 50 times and event A occurs 17 times, then relative frequency of A = ___.

$\frac{17}{50}$

60 If an experiment was performed 100 times and the relative frequency of event A was $\frac{3}{5}$, then A occurred ___ times out of the 100 experiments.

60

61 An experiment was performed 50 times, and the relative frequency of event A was 1. To find how many times event A occurred, we do the following:

Relative frequency of $A = \dfrac{n(A)}{N}$ $1 = \dfrac{n(A)}{50}$ $\therefore\ n(A) = $ ___.

50

62 If the relative frequency of event A was $\frac{3}{10}$ during 100 trials of an experiment, how many times did event A occur?

30

63 If an experiment is performed N times, then for any event A, the number of times A occurred must fall between 0 and N. Writing this symbol symbolically, we have ___ $\leq n(A) \leq$ ___. (Copy the $\leq n(A) \leq$ when you answer.)

$0 \leq n(A) \leq N$

64 If an experiment is performed N times, then for any event A, ___ $\leq$ relative frequency of $A \leq$ ___.
(Copy the $\leq$ relative frequency of $A \leq$ when you answer.)

$0 \leq$ relative frequency of $A \leq 1$

65 An experiment was performed 100 times and during these 100 trials,
Relative frequency of event A = 0.32
Relative frequency of event B = 0.61
Relative frequency of event C = 0.07
Find: (1) $n(A)$ (2) $n(B)$ (3) $n(C)$

(1) 32   (2) 61   (3) 7

66 A coin was tossed 10 times, and a head appeared three times out of the 10 trials. The coin was tossed 10 more times, and a head appeared six times out of the 10 trials.

After 10 trials, the relative frequency of $H = \frac{3}{10} = 0.3$

After 20 trials, the relative frequency of $H = \frac{3 + 6}{10 + 10} = \frac{9}{20} = 0.45$

Suppose the coin is tossed 10 more times with H appearing five times; then, after 30 trials, the relative frequency of

$$H = \frac{3 + 6 + 5}{10 + 10 + 10} = \text{\_\_\_\_\_}.$$

$\frac{14}{30}$ or about 0.47

67 After each 10 tosses of a coin, the number of heads was recorded in the following chart

Tosses	First 10	Second 10	Third 10	Fourth 10	Fifth 10	Sixth 10
Number of H ...	6	5	6	4	6	5

After 10 tosses, relative frequency of $H = 6/10$ or 0.6
After 20 tosses, relative frequency of $H = 11/20$ or 0.55

(1) After 30 tosses, relative frequency of $H = $ ___ or ___
(2) After 40 tosses, relative frequency of $H = $ ___ or ___
(3) After 50 tosses, relative frequency of $H = $ ___ or ___
(4) After 60 tosses, relative frequency of $H = $ ___ or ___

(1) $\frac{17}{30}$ or about 0.57 (2) $\frac{21}{40}$ or about 0.52
(3) $\frac{27}{50}$ or about 0.54 (4) $\frac{32}{60}$ or about 0.53

68 A hat contains eight red balls, two white balls, and five blue balls. A ball is drawn from the hat, its color is noted, and the ball is returned to the hat. The table below records the results for each of five sets of 100 trials of the experiment.

	Set 1	Set 2	Set 3	Set 4	Set 5
Number of R	56	52	50	55	56
Number of W	13	15	16	13	10
Number of B	31	33	34	32	34

After 100 trials, the relative frequency of $R = \frac{56}{100} = 0.56$

After 200 trials, the relative frequency of $R = \frac{52 + 56}{100 + 100} = \frac{108}{200} = 0.54$

After 300 trials, the relative frequency of $R = \frac{50 + 52 + 56}{100 + 100 + 100} = \frac{158}{300} = 0.53$

After 400 trials, the relative frequency of $R = \frac{213}{400} = 0.53$

▼

We shall put these relative frequencies in a table.

After	100 trials	200 trials	300 trials	400 trials	500 trials
Relative frequency of R	0.56	0.54	0.53	0.53	
Relative frequency of W					
Relative frequency of B					

Complete the table.

After	100 trials	200 trials	300 trials	400 trials	500 trials
Relative frequency of R	0.56	0.54	0.53	0.53	0.54
Relative frequency of W	0.13	0.14	0.15	0.14	0.13
Relative frequency of B	0.31	0.32	0.33	0.325	0.33

●**69** After 5,000 tosses of a coin, the relative frequency of H is 0.5062. (1) How many heads appeared during the *first 5,000* tosses? During the *next 1,000* tosses, H appeared 503 times. (2) Find the relative frequency of H after the 6,000 tosses.

(1) $0.5062 = \frac{n(H)}{5,000}$ $n(H) = 2,531$

(2) After 6,000, relative frequency of $H = 3,034/6,000 = 0.5057$

70 Joe Zilch tossed a coin 100 times, and H appeared 40 times. During the next 500 tosses, H appeared 247 times.
(1) Find the relative frequency of H after 100 tosses.
(2) Find the relative frequency of H after 600 tosses.

(1) 0.4   (2) $\frac{287}{600} = 0.48$

71 For certain types of experiments, as N becomes large, the relative frequency of an event A will not vary appreciably from one large set of trials to another. For example, it has been verified by experiment, and to most people it is intuitively obvious, that for *a large number of* tosses of a coin, the relative frequency of H will be reasonably close to ___.

$\frac{1}{2}$

72 After all, even though there is much chance governing our lives, we have come to expect a certain amount of regularity. If we were not fairly certain that the relative frequency of 1,000-inch rainstorms is close to 0 and that this relative frequency will not change very much, then arks would be selling well.

▼

Similarly, if we were not sure that the relative frequency of walking across a street safely would remain close to 1, the number of trials would become very small.
One of the reasons that going over the Niagara Falls in a barrel has not caught on as a popular sport is that the relative frequency of success is close to 0 and is likely to remain so. During the last 1,000 flights of the Trans-Guavian Airline, the relative frequency of crashes has been 0.98. Would you like to be a stewardess or engineer for the next 100 flights?

No, not unless you like to live dangerously.

73 Toss a coin 50 times and record the number of heads which appear.

There is no "correct" answer other than the number of heads you got.
If your answer is less than 18 or greater than 32, however, you have just seen a relatively unusual event, since if the coin is honest and the experiment is performed honestly, about 95 per cent of the time, H will appear somewhere between 18 and 32 times out of 50 tosses.

74 So we see that for some experiments, when N is large, the relative frequency of event A will not vary appreciably from one large set of experiments to another. Moreover, it has been found that as an experiment is performed under essentially the same conditions, as N *becomes very large,* the relative frequency of event A "settles down" and ultimately ranges over a rather restrictive set of values. It would be highly unusual to take a given die, toss it 1,000 times, find the relative frequency of the appearance of the 2 to be 0.17, and then, after another 1,000 tosses of the same die, find that the relative frequency of the appearance of the 2 had become 0.4. In fact, let us see what must happen to change the relative frequency this much.
(1) If after 1,000 tosses, relative frequency of 2 = 0.17, $n(2)$ = ___.
(2) If after 2,000 tosses, relative frequency of 2 = 0.4, $n(2)$ = ___.

(1) 170   (2) 800

75 If after 1,000 tosses of a die, the relative frequency of 2 = 0.17, the 2 has appeared 170 times. If after 2,000 tosses of a die, the relative frequency of 2 = 0.4, the 2 has appeared 800 times. Therefore, during the second 1,000 tosses, 2 would have had to appear ___ times. $800 - 170$

630

Self-test I

1 A coin has been tossed with the following results: *HHTTTHTHHH*.
(1) $N = \underline{10}$ (2) $n(H) = \underline{6}$ (3) $n(T) = \underline{4}$

2 A coin was tossed 200 times, and the relative frequency of *H*
was $\frac{3}{5}$. (1) Find $n(H)$.   (2) Find $N(T)$.
$\frac{3}{5} * 200 = 120$ 80

3 An experiment was performed 100 times. Let *A* be a particular
event. (1) The smallest possible value which $n(A)$ could have
is $\underline{0}$. Therefore (2) the smallest possible value the relative
frequency of event *A* could have is $\underline{0}$. (3) The largest possible
value which $n(A)$ could have is $\underline{100}$. Therefore (4) the largest
possible value the relative frequency of event *A* could have is $\underline{1}$.

4 Suppose a die is tossed 10 times with the following results:
1, 6, 6, 5, 2, 4, 2, 6, 5, 3.
Let *A* be the event that an odd number appears.
Let *B* be the event that a number greater than 3 appears.
(1) $N = \underline{10}$ (2) $n(A) = \underline{4}$ (3) $n(B) = \underline{6}$
(4) $n(A \text{ or } B) = \underline{8}$ (5) $n(A \text{ and } B) \underline{2}$

5 A box contained one red ball *R* and one white ball *W*. A ball was
drawn from the box, its color was noted, and the ball returned to
the box. In the first 100 draws, *R* appeared 60 times. During
the next 400 draws, *R* appeared an additional 190 times.
(1) Find the relative frequency of *R* after 100 draws. $.6$
(2) Find the relative frequency of *R* after 500 draws. $.5$

6 A coin is tossed 451 times. The relative frequency for heads was
found to be 0.55. If the coin were tossed 756 more times, the
relative frequency for heads would most likely be which of the
following: 0.35; 0.59; 0.78; (0.53?)

$= \frac{n(\checkmark)}{2000} = .4$ 800
$.4$ $\underline{170}$

part ii SAMPLE SPACES AND EVENTS

So "Relative Frequency", $\dfrac{n(A)}{N}$, is a representation of actual or "what if" measurements. As $N \to \infty$,

$$\dfrac{n(A)}{N} \to P(A) \quad or \quad in \; Cecil \; Holmespeak,$$

$$\underset{N \to \infty}{LIMIT} \; \dfrac{n(A)}{N} = P(A)$$

It is essential to remember that we are dealing with experiments which are capable of being performed a large number of times under essentially the same conditions. If, for example, in one of the experiments of growth of seeds mentioned earlier, we were to vary appreciably the moisture, sunlight, soil, etc., from one experiment to another, the relative frequency of S (success) would probably vary appreciably. If, however, the experiment has been performed 1,000 times under essentially the same conditions with relative frequency of $S = 0.8$; then, after 2,000 trials, we would expect the relative frequency of S to be close to 0.8.

---

76 So we assume that, with certain experiments, there is some "ideal" number which we are approximating when computing the relative frequency of event A. *This ideal number is called the probability of A and is denoted by P(A).*
We assume that $P(A)$ is a number such that, as the number of trials of the experiment becomes large, the relative frequency of event A will ultimately get closer and closer to $P(A)$. If A is the event of throwing a 7 with a pair of dice, and we say that $P(A) = \frac{1}{6}$, we mean that as the number of trials of throwing a pair of dice becomes large, we expect the relative frequency of event A will become very close to ___.

$\frac{1}{6}$

77 So, in a given experiment, if we refer to the *probability of event A,*
P(A), we are referring to a(n) (1) _____ to which, after a
large number of trials of the experiment, we expect the relative
frequency of event *A* to be near. Thus, if we say that the probability of tossing a 7 with a pair of dice is $\frac{1}{6}$, we mean that, after a
large number of tosses, the relative frequency of 7 will be close
to (2) ___.

(1) ideal number   (2) $\frac{1}{6}$

78 The "ideal" number to which, after a large number of trials of an
experiment, we expect the relative frequency of an event *A* to be
near is called the (1) _____ of event *A* and is designated by *P(A).*
If *H* is the event that a coin turns up heads, by $P(H) = \frac{1}{2}$ we mean
that in tossing a coin a large number of times, we expect the relative frequency of *H* to be close to $\frac{1}{2}$. We do not mean that, if the
coin is tossed 10 times, heads cannot appear 10 times, for example,
but that the more likely *number* of times for *H* to appear would be
(2) ___.

(1) probability   (2) five

comment

Suppose an experiment consists of tossing 10,000 coins and event *A*
is that 5,100 or more heads appear. The task of finding the relative frequency of event *A* for a large number of trials of the experiment would be enormous. In addition, it would seem that the value
we are trying to estimate *P(A)* will depend completely on a simpler
probability—the probability of *H* on a single toss of a coin. This
problem and others similar to it lead us to try to develop a mathematical model for such experiments in order to get techniques for
computing probabilities of complicated events, assuming that we
know or can estimate probabilities of simple events.

In building such a model, we will be guided by specific examples of
experiments. One must always be careful, however, in trying to
apply a model to a specific situation, to be sure that the assumptions made in constructing the model are reasonably satisfied by
the experiment under consideration. For example, the assumptions
used to develop plane geometry you have studied are reasonably
satisfied when applying the geometry to a situation on a fairly flat
field. But the assumptions are not reasonably satisfied by a situation on a sphere, and one would not expect to apply theorems of
plane geometry to figures drawn on a sphere.

79 Consider the following experiment. A person suffering from hay fever is injected with serum X. After 24 hours, it is determined if his condition has improved I, remained the same S, or become worse W. This experiment was performed on 100 persons with the following results:

Condition	I	S	W
Number of persons	38	42	20

Find (1) the relative frequency of I, (2) the relative frequency of S, (3) the relative frequency of W. (4) The sum of the relative frequencies would be $\frac{38}{100} + \frac{42}{100} + \frac{20}{100} =$ ___.

(1) $\frac{38}{100}$ (2) $\frac{42}{100}$ (3) $\frac{20}{100}$ (4) $\frac{100}{100}$ or 1

●80 Consider another simple experiment. From a set of registered Republicans and Democrats we select a person, ask him his party, and ask whether he approves of the handling of foreign affairs by the present administration. Let us indicate Republicans by R, Democrats by D, approves by Y (yes), disapproves by N (no), or has no opinion by U (undecided). 200 trials of this experiment produced the following results:

	Y	N	U
R	41	32	14
D	80	23	10

Find the relative frequency of (1) RY, (2) RN, (3) RU, (4) DY, (5) DN, (6) DU. (7) What is the sum of the relative frequencies?

(1) $\frac{41}{200}$ (2) $\frac{32}{200}$ (3) $\frac{14}{200}$ (4) $\frac{80}{200}$ (5) $\frac{23}{100}$ (6) $\frac{10}{200}$ (7) 1

81 Recall from our previous work. If an experiment is performed N times, then for any event A, ___ $\leq n(A) \leq$ ___
(Copy the $\leq n(A) \leq$ when you answer.)

$0 \leq n(A) \leq N$

82 Therefore, in a given experiment, for any event A,
___ $\leq$ relative frequency of $A \leq$ ___
(Copy the $\leq$ relative frequency of $A \leq$ when you answer.)

$0 \leq$ relative frequency of $A \leq 1$

83 Suppose records of a local hospital show that of the last 100 children born there, 47 were girls and 53 were boys.
(1) Relative frequency of $G =$ ___ $\frac{n(G)}{N} = \frac{47}{100}$

▼

(2) Relative frequency of $B =$ ___
(3) The sum of the relative frequencies = ___

(1) $\frac{47}{100}$ (2) $\frac{53}{100}$ (3) 1

84 So we have the following information to guide us: If we perform an experiment N times and consider the relative frequencies of the various events, we find:
(1) ___ $<$ relative frequency of any event $<$ ___
(2) The sum of the relative frequencies of the various events = ___
(Copy the $\leq$ relative frequency of any event $\leq$ when you answer.)

(1) $0 \leq$ relative frequency of any event ≤ 1
(2) 1

85 For example, suppose a card is drawn from an ordinary deck of cards, its suit recorded, and the card replaced. 100 trials of this experiment resulted as follows: $23\,H$ $27\,C$ $31\,D$ $19\,S$
where H, C, D, and S represent hearts, clubs, diamonds, spades.
(1) Relative frequency of $H =$ ___
(2) Relative frequency of $C =$ ___
(3) Relative frequency of $D =$ ___
(4) Relative frequency of $S =$ ___
(5) The sum of the relative frequencies = ___

(1) $\frac{23}{100}$ (2) $\frac{27}{100}$ (3) $\frac{31}{100}$ (4) $\frac{19}{100}$ (5) 1

86 Of course, in order that the sum of the relative frequencies equal 1, the events must be such that each trial of the experiment must result in exactly one of the events. After all, suppose 10 tosses of a die result in the following: 4, 6, 1, 2, 2, 5, 1, 6, 5, 2. Suppose further that A is the event that an even number appears, B is the event that a number less than 4 appears.
(1) Relative frequency of $A =$ ___
(2) Relative frequency of $B =$ ___
(3) Is the sum of the relative frequencies 1?
The sum of the relative frequencies of events such as these would be 1 only by accident, since some experiments result in neither A or B and some experiments result in both A and B.

(1) $\frac{6}{10}$ (2) $\frac{5}{10}$ (3) no

87 So we shall be concerned with building a model of an experiment which can be performed a large number of times under essentially the same conditions, and at least in the beginning of our study, we shall consider outcomes such that any single trial of the experiment can result in *one and only one* of these outcomes. Then we have that

▼

(1) ___ $\leq$ relative frequency of any outcome $\leq$ ___
(2) The sum of the relative frequencies = ___
Copy the $\leq$ relative frequency of any outcome $\leq$ when you answer.

(1) $0 \leq$ relative frequency of any outcome ≤ 1
(2) 1

88 One other point to keep in mind: We shall be concerned with experiments such that the number of outcomes of the experiment is finite. Keep in mind also that the outcomes must be such that each trial of the experiment must result in exactly _____ of the outcomes.

$\left(\begin{array}{c} or \\ integral \end{array}\right)$

one

89 Thus we proceed as follows. Given any such experiment, we have a set of results such that each trial of the experiment produces one and only one of these results. We define a *sample space* of the experiment to be a set of elements such that each element of the set corresponds to exactly one outcome of the experiment. For example, toss a coin and observe whether a head or a tail appears. We set up the following correspondence:

$e_1 \leftrightarrow$ the coin turns up heads
$e_2 \leftrightarrow$ the coin turns up tails

The sample space S of the experiment is $S = \{$ ___, ___ $\}$.

e_1, e_2

●90 A single die is tossed, and the number of spots on the upper surface is counted. We would probably consider the following outcomes:

$e_1 \leftrightarrow$ the number appearing is a 1
$e_2 \leftrightarrow$ the number appearing is a 2
$e_3 \leftrightarrow$ the number appearing is a 3
$e_4 \leftrightarrow$ the number appearing is a 4
$e_5 \leftrightarrow$ the number appearing is a 5
$e_6 \leftrightarrow$ the number appearing is a 6

Thus, this sample space $S = \{$ $\}$.

e_1, e_2, e_3, e_4, e_5, e_6

91 In a survey among a collection of registered Republicans and Democrats, we wish to find their opinions on the current administration's domestic affairs. A sample space for this experiment might consist of six outcomes:

▼

$e_1 \longleftrightarrow$ the person sampled is a Republican who approves
$e_2 \longleftrightarrow$ the person sampled is a Republican who disapproves
$e_3 \longleftrightarrow$ the person sampled is a Republican who is undecided
$e_4 \longleftrightarrow$ the person sampled is a Democrat who approves
$e_5 \longleftrightarrow$ _____
$e_6 \longleftrightarrow$ _____

This sample space $S = \{$ $\}$

the person sampled is a Democrat who disapproves
the person sampled is a Democrat who is undecided
(Of course you may have them in a different order.)
e_1, e_2, e_3, e_4, e_5, e_6

92 The manager of the East End Eagles is keeping a record of each
pitch thrown to Slugger McGoon, his star batter. He records if the
ball thrown was, in his opinion, a strike or a ball, and whether
McGoon swung at it or let it go. We would consider these four outcomes:

$e_1 \longleftrightarrow$ the pitch was a strike at which McGoon swung
$e_2 \longleftrightarrow$ the pitch was a ball at which McGoon swung
$e_3 \longleftrightarrow$ _____
$e_4 \longleftrightarrow$ _____

Set up a sample space for this experiment.

the pitch was a strike which McGoon let go
the pitch was a ball which McGoon let go
$S = \{e_1,\ e_2,\ e_3,\ e_4\}$

●93 A hospital keeps a record of the sex of newborn babies. Here,
there are just two outcomes:

$e_1 \longleftrightarrow$ the baby is a boy
$e_2 \longleftrightarrow$ the baby is a girl
$S = \{e_1, e_2\}$ is called a ____ ____.

sample space

94 An experiment is performed as follows: A coin is tossed. If a
head turns up, a die is rolled and its number recorded. If a tail
turns up, a ball is drawn from a hat containing one red ball, one
white ball, and one blue ball. There would be nine outcomes:

$e_1 \longleftrightarrow$ the coin is a head and the die turns up 1
$e_2 \longleftrightarrow$ the coin is a head and the die turns up 2

$6 + 3$

$e_3 \longleftrightarrow$ _____
$e_4 \longleftrightarrow$ _____
$e_5 \longleftrightarrow$ _____
$e_6 \longleftrightarrow$ _____

▼

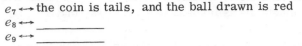

$e_7 \leftrightarrow$ the coin is tails, and the ball drawn is red
$e_8 \leftrightarrow$ _____
$e_9 \leftrightarrow$ _____
The sample space $S =$ _____

$e_3 \leftrightarrow$ the coin is heads and the die turns up 3
$e_4 \leftrightarrow$ the coin is heads and the die turns up 4
$e_5 \leftrightarrow$ the coin is heads and the die turns up 5
$e_6 \leftrightarrow$ the coin is heads and the die turns up 6
$e_8 \leftrightarrow$ the coin is tails and the ball drawn is white
$e_9 \leftrightarrow$ the coin is tails and the ball drawn is blue

(The order may be different.)
$\{e_1,\ e_2,\ e_3,\ e_4,\ e_5,\ e_6,\ e_7,\ e_8,\ e_9\}$

95 So, in a given experiment, if we have *outcomes* A_1, A_2,. . ., A_n such that any single trial of the experiment can result in exactly one of the outcomes, we associate with each of the outcomes an *element* e_1, e_2,. . ., e_n and the $S = \{e_1,\ e_2,. . .,\ e_n\}$ is called a _____ of this experiment.

sample space

96 In a coin-tossing experiment there are just two *outcomes:*
The coin is a head
The coin is a tail
We associate each of the outcomes with one _____ e_1, e_2 and then list our sample space $S = \{e_1,\ e_2\}$.

element

97 When drawing single balls in a ball-drawing experiment with three balls, a red, a white, and a blue, there are just three _____:
A red ball is drawn
A white ball is drawn
A blue ball is drawn
We associate each of these _____ with one element e_1, e_2, e_3 and then list our sample space $S = \{e_1,\ e_2,\ e_3\}$.

outcomes,   outcomes

•**98** A man tries to light a lighter and records success S or failure F.
The lighter lights $\quad$ } These are called the (1) _____
The lighter fails to light
Each of the above is associated with exactly one (2) _____ e_1, e_2, and then $S = \{e_1,\ e_2\}$ is called a (3) _____ of the experiment.

(1) outcomes   (2) element   (3) sample space

99 Suppose a single die is tossed. We *might* say that $S = \{e_1, e_2, e_3, e_4\}$ where

$e_1 \longleftrightarrow$ the outcome that the number of spots is even
$e_2 \longleftrightarrow$ the outcome that the number of spots is a 1
$e_3 \longleftrightarrow$ the outcome that the number of spots is a 3
$e_4 \longleftrightarrow$ the outcome that the number of spots is a 5

Note that each trial of the experiment can result in one and only one of the outcomes. However, unless there is some good reason for such a sample space, it would be natural to construct a sample space of six elements, say $a_1, a_2, a_3, a_4, a_5, a_6$, where
$a_1 \longleftrightarrow$ the outcome that the number of spots is 1
Complete the enumeration of $a_2, a_3, a_4, a_5,$ and a_6.

$a_2 \longleftrightarrow$ the outcome that the number of spots is 2
$a_3 \longleftrightarrow$ the outcome that the number of spots is 3
$a_4 \longleftrightarrow$ the outcome that the number of spots is 4
$a_5 \longleftrightarrow$ the outcome that the number of spots is 5
$a_6 \longleftrightarrow$ the outcome that the number of spots is 6

100 Similarly, if an experiment consists of tossing two coins, one might say that $S = \{a_1, a_2, a_3\}$ where

$a_1 \longleftrightarrow$ no heads appear
$a_2 \longleftrightarrow$ one head appears
$a_3 \longleftrightarrow$ two heads appear

but we will consider simpler outcomes and say that
$S = \{e_1, e_2, e_3, e_4\}$ where

$e_1 \longleftrightarrow$ coin 1 turns up tails and coin 2 turns up tails
$e_2 \longleftrightarrow$ coin 1 turns up heads and coin 2 turns up tails
$e_3 \longleftrightarrow$ _____
$e_4 \longleftrightarrow$ _____

coin 1 turns up tails and coin 2 turns up heads
coin 1 turns up heads and coin 2 turns up heads

101 In problems of tossing a number of coins, we will ordinarily consider the coins to be tossed in some order and indicate the outcome as follows: Suppose three coins are tossed. One outcome might be that the first coin turns up heads, the second coin turns up tails, and the third coin turns up heads. We would indicate this outcome by HTH. Then the sample space for the experiment of tossing three coins contains eight elements:

$e_1 \longleftrightarrow HHH$ $e_2 \longleftrightarrow HHT$ $e_3 \longleftrightarrow HTH$ $e_4 \longleftrightarrow THH$
$e_5 \longleftrightarrow$ _____ $e_6 \longleftrightarrow$ _____ $e_7 \longleftrightarrow$ _____ $e_8 \longleftrightarrow$ _____

HTT THT TTH TTT
(Of course your order might be different.)

●102 If a hat contains three red balls and two white balls and an experiment consists of drawing a single ball out of the hat and noting its
color, we might be tempted to say that $S = \{a_1, a_2\}$ where $a_1 \leftrightarrow$ the
ball is red and $a_2 \leftrightarrow$ the ball is white.
But the element a_1 really corresponds to three simpler outcomes,
and a_2 really corresponds to two simpler outcomes. That is, the
outcome that the ball is red can come about in three different
ways—one for each of the red balls. So in this type of problem,
we would, for convenience, number the balls R_1, R_2, R_3, W_1, W_2
and then our sample space has five elements.
(1) List the five possible outcomes. (2) $S =$ _____

(1) $e_1 \leftrightarrow$ the ball drawn is R_1
$e_2 \leftrightarrow$ the ball drawn is R_2
$e_3 \leftrightarrow$ the ball drawn is R_3
$e_4 \leftrightarrow$ the ball drawn is W_1
$e_5 \leftrightarrow$ the ball drawn is W_2
(2) $\{e_1, e_2, e_3, e_4, e_5\}$

103 A hat contains three red and two white balls. *Two* balls are drawn,
and their color is noted. To set up the sample space of the experiment, once again we consider the balls to be numbered R_1, R_2, R_3,
W_1, W_2. It is easier to think of one ball being drawn and then the
second ball being drawn; and if, for example, the first ball is R_1
and the second is R_2, we indicate this outcome $R_1 R_2$. Then
$S = \{e_1, \ldots, e_{20}\}$ where

$e_1 \leftrightarrow R_1 R_2$ $e_2 \leftrightarrow R_1 R_3$ $e_3 \leftrightarrow R_1 W_1$
$e_4 \leftrightarrow R_1 W_2$ $e_5 \leftrightarrow R_2 R_1$ $e_6 \leftrightarrow R_2 R_3$
$e_7 \leftrightarrow R_2 W_1$ $e_8 \leftrightarrow R_2 W_2$ $e_9 \leftrightarrow R_3 R_1$

Complete the 20 possible outcomes.

But what if 18 Red,
13white + 23 Blue —
what's the total outcomes
What's the math?
see #108

$e_{10} \leftrightarrow R_3 R_2$ $e_{11} \leftrightarrow R_3 W_1$ $e_{12} \leftrightarrow R_3 W_2$
$e_{13} \leftrightarrow W_1 R_1$ $e_{14} \leftrightarrow W_1 R_2$ $e_{15} \leftrightarrow W_1 R_3$
$e_{16} \leftrightarrow W_1 W_2$ $e_{17} \leftrightarrow W_2 R_1$ $e_{18} \leftrightarrow W_2 R_2$
$e_{19} \leftrightarrow W_2 R_3$ $e_{20} \leftrightarrow W_2 W_1$

104 If a pair of dice is tossed, there are 36 elements in the sample
space. You might think of the one die being red and the other
white. The red die can turn up in any one of six ways, and with
each of these the white die can turn up in six ways. Let us indicate each as follows: If the red die turns up 3 and the white die
turns up 1, then this outcome is indicated by (3, 1). Note, the
number on the red die is listed first. The 36 outcomes are:

▼

$6 * 6 = 36$

(1, 1)   (1, 2)   (1, 3)   (1, 4)   (1, 5)   (1, 6)
(2, 1)   (2, 2)   (2, 3)   (2, 4)   (2, 5)   (2, 6)
Complete the list of outcomes.

(3, 1)   (3, 2)   (3, 3)   (3, 4)   (3, 5)   (3, 6)
(4, 1)   (4, 2)   (4, 3)   (4, 4)   (4, 5)   (4, 6)
(5, 1)   (5, 2)   (5, 3)   (5, 4)   (5, 5)   (5, 6)
(6, 1)   (6, 2)   (6, 3)   (6, 4)   (6, 5)   (6, 6)

105 Now, with each outcome A of an experiment, there is assumed to
be a value $P(A)$ called the probability of A such that the relative
frequency of event A will become relatively close to $P(A)$ if the
number of trials becomes large. Therefore, in our sample space,
we will associate with each element e_i a number indicated by $P(e_i)$
called the probability of e_i. Recall that, if the outcomes were such
that any trial of the experiment could result in exactly one of the
outcomes, then
(1) ___ $\leq$ relative frequency of $A \leq$ ___
(2) Sum of the relative frequencies = ___

(1) 0, 1   (2) 1

106 Therefore, it is natural that in assigning the probability values to
each of the elements in the sample space, we place two restrictions
upon the values:
(1) ___ $\leq P(e_i) \leq$ ___ for $i = 1, 2, 3, \ldots, n$
(2) $P(e_i) + P(e_2) + \cdots + P(e_n) =$ ___

(1) 0, 1   (2) 1

107 So now, given an experiment, our model consists of a sample space
of N elements $e_1, e_2, \ldots, e_n$, each of which corresponds to an outcome of the experiment and such that any trial of the experiment results in exactly (1) *one* of the outcomes. Furthermore, to each
element of the sample space there corresponds a number
$P(e_1), P(e_2), \ldots, P(e_n)$ such that (2) $0 \leq P(e_i) \leq 1$ for
$i = 1, 2, \ldots, n$ and (3) $P(e_1) + P(e_2) + \cdots + P(e_n) = 1$

(1) one   (2) 0, 1   (3) 1

108 The obvious question is: How do we assign the values $P(e_1), P(e_2)$,
$\ldots, P(e_n)$ to the elements of the sample space? For some experiments, we must, if possible, perform the experiment a large number of times and use the relative frequencies as approximations of
the $P(e_i)$. For example, if A is the event that a light bulb chosen
from a certain production line is defective, we might find the relative frequency of event A for a large number of trials. Suppose the
relative frequency of A is found to be 0.013 for a large N. Then, in

▼

our sample space, if $e_1 \leftrightarrow$ the light bulb chosen is defective, we would have little choice but to let $P(e_1) = $ ___.

0.013   Although 0.013 is undoubtedly not correct for the probability of event A, we know that for a large number of trials, the relative frequency of event A should ultimately be close to $P(A)$.

---

comment

If an experiment consists of observing whether any precipitation falls during a day in Cleveland, Ohio, then, our sample space consists of two elements:

$e_1 \leftrightarrow$ some precipitation fell during the day
$e_2 \leftrightarrow$ no precipitation fell during the day

Now, in assigning the values $P(e_1)$ and $P(e_2)$, unless you wish to make a wild guess, you would check the past weather reports of Cleveland and find the relative frequency of the outcomes corresponding to e_1 and e_2. Then assign $P(e_1)$ and $P(e_2)$ these values.

If no past records are available, we might perform the experiment ourselves a large number of times. If this is impractical, we might be forced to use information from some locality close to Cleveland whose weather is similar. But in all cases, we must remember that we have less confidence in the values $P(e_1)$ and $P(e_2)$ since all these are approximations of the probabilities.

---

109 There are experiments, however, where we feel relatively free to assign the values $P(e_1), P(e_2), \ldots, P(e_n)$ without resorting to approximations. In some simple experiments, there is a certain symmetry which carries over to the set of outcomes, and we feel that there is no reason for the probability of one outcome to be any different from the probability of another. For example, in an *honest* toss of an *honest* coin,

$e_1 \leftrightarrow$ the coin turns up heads
$e_2 \leftrightarrow$ the coin turns up tails

It appears obvious that the probability of a head and the probability of a tail should be equal, and since $P(e_1) + P(e_2) = 1$, we would let $P(e_1) = $ ___ and $P(e_2) = $ ___.

$\frac{1}{2}$, $\frac{1}{2}$

●110 Similarly, in an honest toss of an honest die, we feel confident in assigning *equal* values to each element in the sample space; so, if

▼

$e_1 \longleftrightarrow$ the die turns up 1 $e_2 \longleftrightarrow$ the die turns up 2
$e_3 \longleftrightarrow$ the die turns up 3 $e_4 \longleftrightarrow$ the die turns up 4
$e_5 \longleftrightarrow$ the die turns up 5 $e_6 \longleftrightarrow$ the die turns up 6

So, since $P(e_1) + P(e_2) + \cdots + P(e_6) = 1$, if each $P(e_i)$ is to have the same value, we would let
$P(e_1) = \underline{\quad} \qquad P(e_2) = \underline{\quad} \qquad P(e_3) = \underline{\quad} \qquad P(e_4) = \underline{\quad} \qquad P(e_5) = \underline{\quad}$
$P(e_6) = \underline{\quad}$

$\frac{1}{6}, \quad \frac{1}{6}, \quad \frac{1}{6}, \quad \frac{1}{6}, \quad \frac{1}{6}, \quad \frac{1}{6}$

---

111 Similarly, if a hat contains three red balls and two white balls and a single ball is chosen at random from the hat, then
$S = \{e_1, e_2, \ldots, e_5\}$ where

$e_1 \longleftrightarrow R_1$ is chosen $e_2 \longleftrightarrow R_2$ is chosen $e_3 \longleftrightarrow R_3$ is chosen
$e_4 \longleftrightarrow W_1$ is chosen $e_5 \longleftrightarrow W_2$ is chosen

If the drawing is made honestly, then we intuitively feel that there is no reason that one ball might be chosen any oftener than any other; so we would assign equal values to each of the $P(e_i)$.
$\therefore P(e_1) = \underline{\quad}, \quad P(e_2) = \underline{\quad}, \quad P(e_3) = \underline{\quad}, \quad P(e_4) = \underline{\quad} \quad P(e_5) = \underline{\quad}$

$\frac{1}{5}, \quad \frac{1}{5}, \quad \frac{1}{5}, \quad \frac{1}{5}, \quad \frac{1}{5}$

---

112 Hat 1 contains two red R_1 and R_2 and three white balls W_1, W_2, and W_3. Hat 2 contains one red R_3 and one blue ball B_1. A coin is tossed. If H appears, a ball is drawn from hat 1. If T appears, a ball is drawn from hat 2. One possible outcome is that H appears and R_1 is chosen from hat 1. We shall indicate this by HR_1. Another possible outcome is that T appears and R_3 is chosen from hat 2. We shall indicate this by TR_3.

$\therefore e_1 \longleftrightarrow HR_1 \qquad e_2 \longleftrightarrow TR_3$

(1) $e_3 \longleftrightarrow \underline{\quad}$ (2) $e_4 \longleftrightarrow \underline{\quad}$
(3) $e_5 \longleftrightarrow \underline{\quad}$ (4) $e_6 \longleftrightarrow \underline{\quad}$
(5) $e_7 \longleftrightarrow \underline{\quad}$

---

(1) HR_2 (2) HW_1 (3) HW_2 (4) HW_3 (5) TB_1
Your order may be different.

---

113 In frame 112, after some thought, you should see that assigning equal probabilities to each element of the sample space is not reasonable. After all, if you were to perform the experiment 1,000 times, you would expect to get heads and thus into hat 1 about 500 times. Also you would expect to get tails and thus into hat 2 about 500 times. So you would expect the sum of the relative frequencies of outcomes from hat 1 to total about $\frac{1}{2}$ and the sum of the relative frequencies of outcomes from hat 2 to total about $\frac{1}{2}$.

▼

$$(1)\ P(e_1) = \underline{\quad}$$
$$(2)\ P(e_3) = \underline{\quad}$$
$$(3)\ P(e_4) = \underline{\quad}$$
$$(4)\ P(e_5) = \underline{\quad}$$
$$(5)\ P(e_6) = \underline{\quad}$$
sum $\frac{1}{2}$

$$(6)\ P(e_2) = \underline{\quad}$$
$$(7)\ P(e_7) = \underline{\quad}$$
sum $\frac{1}{2}$

But, What probabilities would you assign to the elements?

(1) $\frac{1}{10}$ (2) $\frac{1}{10}$ (3) $\frac{1}{10}$ (4) $\frac{1}{10}$ (5) $\frac{1}{10}$ (6) $\frac{1}{4}$ (7) $\frac{1}{4}$

114 There are four packages, each has two sandwiches in it:
Package 1 has two ham sandwiches
Package 2 has one ham and one cheese sandwich
Package 3 has one ham and one cheese sandwich
Package 4 has two cheese sandwiches
An experiment consists of picking a package at random, and then picking at random one of the sandwiches out of the package and seeing what kind it is.

$e_1 \longleftrightarrow$ package 1 is chosen and H_1 sandwich is chosen.

Complete the listing of the sample space and assign probabilities.

$e_2 \longleftrightarrow$ package 1 is chosen and H_2 sandwich is chosen
$e_3 \longleftrightarrow$ package 2 is chosen and H_3 sandwich is chosen
$e_4 \longleftrightarrow$ package 2 is chosen and C_1 sandwich is chosen
$e_5 \longleftrightarrow$ package 3 is chosen and H_4 sandwich is chosen
$e_6 \longleftrightarrow$ package 3 is chosen and C_2 sandwich is chosen
$e_7 \longleftrightarrow$ package 4 is chosen and C_3 sandwich is chosen
$e_8 \longleftrightarrow$ package 4 is chosen and C_4 sandwich is chosen

$P(e_i) = \frac{1}{8}$ for $i = 1, 2, \ldots, 8$

115 Now we have: With each experiment there is a set of outcomes such that any trial of the experiment must result in exactly (1) _____ outcome(s). Our model consists of a set of elements such that each element corresponds to one of the outcomes. This set of elements is called the (2) _____ of the experiment. Suppose $S = \{e_1, e_2, \ldots, e_n\}$ To each point, say e_i, a number $P(e_i)$ is assigned such that (3) ___ $\leq P(e_i) \leq$ ___, (4) the sum of all $P(e_i) = $ ___

(1) one   (2) sample space   (3) 0, 1   (4) 1

116 Recall, our reason for constructing a model was to find ways of computing probabilities of complicated outcomes if the probabilities of simpler outcomes are known. So we assume now that with a given experiment we have a sample space $S = \{e_1, e_2, \ldots, e_n\}$ and corresponding to each point e_i ($i = 1, 2, \ldots, n$) of the sample space there is a number $P(e_i)$ called the probability of e_i such that:

▼

(1) ___ $\leq P(e_i) \leq$ ___ for $i = 1, 2, \ldots, n$

(2) $P(e_1) + P(e_2) + \cdots + P(e_n) =$ ___

---

(1) 0, 1   (2) 1

---

117 Suppose a sample space consists of: $S = \{e_1, e_2, e_3, e_4, e_5, e_6\}$

(1) If $A = \{e_2, e_4, e_5\}$, is A a subset of S?

(2) Any subset of a sample space is called an *event*. You can see that A is an _____.

---

(1) yes   (2) event

---

118 Items 1 to 4 below contain some familiar facts about an experiment in which two coins are tossed. Event A, which consists of only one head in a single trial, is considered:

1. Outcomes: HH HT TH TT

2. Elements: e_1 e_2 e_3 e_4

3. Sample space: $S = \{e_1, e_2, e_3, e_4\}$

4. Subset of S: $A = \{e_2, e_3\}$

Each *outcome* in item 1 is associated with one *element* in item 2. The set of elements S in item 3 is a *sample space* for the experiment, and A in item 4 is referred to as an *event* because A is a _____ of S.

---

subset

---

119 Consider the experiment of tossing three coins.

$S = \{e_1, e_2, \ldots, e_8\}$ where

$e_1 \leftrightarrow HHH$ $e_2 \leftrightarrow HHT$ $e_3 \leftrightarrow HTH$ $e_4 \leftrightarrow THH$

$e_5 \leftrightarrow TTH$ $e_6 \leftrightarrow THT$ $e_7 \leftrightarrow HTT$ $e_8 \leftrightarrow TTT$

If event A is that *at least* two heads appear, we know that A is a subset of S and is equal to $\{e_1, e_2, e_3, e_4\}$. Let B be a subset of S and contain those elements of S which correspond to outcomes containing three tails. Then (1) $B = \{$ ___ $\}$, and B is referred to as an (2) _____.

---

(1) e_8 (2) event

●**120** Given a sample space S, any subset of S is called an _____.

---

event

121 Consider again the experiment in which two coins are tossed and A is the event that only one head appears:

1. Outcomes: HH HT TH TT
2. Elements: e_1 e_2 e_3 e_4
3. Sample space: $S = \{e_1, e_2, e_3, e_4\}$
4. Event A: $A = \{e_2, e_3\}$

Event = outcome.

Sometimes we will relax our use of terminology and use the word *outcome* to mean *event*. This means that although item 1 above is a list of all possible outcomes for the experiment, item 4 could be read not only *event A*, but also _____ A.

outcome

122 (a) Let an experiment consist of tossing a die, and let outcome B be that the number turning up is even:
$S = \{e_1, e_2, e_3, e_4, e_5, e_6\}$ where

$e_1 \leftrightarrow$ the die turns up 1 $e_2 \leftrightarrow$ the die turns up 2
$e_3 \leftrightarrow$ the die turns up 3 $e_4 \leftrightarrow$ the die turns up 4
$e_5 \leftrightarrow$ the die turns up 5 $e_6 \leftrightarrow$ the die turns up 6

Then (1) $B = \{$ _____ $\}$.
(b) Although B in part a is referred to as an outcome, we will usually refer to such a subset of a sample space as an (2) _____.

(1) e_2, e_4, e_6 (2) event

123 *Definition:* Given an event A, the probability of A, $P(A)$, equals the sum of the probabilities of the elements contained in A. For example, in tossing two coins, let A be that exactly one head occurs. To find the probability of A, we do the following:

1. Set up the sample space S:
$S = \{e_1, e_2, e_3, e_4\}$ where $e_1 \leftrightarrow HH$, $e_2 \leftrightarrow HT$, $e_3 \leftrightarrow TH$, $e_4 \leftrightarrow TT$
2. Assign probabilities to the elements in S. In this problem, it seems reasonable to let $P(e_1) = \frac{1}{4}$, $P(e_2) = \frac{1}{4}$, $P(e_3) = \frac{1}{4}$, and $P(e_4) = \frac{1}{4}$.
3. Find A, the subset of S corresponding to event A: $A = \{e_2, e_3\}$
4. Find $P(A)$ by adding the probabilities of the elements in A.
$\therefore P(A) = P(e_2) + P(e_3)$
$P(A) =$ _____

$\frac{1}{4} + \frac{1}{4} = \frac{1}{2}$

124 An experiment consists of drawing two balls from a hat containing two red balls and one white ball. Let event $A =$ the white ball is drawn. Find the probability of A.

▼

1. $S = \{e_1, e_2, e_3, e_4, e_5, e_6\}$ where

   $e_1 \leftrightarrow R_1 R_2$ $e_2 \leftrightarrow R_1 W$ $e_3 \leftrightarrow R_2 R_1$

   $e_4 \leftrightarrow R_2 W$ $e_5 \leftrightarrow W R_1$ $e_6 \leftrightarrow W R_2$

2. It seems reasonable to let $P(e_i) = \frac{1}{6}$ for $i = 1, 2, \ldots, n$
3. $A = \{e_2, e_4, e_5, e_6\}$
4. $\therefore P(A) = P(e_2) + P(e_4) + P(e_5) + P(e_6)$

   = _____

$\frac{1}{6} + \frac{1}{6} + \frac{1}{6} + \frac{1}{6} = \frac{4}{6}$ or $\frac{2}{3}$ *Back of Book*

125 An experiment consists of tossing a pair of dice. Let event A be
that the *sum* of the spots is 4. Find $P(A)$. The sample space S is
listed on Panel 1. $A = \{e_3, e_8, e_{13}\}$
$\therefore P(A) = P(e_3) + P(e_8) + P(e_{13})$
    = ___ + ___ + ___ = ___

$\frac{1}{36} + \frac{1}{36} + \frac{1}{36} = \frac{3}{36}$ or $\frac{1}{12}$

126 An experiment consists of tossing a pair of dice. Let event A be
that the sum of the spots is less than 4. Find $P(A)$.
From Panel 1, (1) $A = \{$___, ___, ___$\}$
$\therefore$ (2) $P(A) = P(\ ) + P(\ ) + P(\ )$ [Copy the $P(\ )$ in your answer.]
    (3)   = ___ + ___ + ___ = ___

(1) e_1, e_2, e_7
(2) $P(e_1)$ $P(e_2)$ $P(e_7)$
(3) $\frac{1}{36} + \frac{1}{36} + \frac{1}{36} = \frac{3}{36}$ or $\frac{1}{12}$

•**127** In an experiment of tossing two dice, let event A be that the sum of
the spots is 7. Find $P(A)$. Use Panel 1.

$\frac{6}{36}$ or $\frac{1}{6}$
Here is the detailed work.
$A = \{e_6, e_{11}, e_{16}, e_{21}, e_{26}, e_{31}\}$
$P(A) = P(e_6) + P(e_{11}) + P(e_{16}) + P(e_{21}) + P(e_{26}) + P(e_{31})$
    $= \frac{1}{36} + \frac{1}{36} + \frac{1}{36} + \frac{1}{36} + \frac{1}{36} + \frac{1}{36} = \frac{6}{36}$ or $\frac{1}{6}$

128 The definition that $P(A)$ = sum of probabilities of the elements contained in A is reasonable if you consider relative frequencies. Suppose an experiment consists of tossing three coins.

Let $e_1 \leftrightarrow HHH$ $e_2 \leftrightarrow HHT$ $e_3 \leftrightarrow HTH$

   $e_4 \leftrightarrow THH$ $e_5 \leftrightarrow HTT$ $e_6 \leftrightarrow THT$

   $e_7 \leftrightarrow TTH$ $e_8 \leftrightarrow TTT$

▼

Suppose 100 trials of the experiment resulted in:

HHH occurred 13 times   *HHT* occurred 10 times
HTH occurred 12 times   *THH* occurred 14 times
HTT occurred 13 times   *THT* occurred 15 times
TTH occurred 12 times   *TTT* occurred 12 times

If we wish to find the relative frequency of the outcome B that *at least* two heads occurred, we see that: Relative frequency of $B =$ ___.

$$\frac{12+13+10+14}{100} = \frac{49}{100}$$ Note that the relative frequency of B is the sum of the relative frequencies of the simpler outcomes in which B occurs.

129 So, if an experiment is performed N times and we have listed a set of outcomes such that each performance of the experiment can result in *one and only one of these outcomes*, and if we consider some more complicated outcome X which occurs whenever certain of our simpler outcomes, say $A, C,$ and D occur, we see that the relative frequency of X = relative frequency of A + relative frequency of C + relative frequency of D. Therefore, it seems reasonable to define:
If $S = \{e_1, e_2, \ldots, e_n\}$
and $A = \{e_{A_1} + e_{A_2} + \ldots + e_{A_k}\}$
then $P(A) =$

$$P(e_{A_1}) + P(e_{A_2}) + \cdots + P(e_{A_k})$$

130 An experiment consists of tossing three coins. Let event A be that at least two heads occur.
(1) Set up a sample space S of the experiment.
    $S =$ _____ where

    $e_1 \leftrightarrow HHH$ $e_2 \leftrightarrow HHT$ $e_3 \leftrightarrow HTH$
    $e_4 \leftrightarrow THH$ $e_5 \leftrightarrow HTT$ $e_6 \leftrightarrow THT$
    $e_7 \leftrightarrow TTH$ $e_8 \leftrightarrow TTT$

(2) Assign probabilities to each element in S.
    $P(e_1) + P(e_2) + \cdots + P(e_8) = 1$
    Therefore the probability for each element = ___
(3) Identify the subset A of S:
    $A =$ _____
(4) Find $P(A)$:
    $P(A) =$ ___

(1) $\{e_1, e_2, e_3, e_4, e_5, e_6, e_7, e_8\}$ (2) $\frac{1}{8}$
(3) $\{e_1, e_2, e_3, e_4\}$ (4) $\frac{4}{8}$ or $\frac{1}{2}$

131 We can say that our procedure for a given experiment is: We list outcomes in such a way that each trial of the experiment must result in exactly (1) _one_ of the (2) _outcomes_

---

(1) one   (2) outcomes

---

132 For this set of outcomes, we establish a set of elements such that there is a 1 to 1 correspondence between the outcomes of the experiment and elements of this set. This set of elements is called a_____ for the experiment.

---

sample space

---

133 With each element e_i of any sample space there is assigned a number $P(e_i)$ called the probability of e_i. There are two restrictions on the probabilities assigned:
(1) ___ $\leq P(e_i) \leq$ ___ for $i = 1, 2, \ldots, n$
(2) $P(e_1) + P(e_2) + \cdots + P(e_n) =$ ___
[Copy the $\leq P(e_i) \leq$ when you answer.]

---

(1) $0 \leq P(e_i) \leq 1$ (2) 1

---

134 The probabilities assigned to the elements of the sample space *might* be determined by careful thought. For example, if a sample space consists of 11 elements and it seems reasonable that all the outcomes corresponding to these elements have the same chance to occur, we would feel confident in assigning equal probabilities to each element of the sample space; that is,
$P(e_1) = P(e_2) = \cdots = P(e_{11}) =$ ___.

$\frac{1}{11}$ (since they are to be equal and their sum must be 1)

---

135 If we are not confident in the reasonableness of assigning probabilities by reflection, we might, if possible, perform the experiment a large number of times and use the _____ of each outcome as an approximation of the probabilities.

---

relative frequency

---

136 Given an experiment having a sample space $S = \{e_1, e_2, \cdots, e_n\}$, any subset of S is called an_____.

---

event

●**137** Finally, given a sample space S of an experiment, and probabilities $P(e_1), P(e_2), \ldots, P(e_n)$ assigned to each element of S, if $A = \{e_{i_1}, e_{i_2}, \ldots, e_{i_k}\}$ is an event in S, then the probability of A, $P(A) = $ _____ .

$P(e_{i_1}) + P(e_{i_2}) + \ldots + P(e_{i_k})$

138 Suppose $S = \{e_1, e_2, e_3, e_4, e_5\}$ is the sample space of an experiment and $P(e_1) = 0.1$, $P(e_2) = 0$, $P(e_3) = 0.6$, $P(e_4) = 0.25$, $P(e_5) = 0.05$.
If $A = \{e_2, e_3, e_5\}$, $P(A) = $ _____ .

$P(e_2) + P(e_3) + P(e_5) = 0 + 0.6 + 0.05 = 0.65$

139 Suppose you were told that, for a certain experiment, $S = \{e_1, e_2, e_3, e_4\}$ and $P(e_1) = 0.3$, $P(e_2) = 0.2$, $P(e_3) = 0.2$, $P(e_4) = 0.1$. What would be your objection?

The sum of the probabilities of the elements of S must = 1. Something is wrong.

140 Suppose you were told that, for some experiment, $S = \{e_1, e_2, e_3, e_4\}$ where $P(e_1) = 0.3$, $P(e_2) = 0.6$, $P(e_3) = -0.3$, and $P(e_4) = 0.4$. What would be your objection?

One of the restrictions in assigning the $P(e_i)$ is that for each $P(e_i)$, $0 \leq P(e_i) \leq 1$, but someone has given $P(e_3) \leq 0$. Something is wrong.

141 Suppose $S = \{e_1, e_2, e_3, e_4, e_5\}$ for some experiment and $P(e_1) = 0.3$, $P(e_2) = 0.2$, $P(e_3) = 0.02$, $P(e_4) = 0.25$. Find $P(e_5)$.

0.23, since $P(e_1) + P(e_2) + \cdots + P(e_5) = 1$

142 Suppose a *dishonest* die is such that, in an experiment of rolling it, $S = \{e_1, e_2, e_3, e_4, e_5, e_6\}$.

$e_1 \longleftrightarrow$ the die turns up a 1 $P(e_1) = 0.1$
$e_2 \longleftrightarrow$ the die turns up a 2 $P(e_2) = 0.1$
$e_3 \longleftrightarrow$ the die turns up a 3 $P(e_3) = 0.1$
$e_4 \longleftrightarrow$ the die turns up a 4 $P(e_4) = 0.1$
$e_5 \longleftrightarrow$ the die turns up a 5 $P(e_5) = 0.1$
$e_6 \longleftrightarrow$ the die turns up a 6 $P(e_6) = 0.5$

▼

If A is the event that an even number turns up, then (1) $A =$ _____ and (2) $P(A) =$ ___.

(1) $\{e_2, e_4, e_6\}$ (2) 0.7

143 For a certain experiment, $S = \{e_1, e_2, e_3, e_4, e_5\}$ and all $P(e_i)$ are equal for $i = 1, 2, \ldots, 5$. Suppose $A = \{e_1, e_2, e_4\}$. Find $P(A)$.

$P(e_1) = P(e_2) = P(e_3) = P(e_4) = P(e_5) = \frac{1}{5}$
$P(A) = P(e_1) + P(e_2) + P(e_4)$
$\quad = \frac{1}{5} + \frac{1}{5} + \frac{1}{5} = \frac{3}{5}$

144 From Panel 1, if A is the event that the sum of the spots in a roll of two dice is 11, find $P(A)$.   Two "ways" to roll 11.

$A = \{e_{30}, e_{35}\}$ $P(A) = P(e_{30}) + P(e_{35})$
$\quad = \frac{1}{36} + \frac{1}{36} = \frac{1}{18}$

145 In an experiment of rolling two dice, if A is the event that the sum of the spots is 2, find $P(A)$. See Panel 1.

$A = \{e_1\}$, $P(A) = P(e_1)$ Only one "way" a 2 can roll
$\quad = \frac{1}{36}$

146 Look at Panel 1. If B is the event that the sum of the dice is 3, find $P(B)$.

$B = \{e_2, e_7\}$, $P(B) = P(e_2) + P(e_7)$
$\quad = \frac{1}{18}$

147 Look at Panel 1. If C is the event that the sum of the spots is 4, find $P(C)$.   3 "ways"

$C = \{e_3, e_8, e_{13}\}$, $P(C) = \frac{3}{36} = \frac{1}{12}$

148 Look at Panel 1. If event E is that the number of spots on each die is the same, find $P(E)$.

$E = \{e_1, e_8, e_{15}, e_{22}, e_{29}, e_{36}\}$
$P(E) = P(e_1) + P(e_8) + P(e_{15}) + P(e_{22}) + P(e_{29}) + P(e_{36})$
$\quad = \frac{6}{36} = \frac{1}{6}$

149 From a set of five boys A,B,C,D,E a committee of three boys is to be chosen. For this experiment, $S = \{e_1, \ldots, e_{10}\}$ where

$$e_1 \leftrightarrow ABC \quad e_2 \leftrightarrow ABD \quad e_3 \leftrightarrow ABE \quad e_4 \leftrightarrow ACD \quad e_5 \leftrightarrow ACE$$
$$e_6 \leftrightarrow ADE \quad e_7 \leftrightarrow BCD \quad e_8 \leftrightarrow BCE \quad e_9 \leftrightarrow BDE \quad e_{10} \leftrightarrow CDE$$

Note that there is no reason to consider the order in which they are to be chosen. Suppose each element of S has the same probability. If X is the event that C is chosen,
(1) $X = $ _____ (2) $P(X) = $ ___

(1) $\{e_1, e_4, e_5, e_7, e_8, e_{10}\}$ (2) $\frac{3}{5}$

150 Suppose an experiment has a sample space
$$S = \{e_1, e_2, e_3, e_4, e_5\}$$
and $A = \{e_1, e_2, e_5\}$ is an event
If an outcome corresponding to e_1, e_2, or e_5 occurs, we say that event A has occurred.
Event A has not occurred if any of the outcomes corresponding to the elements ___ or ___ occurs.

e_3, e_4

Self-test II

1 Consider the following experiment: From a set of registered voters we select a male M or a female F and ask whether the person would vote for a woman for President of the United States. We indicate yes Y, no N, or undecided U. One hundred trials of this experiment produced the following results:

	Y	N	U
M	15	29	10
F	25	13	8

Find the relative frequency of (1) MY, .15 (2) MN, .29 (3) MU, .10
(4) FY, (5) FN, (6) FU. (7) What is the sum of the relative frequencies? 1.00

2 A hat contains three red balls, two white balls, and one blue ball. The experiment consists of drawing a single ball out of the hat and noting its color. We would probably consider the following outcomes:

▼

$e_1 \leftrightarrow$ the ball drawn is R_1 $e_2 \leftrightarrow$ the ball drawn is R_2
$e_3 \leftrightarrow$ the ball drawn is R_3 $e_4 \leftrightarrow$ the ball drawn is W_1
$e_5 \leftrightarrow$ the ball drawn is W_2 $e_6 \leftrightarrow$ the ball drawn is B_1

This sample space $S =$ $\{e1, e_2, e_3, e_4, e_5, e_6\}$

3 In a coin-tossing experiment there are just two (1) _outcomes_:
The coin is a head
The coin is a tail
We associate each outcome with one (2) _element_ e_1, e_2 and then list
our (3) _sample space_ $S = \{e_1, e_2\}$.

4 Consider an experiment in which three coins are tossed. One outcome might be that the first coin turns up H, the second coin turns up H, and the third coin turns up T. We would indicate this outcome by HHT. The sample space for the experiment of tossing three coins contains eight elements.
(1)   List the elements.
(2) $S =$ $\{e_1, e_2, ..., e_8\}$
(3)   Let outcome A be that *at least* two tails occur.
Then $A =$ _____

5 Look at Panel 1. If A is the event that the sum of the spots is more than 8, find
(1) $A =$ $\{e_{18}, e_{23}, e_{24}, e_{18}\} e_{29}, e_{30}, e_{33}, e_{34}, e_{35}, e_{36}\}$
(2) $P(A)$ $\frac{10}{36}$

part iii

COMPLEMEN-
TARY EVENTS
AND REVIEW

151 *Definition:* Given a sample space S for a certain experiment. If A is an event, then A' (called the *complement of A*) is the set of all elements of S which are not in A. Thus, if $S = \{e_1, e_2, \dots, e_6, e_7\}$ and $A = \{e_1, e_2, e_4\}$, then $A' = $_____.

$\{e_3, e_5, e_6, e_7\}$

152 Graphically, suppose $S = \{e_1, e_2, e_3, e_4, e_5, e_6, e_7\}$.

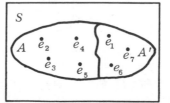

If $A = \{e_2, e_3, e_4, e_5\}$, then $A' = $ _____.

$\{e_1, e_6, e_7\}$

153 Suppose A and A' are as shown:

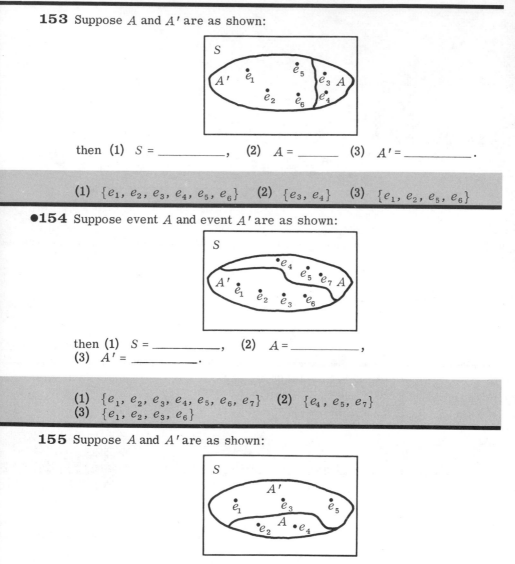

then   (1) $S =$ _____,   (2) $A =$ _____   (3) $A' =$ _____.

    (1) $\{e_1, e_2, e_3, e_4, e_5, e_6\}$ (2) $\{e_3, e_4\}$ (3) $\{e_1, e_2, e_5, e_6\}$

●**154** Suppose event A and event A' are as shown:

then (1) $S =$ _____,   (2) $A =$ _____,
(3) $A' =$ _____.

    (1) $\{e_1, e_2, e_3, e_4, e_5, e_6, e_7\}$ (2) $\{e_4, e_5, e_7\}$
    (3) $\{e_1, e_2, e_3, e_6\}$

155 Suppose A and A' are as shown:

$S = \{e_1, e_2, e_3, e_4, e_5\}$
$P(S) = P(e_1) + P(e_2) + P(e_3) + P(e_4) + P(e_5) =$ ___

    1

156 Given a sample space S of an experiment, $P(S) =$ ___

    1,   since $S = \{e_1, e_2, \ldots, e_n\}$, $P(S) = P(e_1) + P(e_2) + \cdots + P(e_n)$,
        and one of the restrictions on the P's is that their sum $= 1$.

157 Suppose A and A' are as shown:

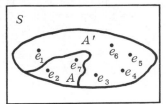

$P(S) \ = P(e_1) + P(e_2) + \cdots + P(e_7) = 1$
$P(A) \ = P(e_2) + P(e_7)$
$P(A') = P(e_1) + P(e_3) + P(e_4) + P(e_5) + P(e_6)$
$\therefore \ \ P(A) + P(A') = \underline{\quad}$

1

158 So we see that

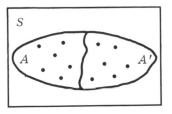

(1) $P(S) = \underline{\quad}$
     $P(A) + P(A') = P(S)$
(2) $P(A) + P(A') = \underline{\quad}$

(1) 1   (2) 1

159 So, in a given experiment, if A is an event, $P(A) + P(A') = \underline{\quad}$

1

160 If $P(A) + P(A') = 1$, then $P(A) = 1 - \underline{\quad}$

$P(A')$

●**161** This technique is sometimes very useful. If A is an event, and if it is easier to compute $P(A')$ than to compute $P(A)$, first find $P(A')$ and then $P(A) = \underline{\quad\quad}$

$1 - P(A')$

162 For example, look at Panel 1. Suppose A is the event that the sum of the spots is less than or equal to 11. Then A' is the event that the sum of the spots is greater than 11.
$A' = \{e_{36}\}$ $P(A') = \frac{1}{36}$ $\therefore P(A) = $ _____

$1 - \frac{1}{36} = \frac{35}{36}$

163 An experiment consists of tossing two coins. We construct S for this experiment in this manner.
(1) $S = $ _____
where (2) $e_1 \leftrightarrow HH$
         (complete outcomes)

(1) $\{e_1, e_2, e_3, e_4\}$ (2) $e_2 \leftrightarrow HT$
                                    $e_3 \leftrightarrow TH$
                                    $e_4 \leftrightarrow TT$

164 An experiment consists of tossing two coins.
$S = \{e_1, e_2, e_3, e_4\}$ where

$e_1 \leftrightarrow HH$ $e_2 \leftrightarrow HT$ $e_3 \leftrightarrow TH$ $e_4 \leftrightarrow TT$

Assuming the probabilities assigned to each element in the sample space are equal, (1) $P(e_1) = $___, (2) $P(e_2) = $ ___, (3) $P(e_3) = $ ___, (4) $P(e_4) = $___.

(1) $\frac{1}{4}$ (2) $\frac{1}{4}$ (3) $\frac{1}{4}$ (4) $\frac{1}{4}$

165 In an experiment of tossing two coins, $S = \{e_1, e_2, e_3, e_4\}$ where

$e_1 \leftrightarrow HH$
$e_2 \leftrightarrow HT$ and $P(e_1) = P(e_2) = P(e_3) = P(e_4)$
$e_3 \leftrightarrow TH$
$e_4 \leftrightarrow TT$

Suppose A is the event that exactly one head appears in the toss of two coins.
(1) $A = $ _____   (2) $P(A) = $ _____

(1) $\{e_2, e_3\}$ (2) $P(e_2) + P(e_3) = \frac{1}{4} + \frac{1}{4} = \frac{1}{2}$

166 An experiment consists of tossing two coins. $S = \{e_1, e_2, e_3, e_4\}$ where

$e_1 \leftrightarrow HH$ $P(e_1) = \frac{1}{4}$
$e_2 \leftrightarrow HT$ $P(e_2) = \frac{1}{4}$
$e_3 \leftrightarrow TH$ $P(e_3) = \frac{1}{4}$
$e_4 \leftrightarrow TT$ $P(e_4) = \frac{1}{4}$

▼

Suppose event A is that at least one head appears.
(1) $A =$ _____   (2) $P(A) =$ _____

---

(1) $\{e_1, e_2, e_3\}$ (2) $P(e_1) + P(e_2) + P(e_3) = \frac{1}{4} + \frac{1}{4} + \frac{1}{4} = \frac{3}{4}$

167 An experiment consists of tossing two coins.
$S = \{e_1, e_2, e_3, e_4\}$ where

$e_1 \longleftrightarrow HH$
$e_2 \longleftrightarrow HT$ and $P(e_1) = P(e_2) = P(e_3) = P(e_4) = \frac{1}{4}$
$e_3 \longleftrightarrow TH$
$e_4 \longleftrightarrow TT$

Let event A be that exactly two tails occur in tossing two coins.
(1) $A =$ ____   (2) $P(A) =$ ___

---

(1) $\{e_4\}$ (2) $\frac{1}{4}$

168 An experiment consists of tossing three coins. List a sample
space for this experiment.

$S = \{e_1, e_2, e_3, e_4, e_5, e_6, e_7, e_8\}$ where

$e_1 \longleftrightarrow HHH$ $e_2 \longleftrightarrow HHT$ $e_3 \longleftrightarrow HTH$ $e_4 \longleftrightarrow THH$
$e_5 \longleftrightarrow HTT$ $e_6 \longleftrightarrow THT$ $e_7 \longleftrightarrow TTH$ $e_8 \longleftrightarrow TTT$

You of course might have them listed in a different order. Copy
this list of S on a separate sheet of paper and use it for frames
169 to 173.

169 Using the sample space S of frame 168, if each element of the
sample space is to be assigned the same probability, find
$P(e_1), P(e_2), P(e_3), \ldots, P(e_8)$

$P(e_1) = P(e_2) = \cdots = P(e_8) = \frac{1}{8}$

170 In the experiment of tossing three coins, frame 168, if A is the
event that no heads occur, (1) $A =$ ___,   (2) $P(A) =$ ___

---

(1) $\{e_8\}$ (2) $\frac{1}{8}$

171 In the experiment of tossing three coins, frame 168, let B be the
event that exactly one head occurs.
(1) $B =$ _____   (2) $P(B) =$ ___

---

(1) $\{e_5, e_6, e_7\}$ (2) $\frac{3}{8}$

172 In the experiment of tossing three coins, frame 168, let C be the event that exactly two heads occur.
(1) $C =$ _____ (2) $P(C) =$ ___

(1) $\{e_2, e_3, e_4\}$ (2) $\frac{3}{8}$

173 In the experiment of tossing three coins, frame 168, let D be the event that exactly three heads occur.
(1) $D =$ ___ (2) $P(D) =$ ___

(1) $\{e_1\}$ (2) $\frac{1}{8}$

174 Construct a sample space for tossing four coins. There are 16 elements of S.

$S = \{e\,, e_2, \ldots, e_{16}\}$

$e_1 \leftrightarrow HHHH$ $e_2 \leftrightarrow HHHT$ $e_3 \leftrightarrow HHTH$ $e_4 \leftrightarrow HTHH$
$e_5 \leftrightarrow THHH$ $e_6 \leftrightarrow HHTT$ $e_7 \leftrightarrow HTHT$ $e_8 \leftrightarrow HTTH$
$e_9 \leftrightarrow THHT$ $e_{10} \leftrightarrow THTH$ $e_{11} \leftrightarrow TTHH$ $e_{12} \leftrightarrow HTTT$
$e_{13} \leftrightarrow THTT$ $e_{14} \leftrightarrow TTHT$ $e_{15} \leftrightarrow TTTH$ $e_{16} \leftrightarrow TTTT$

Of course, you may have them listed in a different order. Copy this list of S on a separate sheet of paper and use it for frames 175 to 180.

175 In the experiment of tossing four coins, frame 174,
$S = \{e_1, e_2, \ldots, e_{16}\}$. If each element of S is to have the same probability, find $P(e_1), P(e_2), \ldots, P(e_{16})$.

$P(e_1) = P(e_2) = \cdots = P(e_{16}) = \frac{1}{16}$

176 In an experiment of tossing four coins, frame 174, $S = \{e_1, \ldots, e_{16}\}$ where each $P(e_i) = \frac{1}{16}$. Suppose A is the event that exactly four heads occur, (1) $A =$ ___, so (2) $P(A) =$ ___.

(1) $\{e_1\}$ (2) $\frac{1}{16}$

177 In the experiment of tossing four coins, frame 174, if A is the event of getting four tails, (1) $A =$ ___, so (2) $P(A) =$ ___.

(1) $\{e_{16}\}$ (2) $\frac{1}{16}$

178 In the experiment of tossing four coins, frame 174, if A is the event of getting exactly two heads, (1) $A =$ _____, so (2) $P(A) =$ ___

(1) $\{e_6,\ e_7,\ e_8,\ e_9,\ e_{10},\ e_{11}\}$ (2) $\frac{6}{16}$ or $\frac{3}{8}$

179 In the experiment of tossing four coins, frame 174, if A is the event that *at least* two heads occur, (1) $A =$ _____, so (2) $P(A) =$ ___

(1) $\{e_1,\ e_2,\ e_3,\ \ldots,\ e_{11}\}$ (2) $\frac{11}{16}$

180 In the experiment of tossing four coins, frame 174, if A is the event that exactly one head occurs, (1) $A =$ _____, so (2) $P(A) =$ ___

(1) $\{e_{12},\ e_{13},\ e_{14},\ e_{15}\}$ (2) $\frac{4}{16}$ or $\frac{1}{4}$

181 A pencil has a cross section which is octagonal. Three faces are painted white, one face is red, and four faces are blue. The pencil is tossed onto a table and the color of the face turning up is noted. Construct a sample space for this experiment. In this case it would be best to distinguish the faces as W_1, W_2, W_3, R, B_1, B_2, B_3, B_4.

$S = \{e_1,\ e_2,\ \ldots,\ e_8\}$ where

$e_1 \longleftrightarrow W_1$ turns up $e_2 \longleftrightarrow W_2$ turns up
$e_3 \longleftrightarrow W_3$ turns up $e_4 \longleftrightarrow R$ turns up
$e_5 \longleftrightarrow B_1$ turns up $e_6 \longleftrightarrow B_2$ turns up
$e_7 \longleftrightarrow B_3$ turns up $e_8 \longleftrightarrow B_4$ turns up

Copy this list of S on a separate sheet of paper and use it for frames 182 to 186.

182 In the sample space of frame 181, if each element of S is to be assigned equal probabilities, find $P(e_1)$, $P(e_2)$, $\ldots$, $P(e_8)$.

$P(e_1) = P(e_2) = \cdots = P(e_8) = \frac{1}{8}$

183 In frame 181, if A is the event that a red face turns up, (1) $A =$ ___, so (2) $P(A) =$ ___

(1) $\{e_4\}$ (2) $\frac{1}{8}$

184 In frame 181, if C is the event that a white face turns up,
(1) $C =$ _____; (2) find $P(C)$.

> (1) $\{e_1, e_2, e_3\}$ (2) $P(C) = \frac{3}{8}$

185 In frame 181, if D is the event that a blue face turns up,
(1) $D =$ _____; (2) find $P(D)$.

> (1) $\{e_5, e_6, e_7, e_8\}$ (2) $P(D) = \frac{4}{8}$ or $\frac{1}{2}$

186 In frame 181, if E is the event that a white or a blue face turns up,
(1) $E =$ _____; (2) find $P(E)$.

> (1) $\{e_1, e_2, e_3, e_5, e_6, e_7, e_8\}$ or $E' = \{e_4\}$
> (2) $P(E) = P(e_1) + P(e_2) + P(e_3) + P(e_5)$
> $\qquad\qquad + P(e_6) + P(e_7) + P(e_8)$
> $\qquad = \frac{7}{8}$
> or $P(E') = \frac{1}{8}$
> $\qquad P(E) = 1 - P(E') = \frac{7}{8}$

187 Suppose we were given this information and asked to list a sample space. A hat contains some red balls (R), some white balls (W), and some blue balls (B). Two balls are to be drawn from the hat and their colors noted. The best we can do is to list the possible colors of the two balls drawn, with the first ball drawn listed first and the second ball drawn listed second.
$S = \{e_1, e_2, e_3, e_4, e_5, e_6, e_7, e_8, e_9\}$ where

$e_1 \leftrightarrow RR$ $e_2 \leftrightarrow RW$ $e_3 \leftrightarrow RB$

Complete the enumeration of $e_4, \cdots, e_9$.

> $e_4 \leftrightarrow WR$ $e_5 \leftrightarrow WW$ $e_6 \leftrightarrow WB$
> $e_7 \leftrightarrow BR$ $e_8 \leftrightarrow BW$ $e_9 \leftrightarrow BB$

188 In frame 187, we have no way of *reasoning* what probabilities should be assigned to each point in the sample space. We would have some basis for judgment if we knew the number of balls of each color which were in the hat.
Another technique of assigning the $P(e_i)$ would be to perform the experiment a large number of times and use the _____ _____ of each outcome corresponding to an element of S.

> relative frequency

189 Suppose a hat contains a number of balls, some red, some white, and some blue. Two balls are to be drawn in succession from the hat.

▼

Then $S = \{e_1,\ e_2,\ e_3,\ e_4,\ e_5,\ e_6,\ e_7,\ e_8,\ e_9\}$ where

$e_1 \leftrightarrow RR \qquad e_2 \leftrightarrow RW \qquad e_3 \leftrightarrow RB$
$e_4 \leftrightarrow WR \qquad e_5 \leftrightarrow WW \qquad e_6 \leftrightarrow WB$
$e_7 \leftrightarrow BR \qquad e_8 \leftrightarrow BW \qquad e_9 \leftrightarrow BB$

Suppose we are told that

$P(e_1) = 0.2 \qquad P(e_2) = 0.2 \qquad P(e_3) = 0.1$
$P(e_4) = 0.2 \qquad P(e_5) = 0.06 \qquad P(e_6) = 0.07$
$P(e_7) = 0.1 \qquad P(e_8) = 0.07 \qquad P(e_9) = 0$

Does $P(e_1) + P(e_2) + \cdots + P(e_9) = 1$?
Copy this information and use it for frames 190 to 197.

yes

---

190 From frame 189: Let A be the event that at least one white ball is drawn.
(1) $A =$ _____ (2) $P(A) =$ _____

(1) $\{e_2,\ e_4,\ e_5,\ e_6,\ e_8\}$
(2) $P(e_2) + P(e_4) + P(e_5) + P(e_6) + P(e_8)$
$= 0.2 + 0.2 + 0.06 + 0.07 + 0.07$
$= 0.6$

---

191 From frame 189, if B is the event that exactly one white ball is drawn, (1) $B =$ _____; (2) find $P(B)$.

(1) $\{e_2,\ e_4,\ e_6,\ e_8\}$
(2) $P(B) = P(e_2) + P(e_4) + P(e_6) + P(e_8)$
$= 0.2 + 0.2 + 0.07 + 0.07$
$= 0.54$

---

192 In frame 189, if C is the event that the first ball drawn is white,
(1) $C =$ _____; (2) find $P(C)$.

(1) $\{e_4,\ e_5,\ e_6\}$ (2) $P(C) = P(e_4) + P(e_5) + P(e_6)$
$= 0.2 + 0.06 + 0.07$
$= 0.33$

---

193 From frame 189, if D is the event that the second ball drawn is white, (1) $D =$ _____; (2) find $P(D)$.

(1) $\{e_2,\ e_5,\ e_8\}$ (2) $P(D) = P(e_2) + P(e_5) + P(e_8)$
$= 0.2 + 0.06 + 0.07$
$= 0.33$

194 For frame 189, if E is the event that both balls drawn are the same color, **(1)** $E =$ _____; **(2)** find $P(E)$.

(1) $\{e_1, e_5, e_9\}$ **(2)** $P(E) = P(e_1) + P(e_5) + P(e_9)$
$$= 0.2 + 0.06 + 0$$
$$= 0.26$$

195 For frame 189, if F is the event that the two balls drawn are different in color, **(1)** $F =$ _____; **(2)** find $P(F)$.

(1) $\{e_2, e_3, e_4, e_6, e_7, e_8\}$
(2) $P(F) = P(e_2) + P(e_3) + P(e_4) + P(e_6) + P(e_7) + P(e_8)$
$$= 0.2 + 0.1 + 0.2 + 0.07 + 0.1 + 0.07 = 0.74$$
or note $F' = \{e_1, e_5, e_9\}$
$$P(F') = 0.26$$
$$P(F) = 1 - P(F')$$
$$= 0.74$$

196 For frame 189, if G is the event that a red ball is not drawn, **(1)** $G =$ _____; **(2)** find $P(G)$.

(1) $\{e_5, e_6, e_8, e_9\}$
(2) $P(G) = P(e_5) + P(e_6) + P(e_8) + P(e_9)$
$$= 0.06 + 0.07 + 0.07 + 0 = 0.2$$

197 For frame 189, if H is the event that a red ball and a white ball are drawn, **(1)** $H =$ _____; **(2)** find $P(H)$.

(1) $\{e_2, e_4\}$ **(2)** $P(H) = P(e_2) + P(e_4)$
$$= 0.2 + 0.2 = 0.4$$

comment

At present, given an experiment and an event A, if you wish to find $P(A)$ you should follow this procedure:

1. Set up a sample space S for the experiment.
2. Assign probabilities to each element of S.
3. Identify A as a subset of S.
4. Then $P(A) =$ the sum of the probabilities of the elements of A.

198 A hat contains four red balls, two white balls, and one blue ball.
Experiment: Draw a single ball from the hat.
Event A: A white ball is drawn.

▼

Find *P(A)* following this procedure:

1. Set up a sample space S for the experiment.
   (1) $S = \{$ _____ $\}$ where
   (2) $e_1 \leftrightarrow$ ___ (3) $e_2 \leftrightarrow$ ___
   (4) $e_3 \leftrightarrow$ ___ (5) $e_4 \leftrightarrow$ ___
   (6) $e_5 \leftrightarrow$ ___ (7) $e_6 \leftrightarrow$ ___
   (8) $e_7 \leftrightarrow$ ___
2. Assign probabilities to each element of S.
   (9) Let $P(e_1) = P(e_2) = \cdots = P(e_7) =$ ___
3. Identify A as a subset of S.
   (10) $A = \{$ ___ $\}$
4. Then $P(A) =$ the sum of the probabilities of the elements of A.
   (11) $P(A) =$ ___ $+$ ___ $=$ ___

---

(1) $e_1,\ e_2,\ e_3,\ e_4,\ e_5,\ e_6,\ e_7$
(2) R_1 (3) R_2 (4) R_3 (5) R_4 (6) W_1 (7) W_2
(8) B_1 (9) $\frac{1}{7}$ (10) $e_5,\ e_6$ (11) $\frac{1}{7} + \frac{1}{7} = \frac{2}{7}$

---

199 *Experiment:* A hat contains two red balls and one white ball. A ball is drawn, its color noted, and returned to the hat. A second ball is drawn and its color noted.
Event A: The two balls drawn are of different color.
Find *P(A)* following this procedure:
(1) Set up a sample space for the experiment.
(2) Assign probabilities to each element of S.
(3) Identify A as a subset of S.
(4) Find *P(A)*.

---

(1) $S = \{e_1,\ e_2,\ \ldots,\ e_9\}$ where

$e_1 \leftrightarrow R_1R_1$ $e_2 \leftrightarrow R_1R_2$ $e_3 \leftrightarrow R_1W$
$e_4 \leftrightarrow R_2R_1$ $e_5 \leftrightarrow R_2R_2$ $e_6 \leftrightarrow R_2W$
$e_7 \leftrightarrow WR_1$ $e_8 \leftrightarrow WR_2$ $e_9 \leftrightarrow WW$

(2) It seems reasonable to assign equal probabilities to the elements of S, so let $P(e_1) = P(e_2) = \cdots = P(e_9) = \frac{1}{9}$
(3) $A = \{e_3,\ e_6,\ e_7,\ e_8\}$
(4) $P(A) = P(e_3) + P(e_6) + P(e_7) + P(e_8)$
   $= \frac{1}{9} + \frac{1}{9} + \frac{1}{9} + \frac{1}{9} = \frac{4}{9}$

●**200** *Experiment:* A hat contains two red balls and one white ball. A ball is chosen, its color noted, and without replacing the first ball, a second ball is chosen and its color noted.

▼

Event A: The two balls drawn are of different color.
Find $P(A)$.

In this case, since the first ball drawn is not replaced,
$S = \{e_1,\ e_2,\ e_3,\ e_4,\ e_5,\ e_6\}$ where

$e_1 \leftrightarrow R_1R_2$ $e_2 \leftrightarrow R_1W$ $e_3 \leftrightarrow R_2R_1$
$e_4 \leftrightarrow R_2W$ $e_5 \leftrightarrow WR_1$ $e_6 \leftrightarrow WR_2$
and we let $P(e_1) = P(e_2) = \cdots = P(e_6) = \frac{1}{6}$
$A = \{e_2,\ e_4,\ e_5,\ e_6\}$ $\therefore P(A) = \frac{2}{3}$

201 No matter what technique is used to assign probabilities to the
elements of S, there are certain restrictions on the probabilities
attached to the elements, that is, if $S = \{e_1,\ e_2,\ \ldots,\ e_n\}$ then
(1) ___ $\leq P(e_i) \leq$ ___ for $i = 1, 2, \ldots, n$
(2) $P(e_1) + P(e_2) + \cdots + P(e_n) =$ ___

(1) 0,   1   (2) 1

202 *Experiment:* A survey is to be made of families having exactly two
children, recording B for boy or G for girl for the older child, and
recording B or G for the younger child, in that order.
Construct the sample space for this experiment.

$S = \{e_1,\ e_2,\ e_3,\ e_4\}$ where

$e_1 \leftrightarrow BB$ $e_2 \leftrightarrow BG$
$e_3 \leftrightarrow GB$ $e_4 \leftrightarrow GG$

203 Assuming each element of the sample space of frame 202 has the
same probability,

$e_1 \leftrightarrow BB$ $e_2 \leftrightarrow BG$
$e_3 \leftrightarrow GB$ $e_4 \leftrightarrow GG$

(1) Then $P(e_1) = P(e_2) = P(e_3) = P(e_4) =$ ___
(2) If A is the event that a family of two children has one girl and
one boy, find $P(A)$.

(1) $\frac{1}{4}$
(2) $A = \{e_2,\ e_3\}$ $P(A) = P(e_2) + P(e_3) = \frac{1}{2}$

●**204** *Experiment:* A single die is thrown and the number of spots on the top face is counted.
Event A: The number of spots is less than 3.
Find $P(A)$.

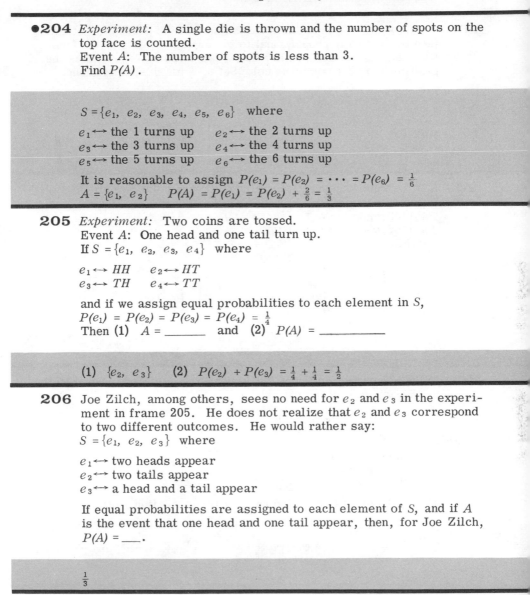

$S = \{e_1,\ e_2,\ e_3,\ e_4,\ e_5,\ e_6\}$ where

$e_1 \longleftrightarrow$ the 1 turns up $\qquad e_2 \longleftrightarrow$ the 2 turns up
$e_3 \longleftrightarrow$ the 3 turns up $\qquad e_4 \longleftrightarrow$ the 4 turns up
$e_5 \longleftrightarrow$ the 5 turns up $\qquad e_6 \longleftrightarrow$ the 6 turns up

It is reasonable to assign $P(e_1) = P(e_2) = \cdots = P(e_6) = \frac{1}{6}$
$A = \{e_1,\ e_2\} \qquad P(A) = P(e_1) = P(e_2) + \frac{2}{6} = \frac{1}{3}$

205 *Experiment:* Two coins are tossed.
Event A: One head and one tail turn up.
If $S = \{e_1,\ e_2,\ e_3,\ e_4\}$ where

$e_1 \longleftrightarrow HH \qquad e_2 \longleftrightarrow HT$
$e_3 \longleftrightarrow TH \qquad e_4 \longleftrightarrow TT$

and if we assign equal probabilities to each element in S,
$P(e_1) = P(e_2) = P(e_3) = P(e_4) = \frac{1}{4}$
Then **(1)** $A =$ _____ and **(2)** $P(A) =$ _____

(1) $\{e_2,\ e_3\}$ **(2)** $P(e_2) + P(e_3) = \frac{1}{4} + \frac{1}{4} = \frac{1}{2}$

206 Joe Zilch, among others, sees no need for e_2 and e_3 in the experiment in frame 205. He does not realize that e_2 and e_3 correspond to two different outcomes. He would rather say:
$S = \{e_1,\ e_2,\ e_3\}$ where

$e_1 \longleftrightarrow$ two heads appear
$e_2 \longleftrightarrow$ two tails appear
$e_3 \longleftrightarrow$ a head and a tail appear

If equal probabilities are assigned to each element of S, and if A is the event that one head and one tail appear, then, for Joe Zilch, $P(A) =$ ___ .

$\frac{1}{3}$

207 Reassure yourself by doing the following: Toss two coins 50 times, recording
The number of times two heads appear
The number of times two tails appear
The number of times one head and one tail appear

Unless something *very* unusual happens, a head and a tail should occur about twice as often as two heads (or two tails). If Joe were correct, each event would occur about the same number of times (about 17).

208 *Experiment:* A single die is loaded so that the probability of each face turning up is proportional to the number of dots on the face (for example, the probability that a two turns up is two times the probability that a one turns up). Set up S for this experiment.

$S = \{e_1,\ e_2,\ e_3,\ e_4,\ e_5,\ e_6\}$ where

$e_1 \longleftrightarrow$ the 1 turns up $e_2 \longleftrightarrow$ the 2 turns up
$e_3 \longleftrightarrow$ the 3 turns up $e_4 \longleftrightarrow$ the 4 turns up
$e_5 \longleftrightarrow$ the 5 turns up $e_6 \longleftrightarrow$ the 6 turns up

209 Now we want to assign probabilities to each point of S for the experiment in frame 208.
$P(e_2) = 2P(e_1)$ $P(e_3) = 3P(e_1)$ $P(e_4) = 4P(e_1)$
$P(e_5) = 5P(e_1)$ $P(e_6) = 6P(e_1)$
Therefore since $P(e_1) + P(e_2) + \cdots + P(e_6) = 1$
$$P(e_1) + 2P(e_1) + \cdots + 6P(e_1) = 1$$
$$21P(e_1) = 1$$
$$P(e_1) = \tfrac{1}{21}$$
(1) $P(e_2) = $___   (2) $P(e_3) = $___   (3) $P(e_4) = $___
(4) $P(e_5) = $___   (5) $P(e_6) = $___

(1) $\frac{2}{21}$ (2) $\frac{3}{21}$ (3) $\frac{4}{21}$ (4) $\frac{5}{21}$ (5) $\frac{6}{21}$

210 In the experiment in frame 208, recall that a die was loaded so that $S = \{e_1,\ e_2,\ e_3,\ e_4,\ e_5,\ e_6\}$ where

$e_1 \longleftrightarrow$ the 1 turns up $P(e_1) = 1/21$
$e_2 \longleftrightarrow$ the 2 turns up $P(e_2) = 2/21$
$e_3 \longleftrightarrow$ the 3 turns up $P(e_3) = 3/21$
$e_4 \longleftrightarrow$ the 4 turns up $P(e_4) = 4/21$
$e_5 \longleftrightarrow$ the 5 turns up $P(e_5) = 5/21$
$e_6 \longleftrightarrow$ the 6 turns up $P(e_6) = 6/21$

If A is the event that an odd number turns up, find $P(A)$.

$A = \{e_1,\ e_3,\ e_5\}$ $P(A) = P(e_1) + P(e_3) + P(e_5)$
$$= \tfrac{1}{21} + \tfrac{3}{21} + \tfrac{5}{21}$$
$$= \tfrac{9}{21} = \tfrac{3}{7}$$

211 *Experiment:* A single die is tossed.
Let $S = \{e_1,\ e_2,\ e_3,\ e_4,\ e_5,\ e_6\}$ where

$e_1 \longleftrightarrow$ the 1 turns up $e_2 \longleftrightarrow$ the 2 turns up
$e_3 \longleftrightarrow$ the 3 turns up $e_4 \longleftrightarrow$ the 4 turns up
$e_5 \longleftrightarrow$ the 5 turns up $e_6 \longleftrightarrow$ the 6 turns up

the set of elements $\{e_1,\ e_2,\ e_3,\ e_4,\ e_5,\ e_6\}$ is called a _____.

sample space   (of the experiment)

212 From the experiment of frame 211, we set up a sample space
$S = \{e_1,\ e_2,\ e_3,\ e_4,\ e_5,\ e_6\}$
The step usually performed next is to assign a value representing
the probability to each element of the sample space. The value
assigned for example to e_3 is indicated by (1) ___ and is called the
(2) _____.

(1) $P(e_3)$ (2) probability of e_3

213 With each element of the sample space of frame 211,
$S = \{e_1,\ e_2,\ e_3,\ e_4,\ e_5,\ e_6\}$, we associate a number called the
probability of that element. No matter what technique is used in
assigning these numbers, there are two conditions which must be
satisfied by the probabilities, namely:
(1) ___ $\leq P(e_i) \leq$ ___ for $i = 1, 2, 3, 4, 5, 6$
(2) $P(e_1) + P(e_2) + \cdots + P(e_6) =$ ___

(1) 0,   1   (2) 1

214 For any experiment of the type we have been discussing, if
$S = \{e_1,\ e_2,\ \ldots,\ e_n\}$ then, in assigning the values
$P(e_1),\ P(e_2),\ P(e_3),\ \ldots,\ P(e_n)$, we must be sure that
(1)_____,   (2) _____

(1) $0 \leq P(e_1) \leq 1$ $i = 1, 2,\ \ldots, n$
(2) $P(e_1) + P(e_2) + \cdots + P(e_n) = 1$

215 Given an experiment and a sample space $S = \{e_1,\ e_2,\ e_3,\ e_4\}$.
Suppose $P(e_1) = 0.2$, $P(e_2) = 0.4$, $P(e_3) = 0.1$. Find $P(e_4)$.

0.3,   since the sum must be 1

216 Given a sample space $S = \{e_1,\ e_2,\ e_3\}$ for an experiment, if you are
told that $P(e_2) = 2P(e_1)$ and $P(e_3) = 3P(e_1)$, find (1) $P(e_1)$,
(2) $P(e_2)$,   (3) $P(e_3)$.

$P(e_1) + P(e_2) + P(e_3) = 1$
but $P(e_2) = 2P(e_1)$ $P(e_3) = 3P(e_1)$
Substituting:
(1) $P(e_1) + 2P(e_1) + 3P(e_1) = 1$
$6P(e_1) = 1$
$P(e_1) = \frac{1}{6}$
(2) $P(e_2) = 2P(e_1) = \frac{2}{6} = \frac{1}{3}$
(3) $P(e_3) = 3P(e_1) = \frac{3}{6} = \frac{1}{2}$

217 Given a sample space $S = \{e_1, e_2, e_3, e_4, e_5\}$ for an experiment, suppose $P(e_1) = 0.1$, $P(e_2) = 0.2$ and the remaining probabilities are equal to each other.
$P(e_1) + P(e_2) + P(e_3) + P(e_4) + P(e_5) = 1$
$0.1 + 0.2 + P(e_3) + P(e_4) + P(e_5) = 1$
$P(e_3) + P(e_4) + P(e_5) = 0.7$
Find (1) $P(e_3)$, (2) $P(e_4)$, (3) $P(e_5)$.

(1) $P(e_3) = 7/30$ (2) $P(e_4) = 7/30$ (3) $P(e_5) = 7/30$

●**218** Suppose for a given experiment $S = \{e_1, e_2, e_3, e_4\}$ and you are told that $P(e_1) = 0.6$, $P(e_2) = 0.3$, $P(e_3) = -0.2$, $P(e_4) = 0.3$. What would be your objection?

Each $P(e_i)$ must be such that $0 \leq P(e_i) \leq 1$, but we are given $P(e_3) = -0.2$. Something is wrong.

219 Recall, in the experiment of rolling a die, we had $S = \{e_1, e_2, e_3, e_4, e_5, e_6\}$. S is called a (1) _____. If we assign equal probabilities to each element of the sample space, then $P(e_1) = P(e_2) = \cdots = P(e_6) = $ (2) ___.

(1) sample space   (2) $\frac{1}{6}$

220 Given a sample space $S = \{e_1, e_2, \ldots, e_{10}\}$ for an experiment. Suppose $A = \{e_1, e_3, e_4, e_8\}$
A is a subset of S and is called an _____.

event

221 If $S = \{e_1, e_2, \ldots, e_{10}\}$ is a sample space for an experiment and $P(e_1)$, $P(e_2)$, $\ldots$, $P(e_{10})$ have been determined, in some way or another, then if $A = \{e_1, e_3, e_9\}$, A is called an event and the probability of A, $P(A) = $ _____.

$P(e_1) + P(e_3) + P(e_9)$
Notice that you may not have $\frac{3}{10}$ for an answer, since there is no indication in the experiment that the $P(e)$'s are equal.

222 So, any subset A of a sample space S is an *event*, and if $A = \{e_2, e_4, e_5\}$, then $P(A) = $ _____.

$P(e_2) + P(e_4) + P(e_5)$

223　A hat contains three black balls *(B)* and two white balls *(W).* Two players pick a single ball each, in succession, without replacing the ball chosen, until the white ball is drawn. The player getting the white ball wins. For example, the first player might get, on his first draw, a black ball and then the second player choose a white ball. Let us indicate this by *BW*, where the balls are listed in the order drawn. If *BW* occurs, then the second player wins. Suppose *BBW* occurs. Who has won?

The first player wins since *BBW* means that the first player draws a black ball, then the second player draws a black ball, then the first player draws a white ball.

224　Consider the game of frame 223. A hat contains three black balls *(B)* and two white balls *(W).* Two players draw in succession without replacement, one ball from the hat, continuing until one of them draws out a white ball and wins. Let us construct a sample space S for this game, using the notation of listing the color of the balls in the order chosen. Then

$e_1 \longleftrightarrow W$
$e_2 \longleftrightarrow BW$

(1)　$e_3 \longleftrightarrow$___
(2)　$e_4 \longleftrightarrow$___

(1)　*BBW*　　(2)　*BBBW*

225　From the experiment in frame 223: A hat contains three black balls and two white balls. Two players choose one ball at a time in succession without replacement, until the white ball is drawn. The player who draws the white ball wins.
We have decided on a sample space $S = \{e_1,\ e_2,\ e_3,\ e_4\}$ where
$e_1 \longleftrightarrow W$　　$e_2 \longleftrightarrow BW$
$e_3 \longleftrightarrow BBW$　　$e_4 \longleftrightarrow BBBW$

Copy and keep this information for frames 226 to 235. $e_3 \longleftrightarrow BBW$ corresponds to the outcome of a game in which the first player draws B, the second player draws B, and the first player then draws W. The first player wins. Therefore, e_3 is an outcome in which the first player wins. Similarly,

(1)　For e_1, the _____ player wins
(2)　For e_2, the _____ player wins
(3)　For e_4, the _____ player wins

(1)　first　　(2)　second　　(3)　second

226　A natural problem for this game is that of whether the first player or the second player has a better chance of winning. More formally, let A be the event that the first player wins and let B be

▼

the event that the second player wins.
First, (1) A = {_____} and (2) B = {_____}.

---

(1) $\{e_1, e_3\}$ (2) $\{e_2, e_4\}$

---

227 So we have $S = \{e_1, e_2, e_3, e_4\}$ where

$e_1 \longleftrightarrow W$ $e_2 \longleftrightarrow BW$
$e_3 \longleftrightarrow BBW$ $e_4 \longleftrightarrow BBBW$

Event A: the first player wins: $A = \{e_1, e_3\}$
Event B: the second player wins: $B = \{e_2, e_4\}$
If we can compute $P(A)$ and $P(B)$ then, whichever probability is
larger will indicate which player should win more often if the game
is played a large number of times. Obviously, *if* we were to assign
equal probabilities to each element of S, we would have
(1) $P(e_1) = P(e_2) = P(e_3) = P(e_4) = $ ___
Therefore, (2) $P(A) = $ ___ and (3) $P(B) = $ ___

---

(1) $\frac{1}{4}$ (2) $\frac{1}{2}$ (3) $\frac{1}{2}$

---

228 *However*, assigning equal probabilities to each element of S is
questionable. In fact, consider the following problem.
Experiment: A hat contains three black balls and two white balls.
A single ball is to be drawn from the hat and its color noted.
Event A: The ball drawn is white.
Let $S = \{e_1, e_2, e_3, e_4, e_5\}$ where

$e_1 \longleftrightarrow B_1$
$e_2 \longleftrightarrow B_2$ It seems reasonable to assign equal probabilities to
$e_3 \longleftrightarrow B_3$ the elements.
$e_4 \longleftrightarrow W_1$
$e_5 \longleftrightarrow W_2$

(1) Assign $P(e_1) = P(e_2) = \cdots = P(e_5) = $ ___
(2) $A = $_____
(3) $P(A) = $ _____

---

(1) $\frac{1}{5}$ (2) e_4, e_5 (3) $P(e_4) + P(e_5) = \frac{2}{5}$

---

229 So, looking back at our game, we see that if a hat contains three
black balls and two white balls, the probability that a single ball
drawn from the hat will be white is $\frac{2}{5}$.   This corresponds exactly
to e_1 of the sample space of the game.
But if $P(e_1) = \frac{2}{5}$, what would happen if we decided to let e_2, e_3, e_4,
have the same probabilities as $P(e_1)$?

The sum $P(e_1) + P(e_2) + P(e_3) + P(e_4)$ would $\neq 1$.

230 So, we have $S = \{e_1,\ e_2,\ e_3,\ e_4\}$ where

$e_1 \leftrightarrow W \qquad e_2 \leftrightarrow BW$
$e_3 \leftrightarrow BBW \quad e_4 \leftrightarrow BBBW$

and we have let $P(e_1) = \frac{2}{5}$. It seems reasonable to find $P(e_2)$ in the following manner: A hat contains three black balls and two white balls. Two balls are drawn in succession. If E is the event that the first ball is black and the second ball is white, find $P(E)$. Let $S = \{f_1, f_2, \ldots\}$ where

$f_1 \leftrightarrow B_1 B_2 \qquad f_2 \leftrightarrow B_1 B_3 \qquad f_3 \leftrightarrow B_1 W_1$
$f_4 \leftrightarrow B_1 W_2 \qquad f_5 \leftrightarrow B_2 B_1 \qquad f_6 \leftrightarrow B_2 B_3$
$f_7 \leftrightarrow B_2 W_1 \qquad f_8 \leftrightarrow B_2 W_2$

Finish and find $P(E)$.

$f_9 \leftrightarrow B_3 B_1 \qquad f_{10} \leftrightarrow B_3 B_2 \qquad f_{11} \leftrightarrow B_3 W_1$
$f_{12} \leftrightarrow B_3 W_2 \qquad f_{13} \leftrightarrow W_1 B_1 \qquad f_{14} \leftrightarrow W_1 B_2$
$f_{15} \leftrightarrow W_1 B_3 \qquad f_{16} \leftrightarrow W_1 W_2 \qquad f_{17} \leftrightarrow W_2 B_1$
$f_{18} \leftrightarrow W_2 B_2 \qquad f_{19} \leftrightarrow W_2 B_3 \qquad f_{20} \leftrightarrow W_2 W_1$

Let $P(f_1) = P(f_2) = \cdots = P(f_{20}) = 1/20$
$E = \{f_3, f_4, f_7, f_8, f_{11}, f_{12}\}$
$P(E) = P(f_3) + P(f_4) + P(f_7) + \cdots + P(f_{12}) = 6/20 = 3/10$

231 Therefore, for our game, we have, so far, $P(e_1) = \frac{2}{5}$, $P(e_2) = \frac{3}{10}$. e_3 is the event that the first two balls are black and the third ball is white. To find $P(e_3)$, do the following problem: A hat contains three black balls and two white balls. Three balls are to be drawn in succession. If E is the event that the first two balls are black and the third ball is white, find $P(E)$. (*Note:* S contains 60 elements.)

$S = \{e_1,\ e_2,\ \ldots, e_{60}\}$ (or some other symbol such as g, h, etc.) where

$e_1 \leftrightarrow B_1 B_2 B_3 \qquad e_2 \leftrightarrow B_1 B_2 W_1 \qquad e_3 \leftrightarrow B_1 B_2 W_2$
$e_4 \leftrightarrow B_1 B_3 B_2 \qquad e_5 \leftrightarrow B_1 B_3 W_1 \qquad e_6 \leftrightarrow B_1 B_3 W_2$
$e_7 \leftrightarrow B_2 B_1 B_3 \qquad e_8 \leftrightarrow B_2 B_1 W_1 \qquad e_9 \leftrightarrow B_2 B_1 W_2$
$e_{10} \leftrightarrow B_2 B_3 B_1 \qquad e_{11} \leftrightarrow B_2 B_3 W_1 \qquad e_{12} \leftrightarrow B_2 B_3 W_2$
$e_{13} \leftrightarrow B_3 B_1 B_2 \qquad e_{14} \leftrightarrow B_3 B_1 W_1 \qquad e_{15} \leftrightarrow B_3 B_1 W_2 \qquad$ etc.
$e_{16} \leftrightarrow B_3 B_2 B_1 \qquad e_{17} \leftrightarrow B_3 B_2 W_1 \qquad e_{18} \leftrightarrow B_3 B_2 W_2$
$e_{19} \leftrightarrow B_1 W_1 B_2 \qquad e_{20} \leftrightarrow B_1 W_1 B_3 \qquad e_{21} \leftrightarrow B_1 W_1 W_2$
$e_{22} \leftrightarrow B_1 W_2 B_2 \qquad e_{23} \leftrightarrow B_1 W_2 B_3 \qquad e_{24} \leftrightarrow B_1 W_2 W_1$
$e_{25} \leftrightarrow B_2 W_1 B_1 \qquad e_{26} \leftrightarrow B_2 W_1 B_3 \qquad e_{27} \leftrightarrow B_2 W_1 W_2$

$P(e_1) = \cdots = P(e_{60}) = \frac{1}{60}$
$E = \{e_2, e_3, e_5, e_6, e_8, e_9, e_{11}, e_{12}, e_{14}, e_{15}, e_{17}, e_{18}\}$
$P(E) = 12/60 = 1/5$

232 So, if three balls are drawn in succession from a hat containing three black and two white balls, we decided that the probability that the first two balls are black and the third one white is 1/5. So, for the sample space of our game, we have:

$P(e_1) = 2/5 \quad P(e_2) = 3/10 \quad P(e_3) = 1/5$

If we are correct so far, what is $P(e_4)$?

$P(e_4) = 1/10$, since $P(e_1) + P(e_2) + P(e_3) + P(e_4) = 1$

233 If we are correct so far, we have the following: From a hat containing three black balls and two white balls, two players draw a single ball, in succession, without replacement, until a white ball is drawn. $S = \{e_1, e_2, e_3, e_4\}$ where

$e_1 \leftrightarrow W$ $P(e_1) = 2/5$
$e_2 \leftrightarrow BW$ and we have decided to let $P(e_2) = 3/10$
$e_3 \leftrightarrow BBW$ $P(e_3) = 1/5$
$e_4 \leftrightarrow BBBW$ $P(e_4) = 1/10$

If A is the event that the first player wins,
$A = $ _____ $\therefore P(A) = $ _____

$A = \{e_1, e_3\} \quad P(A) = P(e_1) + P(e_3) = 2/5 + 1/5 = 3/5$

234 In the game, if A is the event that the first player wins, we have $P(A) = 3/5$. If B is the event that the second player wins, $B = \{e_2, e_4\}$; therefore $P(B) = $ ___. So, if you were to play this game, which player would you rather be?

2/5,   First player, unless you enjoy losing more often than winning.

235 For the game, $P(e_1) = \frac{2}{5}$, $P(e_2) = \frac{3}{10}$, $P(e_3) = \frac{1}{5}$, and $P(e_4) = \frac{1}{10}$. So the probability that the first player wins is $\frac{3}{5}$. The game would be fair if each player had the same probability of winning. Of course, the players might take turns being first; so if an even number of games were played, neither would have an advantage. Would the game be fair if we changed the rules so that the second player draws the second and third ball and the first player drew the first and fourth ball?

Yes; then, if A is the event that the first player wins, $A = \{e_1, e_4\}$ and $P(A) = 2/5 + 1/10 = 1/2$.

comment

We could do the problem in the following manner: Assume that the players each draw one ball in succession until four balls are drawn,

and the one drawing a white ball first wins:
Then $S = \{e_1, e_2, \ldots, e_{120}\}$ where

$e_1 \longleftrightarrow B_1 B_2 B_3 W_1$ second player wins
$e_2 \longleftrightarrow B_1 B_2 B_3 W_2$ second player wins   etc.
$e_3 \longleftrightarrow B_1 B_2 W_1 B_3$ first player wins
$e_4 \longleftrightarrow B_1 B_2 W_1 W_2$ first player wins

You would have 120 elements in S. Of them, the first white ball appears on the first drawing in 48 of the points, for example,

$$W_1 B_2 B_2 B_3$$
$$W_1 B_1 B_2 W_2 \quad \text{etc.}$$

The first white ball appears on the second drawing in 36 of the points, for example, $B_1 W_2 W_1 B_2$
$$B_2 W_1 B_3 B_1 \quad \text{etc.}$$

The first white ball appears on the third drawing in 24 of the points, for example, $B_1 B_3 W_1 B_2$
$$B_2 B_1 W_2 W_1 \quad \text{etc.}$$

The first white ball appears on the fourth drawing in 12 of the points, for example, $B_1 B_2 B_3 W_1$
$$B_2 B_1 B_3 W_2 \quad \text{etc.}$$

So, using this technique, we have a sample space containing 120 points. If we let $P(e_1) = P(e_2) = \cdots = P(e_{120}) = 1/120$, which seems reasonable, and if A is the event that the first player wins, we see that A contains exactly those points in which the first white ball to appear is either in the first drawing or the third drawing. Thus, there are 72 points in A. Therefore, $P(A) = \frac{72}{120} = \frac{3}{5}$

So, using either technique, we get the same answer, but both techniques are rather laborious, even for such a simple problem. If the hat contained 50 red balls and 10 white balls, you see that the amount of work required using our present methods would be tremendous. Therefore, it will be necessary to find some techniques which can be used to compute probabilities of complex events, if the probabilities of simpler events are known.

Self-test III

1 Suppose A and A' are as shown:

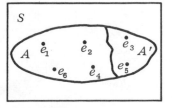

Then **(1)** $S = $ _____,   **(2)** $A = $ _____,   **(3)** $A' = $ _____,
(4) $P(S) = P(e_1) + P(e_2) + P(e_3) + P(e_4) + P(e_5) + P(e_6) = $ ____.

2 If A is an event, and if it is easier to compute $P(A')$ than to compute $P(A)$, first find $P(A')$ and then $P(A)$ = _____ .

3 Suppose, for a given experiment $S = \{e_1, e_2, e_3, e_4, e_5\}$
  (1) You are told $P(e_1) = 0.5$, $P(e_2) = 0.2$, $P(e_3) = 0.1$, $P(e_4) = 0.3$, $P(e_5) = 0.04$, $P(e_6) = 0.06$. What would be your objection?
  (2) You are told $P(e_1) = 0.3$, $P(e_2) = 0.1$, $P(e_3) = 0.2$, $P(e_4) = -0.2$ $P(e_5) = 0.4$, $P(e_6) = 0.2$. What would be your objection?

4 Given an experiment and an event A, if you wish to find $P(A)$ you should follow this procedure:
  (1) Set up a _____ S for the experiment.
  (2) Assign _____ to each element of S.
  (3) Identify A as a _____ of S.
  (4) Then $P(A)$ = the sum of the _____ of the elements of A.

5 *Experiment:* A hat contains three white balls and one blue ball. A ball is chosen, its color noted, and without replacing the first ball, a second ball is drawn and its color noted.
Event A: The two balls drawn are of the same color.
Find $P(A)$.

part iv

COMBINATIONS OF EVENTS AND COMPUTATION OF THEIR PROBABILITIES

1. Intersection of Events and Conditional Probabilities

236 First, we need some new terminology. *Definition:* Given two events A and B of a sample space S for a given experiment, the intersection of A and B, denoted by $A \cap B$, is the set of all elements in both A and B. Note that this corresponds exactly to the definition of intersections of sets.

So, if $S = \{e_1,\ e_2,\ e_3,\ e_4,\ e_5\}$
$A = \{e_2,\ e_4,\ e_5\}$
$B = \{e_1,\ e_2,\ e_3,\ e_5\}$
$A \cap B =$ _____ .

$\{e_2,\ e_5\}$

●237 For a given experiment, if
$S = \{e_1,\ e_2,\ e_3,\ e_4,\ e_5,\ e_6,\ e_7\}$
$A = \{e_1,\ e_3,\ e_6\}$
$B = \{e_2,\ e_4,\ e_5,\ e_6\}$
then $A \cap B =$ ___ .

$\{e_6\}$

238 For a given experiment, if
$S = \{e_1, \ e_2, \ e_3, \ e_4, \ e_5, \ e_6, \ e_7, \ e_8, \ e_9, \ e_{10}\}$
$A = \{e_1, \ e_5, \ e_6\}$
$B = \{e_2, \ e_3, \ e_8\}$
then $A \cap B =$ ___ .

$\emptyset$

239 Graphically, let a sample space S and events A and B for a given experiment be as shown:

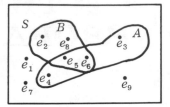

then $A \cap B =$ _____ .

$\{e_5, \ e_6\}$

240 Let a sample space S and events A and B for a given experiment be as shown:

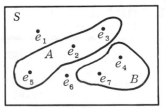

then $A \cap B =$ ___ .

$\emptyset$

241 Look at Panel 1. If A is the event that the first die turns up 1, then $A = \{e_1, \ e_2, \ e_3, \ e_4, \ e_5, \ e_6\}$. If B is the event that the sum of the spots is 5,
(1) $B =$ _____
(2) $A \cap B =$ ___

(1) $\{e_4, \ e_9, \ e_{14}, \ e_{19}\}$ **(2)** $\{e_4\}$

242 Look at Panel 1. Suppose A is the event that both dice have the same number of spots. Then $A = \{e_1, \ e_8, \ e_{15}, \ e_{22}, \ e_{29}, \ e_{36}\}$. On a single trial of an experiment, we say that event A has occurred
▼

if (an outcome corresponding to) e_1, e_8, e_{15}, e_{22}, e_{29}, or e_{36} occurs. Suppose B is the event that the sum of the spots is 3.
(1) $B =$ _____ and B occurs if (2) ___ or (3) ___ occurs.

---

(1) $\{e_2, e_7\}$ (2) e_2 (3) e_7

•**243** Look at Panel 1. Suppose A is the event that the sum of the dots is less than 4. (1) Then $A =$ _____. Suppose B is the event that the first die turns up a 1 and the second die turns up odd.
(2) Then $B =$ _____. Suppose the outcome corresponding to e_3 occurs on a trial of the experiment. (3) Has A occurred?
(4) Has B occurred? Suppose e_1 occurs. (5) Has A occurred?
(6) Has B occurred?

---

(1) $\{e_1, e_2, e_7\}$ (2) $\{e_1, e_3, e_5\}$ (3) no, $e_3 \notin A$
(4) yes, $e_3, \in B$ (5) yes, $e_1 \in A$ (6) yes, $e_1 \in B$

---

244 *Note:* Roughly we say that event A occurs if an element in set A occurs.

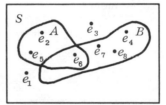

A occurs if e_2, e_5, or e_6 occurs.
B occurs if ___, ___, ___, or ___ occurs.

---

e_4, e_6, e_7, e_8

---

245 For a given experiment, S and events A and B are shown.

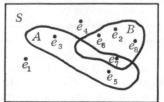

(1) $A =$ _____ (2) $B =$ _____ (3) $A \cap B =$ ___
On a certain trial of the experiment, e_7 occurs.
(4) Has A occurred?   (5) Has B occurred?

---

(1) $\{e_3, e_5, e_7\}$ (2) $\{e_2, e_6, e_7, e_8\}$ (3) $\{e_7\}$
(4) yes   (5) yes

246 Suppose S and events A and B are shown for a given experiment.

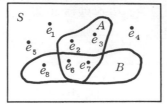

    (1)   For what points of S would both A and B occur at the same time on a given trial of the experiment?

    (2) $A \cap B = $ _____.

---

    (1) e_6 and e_7 (2) $\{e_6, e_7\}$

---

247 Therefore, $A \cap B$ contains exactly those elements whose occurrence on a given trial of the experiment means that both event A and event B have occurred. In fact, $A \cap B$ is often read "event A and B" in probability courses, rather than "A intersection B."
If, for a given experiment
$S = \{e_1, e_2, e_3, e_4, e_5, e_6, e_7, e_8, e_9, e_{10}\}$, event $C = \{e_2, e_3, e_5, e_{10}\}$, and event $D = \{e_3, e_4, e_8, e_{10}\}$, then the event that C and D occur is
$C \cap B = $ _____.

    $\{e_3, e_{10}\}$

---

248 Look at Panel 1. Suppose A is the event that the first die turns up greater than 4. (1) Then $A = $ _____. Suppose B is the event that the sum of the spots on both dice is 9. (2) Then $B = $ _____.
$A \cap B$ is the event that the first die is greater than 4, *and* the sum of the spots is 9. (3) Then $A \cap B = $ _____.

---

    (1) $\{e_{25}, e_{26}, e_{27}, e_{28}, e_{29}, e_{30}, e_{31}, e_{32}, e_{33}, e_{34}, e_{35}, e_{36}\}$
    (2) $\{e_{18}, e_{23}, e_{28}, e_{33}\}$ (3) $\{e_{28}, e_{33}\}$

---

249 Of course, given a sample space S of an experiment and given $P(e_1)$, $P(e_2)$, ..., $P(e_n)$ of the sample space, if A and B are events, we could compute $P(A \cap B)$ by finding $A \cap B$ and adding the probabilities of the elements of $A \cap B$. For example, on Panel 1, if A is the event that the sum of the spots is greater than 8 and B is the event that the second die turns up a 3 or a 6, then to find $A \cap B$,

    (1) $A = $ _____   (2) $B = $ _____   (3) $A \cap B = $ _____
∴ (4) $P(A \cap B) = $ _____

---

    (1) $\{e_{18}, e_{23}, e_{24}, e_{28}, e_{29}, e_{30}, e_{33}, e_{34}, e_{35}, e_{36}\}$
    (2) $\{e_3, e_6, e_9, e_{12}, e_{15}, e_{18}, e_{21}, e_{24}, e_{27}, e_{30}, e_{33}, e_{36}\}$
    (3) $\{e_{18}, e_{24}, e_{30}, e_{33}, e_{36}\}$
    (4) $P(e_{18}) + P(e_{24}) + P(e_{30}) + P(e_{33}) + P(e_{36}) = \frac{1}{36} + \frac{1}{36} + \frac{1}{36} + \frac{1}{36} + \frac{1}{36} = \frac{5}{36}$

250 But this technique is not any simpler than the technique used in Part III. In fact, we are still finding points in an event and computing probabilities by adding the probabilities of the elements in the event. It would be nicer if $P(A \cap B)$ could be computed from $P(A)$ and $P(B)$. (It can sometimes be found this way, but unfortunately not always.)

Suppose:

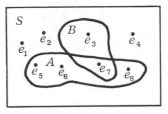

and $P(e_1) = P(e_2) = \cdots = P(e_8) = \frac{1}{8}$

(1) $A = $ _____   (2) $P(A) = $ _____   (3) $B = $ ___
(4) $P(B) = $ _____   (5) $A \cap B = $ ___   (6) $P(A \cap B) = $ ___

(1) $\{e_5, e_6, e_7, e_8\}$ (2) $\frac{4}{8} = \frac{1}{2}$ (3) $\{e_3, e_7\}$ (4) $\frac{2}{8} = \frac{1}{4}$,
(5) $\{e_7\}$ (6) $\frac{1}{8}$
Note: $P(A \cap B) = P(A) \cdot P(B)$. Before you jump to a conclusion, jump to the next problem.

●251 Now look at this problem:

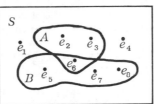

and $P(e_1) = P(e_2) = \cdots = P(e_8) = \frac{1}{8}$
(1) $A = $ _____   (2) $P(A) = $ ___   (3) $B = $ _____
(4) $P(B) = $ _____   (5) $A \cap B = $ ___   (6) $P(A \cap B) = $ ___

(1) $\{e_2, e_3, e_6\}$ (2) $\frac{3}{8}$ (3) $\{e_5, e_6, e_7, e_8\}$ (4) $\frac{4}{8} = \frac{1}{2}$
(5) $\{e_6\}$ (6) $\frac{1}{8}$
Note: $P(A \cap B) \neq P(A) \cdot P(B)$

252 *Experiment:* Two coins are tossed.
Event A: Two heads appear.
For practice in the use of intersections, let us consider event A as the intersection of events B and C where
B is the event that the first coin is a head
C is the event that the second coin is a head

▼

Note: $A = B \cap C$. Let $S = \{e_1,\ e_2,\ e_3,\ e_4\}$ where

$e_1 \leftrightarrow HH \qquad e_2 \leftrightarrow HT$
$e_3 \leftrightarrow TH \qquad e_4 \leftrightarrow TT$

and $P(e_1) = P(e_2) = P(e_3) = P(e_4) = \frac{1}{4}$.
(1) $B =$ _____   (2) $C =$ _____   (3) $B \cap C =$ ___
(4) $P(B \cap C) =$ ___

---

(1) $\{e_1,\ e_2\}$ (2) $\{e_1,\ e_3\}$ (3) $\{e_1\}$ (4) $\frac{1}{4}$

---

253 In Panel 1, let A be the event that the number of spots on the first die is greater than the number of spots on the second die; that is, all $(p,\ q)$ where $p > q$. (1) $A =$ _____ Let B be the event that the sum of the spots on the two dice is less than 5. (2) $B =$ _____ (3) $A \cap B =$ _____. $A \cap B$ is the event that the number of spots on the first die is greater than the number of spots on the second *and* that the sum of the spots is less than 5. (4) $P(A \cap B) =$ _____

---

(1) $\{e_7,\ e_{13},\ e_{14},\ e_{19},\ e_{20},\ e_{21},\ e_{25},\ e_{26},\ e_{27},\ e_{28},\ e_{31},\ e_{32},\ e_{33},\ e_{34},\ e_{35}\}$
(2) $\{e_1,\ e_2,\ e_3,\ e_7,\ e_8,\ e_{13}\}$ (3) $\{e_7,\ e_{13}\}$
(4) $P(e_7) + P(e_{13}) = \frac{2}{36} = \frac{1}{18}$
Note: $P(A) = \frac{15}{36} = \frac{5}{12} \qquad P(B) = \frac{6}{36} = \frac{1}{6}$
$P(A \cap B) \neq P(A) \cdot P(B)$

---

254 *Experiment:* A die is rolled. Find the probability that the die turns up an even number and that the die turns up less than 5.
For practice, let A be the event that an even number turns up, and B be the event that a number less than 5 turns up. Then we want $P(A \cap B)$.
(1) Set up S.   (2) Assign probabilities.   (3) Find A.
(4) Find B.   (5) Find $A \cap B$.   (6) Find $P(A \cap B)$.

---

(1) $S = \{e_1,\ e_2,\ e_3,\ e_4,\ e_5,\ e_6\}$ where

     $e_1 \leftrightarrow a$ 1 turns up $e_2 \leftrightarrow a$ 2 turns up,   etc.

(2) $P(e_1) = P(e_2) = \cdots = P(e_6) = \frac{1}{6}$
(3) $\{e_2,\ e_4,\ e_6\}$ (4) $\{e_1,\ e_2,\ e_3,\ e_4\}$ (5) $\{e_2,\ e_4\}$
(6) $P(e_2) + P(e_4) = 1/6 + 1/6 = 1/3$
[*Note:* In this case, $P(A \cap B) = P(A) \cdot P(B)$]

---

255 In Panel 1, let A be the event that the sum of the dots is 7. Let B be the event that both dice have the same number of dots.
(1) $A =$ _____   (2) $B =$ _____   (3) $A \cap B =$ ___

---

(1) $e_6,\ e_{11},\ e_{16},\ e_{21},\ e_{26},\ e_{31}$
(2) $e_1,\ e_8,\ e_{15},\ e_{22},\ e_{29},\ e_{36}$
(3) $\emptyset$

256 *Definition:* Two events A and B are *mutually exclusive,* if, and only if, their intersection is the empty set.
Experiment: Toss a die.
Event A: The number appearing is odd.
Event B: A 2 or a 4 appears.
$S = \{e_1,\ e_2,\ e_3,\ e_4,\ e_5,\ e_6\}$ where

$e_1 \longleftrightarrow a$ 1 turns up $e_2 \longleftrightarrow a$ 2 turns up   etc.

(1) $A =$ _____   (2) $B =$ _____   (3) $A \cap B =$ ___
$\therefore$ (4) A and B are _____

---

(1) $\{e_1,\ e_3,\ e_5\}$ (2) $\{e_2,\ e_4\}$ (3) $\emptyset$
(4) mutually exclusive

●**257** Suppose a sample space S and events A and B are as shown graphically:

(1) $A =$ _____   (2) $B =$ _____   (3) $A \cap B =$ ___
$\therefore$ (4) A and B are _____

---

(1) $\{e_2,\ e_3,\ e_4\}$ (2) $\{e_6,\ e_7\}$ (3) $\emptyset$
(4) mutually exclusive

---

258 *Experiment:* Two coins are tossed.
$S = \{e_1,\ e_2,\ e_3,\ e_4\}$ where

$e_1 \longleftrightarrow HH$ $e_2 \longleftrightarrow HT$
$e_3 \longleftrightarrow TH$ $e_4 \longleftrightarrow TT$

(1) If event A is that the first coin is a head, $A =$ _____
(2) If event B is that the second coin is a head, $B =$ _____
(3) $A \cap B =$ ___
(4) Are A and B mutually exclusive?

---

(1) $\{e_1,\ e_2\}$ (2) $\{e_1,\ e_3\}$ (3) $\{e_1\}$ (4) no

---

259 Suppose for a given experiment,
$S = \{e_1,\ e_2,\ e_3,\ e_4,\ e_5,\ e_6,\ e_7,\ e_8,\ e_9,\ e_{10}\}$
$A = \{e_2,\ e_5,\ e_6\}$ and $B = \{e_1,\ e_8\}$

▼

On a single trial of the experiment, we say that event A has occurred if (the outcome corresponding to) e_2, e_5, or e_6 occurs. Event
B occurs if____ or ____ occurs.

e_1, e_8

260 For a given experiment,
$S = \{e_1, e_2, e_3, e_4\}$ $A = \{e_1\}$ $B = \{e_1, e_3\}$
Suppose that on a single trial of an experiment, e_1 occurs
(1) Event A _____ (has, has not) occurred.
(2) Event B _____ (has, has not) occurred.
(3) You can see from this experiment that in a *single trial* it
_____ (is, is not) possible for A and B to occur at the same
time.
(4) In this experiment, A and B_____ (are, are not) mutually
exclusive events.

(1) has   (2) has   (3) is   (4) are not

261 For a given experiment,
$S = \{e_1, e_2, e_3, e_4\}$ $A = \{e_1, e_3\}$ $B = \{e_2, e_4\}$
(1) In a single trial of the experiment, suppose e_1 occurs.
  (a) Has event A occurred?
  (b) Has event B occurred?
(2) In a single trial of the experiment, suppose e_4 occurs.
  (a) Has event A occurred?
  (b) Has event B occurred?
(3) In a *single trial* of the experiment, if A occurs, can B occur?
If yes, give an example.
(4) In a *single trial* of the experiment, if B occurs, can A occur?
If yes, give an example.
(5) In this experiment A and B _____ (are, are not) mutually exclusive events.

(1) (a) yes   (b) no
(2) (a) no   (b) yes
(3) no
(4) no
(5) are

262 Two events A and B are mutually exclusive if, and only if, they
have no elements of S in common; that is, if, and only if, $A \cap B = \emptyset$.
Roughly speaking then, if A and B are mutually exclusive events,
and on a single trial of an experiment one of the events occurs, then
the other one_____ (can, cannot) occur.

cannot

●**263** If two events A *and* B are mutually exclusive, then (1) $A \cap B =$ ___
and both of these events (2) _____ (can, cannot) occur at the
same time in a single trial of the experiment.

(1) $\emptyset$ (2) cannot

264 Roughly speaking, if A and B are mutually exclusive, then they
cannot *both* occur on a single trial of an experiment. If, on a
single trial of the experiment, one of the events occurs, then the
other one _____.

cannot or does not

265 Recall: Given a sample space S and an event A, then A', the complement of A, is the set of all elements of S which are not in A.
Thus, $A \cap A' =$ ___.

$\emptyset$

266 Graphically: A and its complement A' are shown:

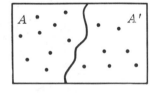

(1) $A \cap A' =$ ___ $\therefore$ (2) A and A' are _____ events.

(1) $\emptyset$ (2) mutually exclusive

267 Let $S = \{e_1, e_2, e_3, e_4, e_5, e_6, e_7, e_8, e_9, e_{10}\}$
and $A = \{e_2, e_3, e_5, e_6\}$ $A' = \{x \mid x \in S$ and $x \notin A\}$
so $A' = \{$_____$\}$

$e_1, e_4, e_7, e_8, e_9, e_{10}$

268 Since we have defined the probability of an event to be the sum of
the probabilities of the elements of the event, it seems reasonable
to define $P(\emptyset) = 0$ since the empty set contains no elements. Thus,
if A and B are mutually exclusive events, then, since
(1) $A \cap B =$ ___, we have that (2) $P(A \cap B) =$ ___.

(1) $\emptyset$ (2) 0

●**269** Given a sample space S for an experiment.   If A and B are mutually exclusive events, then (1) $A \cap B =$ ___ (2) $P(A \cap B) =$ ___

(1) ∅   (2) 0

270 If a sample space S and events A and B are as shown:

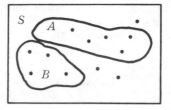

Then ___ = ∅; so A and B are _____ events.

$A \cap B,$ mutually exclusive

271 A sample space S and events A and B are as shown:

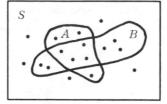

Are A and B mutually exclusive events? Why?

no, $A \cap B \neq \emptyset$

272 Let $S = \{e_1,\ e_2,\ e_3,\ e_4,\ e_5\}$ and $P(e_1) = 0.3$, $P(e_2) = 0.3$, $P(e_3) = 0.2$, $P(e_4) = 0.1$, $P(e_5) = 0.1$.
If $A = \{e_1,\ e_2,\ e_4\}$,   **(1)** $P(A) =$ _____
If $B = \{e_2,\ e_3,\ e_4\}$,   **(2)** $P(B) =$ _____
(3) $A \cap B =$ _____   **(4)** $P(A \cap B) =$ _____

(1) $P(e_1) + P(e_2) + P(e_4) = 0.7$
(2) $P(e_2) + P(e_3) + P(e_4) = 0.6$
(3) $\{e_2, e_4\}$
(4) $P(e_2) + P(e_4) = 0.4$

273 Let $S = \{e_1,\ e_2,\ e_3,\ e_4,\ e_5\}$ and $P(e_1) = 0.3$, $P(e_2) = 0.2$, $P(e_3) = 0.2$, $P(e_4) = 0.1$, $P(e_5) = 0.2$.
If $A = \{e_1,\ e_2,\ e_4\}$,   **(1)** $P(A) =$ _____

▼

If $B = \{e_2, e_3, e_4\}$ (2) $P(B) =$ _____
(3) $A \cap B =$ _____   (4) $P(A \cap B) =$ _____

---

(1) $P(e_1) + P(e_2) + P(e_4) = 0.6$
(2) $P(e_2) + P(e_3) + P(e_4) = 0.5$
(3) $\{e_2, e_4\}$
(4) $P(e_2) + P(e_4) = 0.3$

---

274 A biologist performs the following experiment: A hamster is chosen and a coin is tossed.

1. If the coin turns up heads, the hamster is injected with a vaccine designed to prevent disease X. He is then exposed to disease X.
2. If the coin turns up tails, the hamster is exposed directly to disease X.

In either event, the hamster is observed to see if he contracts disease X, and records are kept, showing whether the hamster was vaccinated *(V)* or not *(V')* and whether the hamster contracted the disease *(X)* or not *(X')*. The 200 trials of the experiment produced the following results:

	X	X'
V	20	70
V'	60	50

Copy this table on a separate sheet of paper, and also record that $V \leftrightarrow$ vaccinated, $V' \leftrightarrow$ not vaccinated, $X \leftrightarrow$ contracted the disease, $X' \leftrightarrow$ did not contract the disease.

Have a correct copy of the table (check it) and a record of what V, V', X, and X' represent.

---

275 Look at the table. It shows the results of 200 experiments. Since every trial results in an outcome which should appear in one and only one of the blocks, the sum of the numbers in the blocks should be _____. Is it?

200,   yes

---

276 If you were asked how many of the 200 hamsters were vaccinated, you would add the numbers in the parts indicated by the crosshatched section of the following table:

▼

How many hamsters were vaccinated?

90

277 If you were asked how many of the 200 hamsters did *not* contract the disease X', you would add the numbers in the parts indicated by the crosshatched sections of the table below:

How many hamsters did not contract the disease?

120

●**278** (1) From the table, how many hamsters contracted the disease?
(2) From the table, how many hamsters were not vaccinated?

(1) 80   (2) 110

279 From the table, we see that 90 of the hamsters were vaccinated. Of the 90 vaccinated hamsters, how many contracted disease X?

20   (from the X column across from V)

●**280** From the table, we see that 90 of the 200 hamsters were vaccinated. Of the 90 vaccinated hamsters, how many did not contract disease X?

70

281 From the table, we see that 110 of the 200 hamsters were not vaccinated. Of the 110 unvaccinated hamsters, how many contracted disease X?

60

282 From the table, we see that 110 of the 200 hamsters were not vaccinated. Of these 110 unvaccinated hamsters, how many did not
contract disease X?

50

283 From the table, we see that 80 of the 200 hamsters contracted disease X. Of the 80 hamsters contracting disease X, (1) ___ have
been vaccinated.
From the table, we see that of the 80 hamsters contracting disease X, (2) ___ of them have not been vaccinated.

(1) 20   (2) 60

284 From the table, we see that 120 of the 200 hamsters did not contract disease X. Of these 120 hamsters not contracting the disease, how many had been vaccinated?

70

285 From the table, how many of the 120 hamsters not contracting
disease X had not been vaccinated?

50

286 Recall: If during N trials of an experiment, event A occurs $n(A)$
times, then the relative frequency of event A = ___.

$\dfrac{n(A)}{N}$

287 Roughly speaking, the relative frequency of event A is the ratio of
the number of times A occurs to the number of times A was given
the opportunity to occur.
If event A occurred 15 times in 35 trials of an experiment, then
relative frequency of A = ___.

$\frac{15}{35}$ or $\frac{3}{7}$

288 Recall also that, for any event A, if the experiment is performed
N times, (1) ___ $\leq n(A) \leq$ ___, therefore (2) ___ $\leq$ relative frequency of $A \leq$ ___.

(1) 0, N (2) 0,   1

289 Finally, recall that, if an experiment is performed a large number
of times, the relative frequency of A can be considered as an approximation for ___.

$P(A)$

---

comment

In fact, we have considered $P(A)$, the probability of event A, as
being an "ideal number" which the relative frequency of A will
ultimately get close to as the number of trials of the experiment
becomes large, and we have constructed our mathematical model
(sample space, event, probability of an event, etc.) using relative
frequencies of events as cues. The hamster problem will be used
to give us some ideas for further theorems.

---

290 Let us use the notation:
V is the event that a hamster was vaccinated.
V' is the event that a hamster was not vaccinated.
X is the event that a hamster contracted disease X.
X' is the event that a hamster did not contract disease X.
Then, from the table, $n(V) = 90$ $n(V') = $___.

110

---

291 From the table, $n(X) = $___

80

●292 From the table, $n(X') = $___

120

---

293 Recall, if event A occurs $n(A)$ times during N trials of an experiment, relative frequency of $A = n(A)/N$. From the table, relative
frequency of $V = $_____.

$\frac{90}{200} = \frac{9}{20}$

●294 From the table, relative frequency of $V' = $_____.

$\frac{110}{200} = \frac{11}{20}$

295 From the table, relative frequency of $X =$ _____.

$\frac{80}{200} = \frac{2}{5}$

296 From the table, relative frequency of $X' =$ _____.

$\frac{120}{200} = \frac{3}{5}$

297 Recall, if A and B are events, $A \cap B$ is the event that A *and* B occur. From the table, $n(V \cap X) =$ ___.

20

298 From the table, $n(V \cap X) = 20$; so relative frequency of $(V \cap X) =$ _____.

$\frac{20}{200} = \frac{1}{10}$

●**299** From the table, relative frequency of $V \cap X' =$ _____.

$\frac{70}{200} = \frac{7}{20}$

300 From the table, relative frequency of $V' \cap X =$ _____.

$\frac{60}{200} = \frac{3}{10}$

301 From the table, the relative frequency of $V' \cap X' =$ _____.

$\frac{50}{200} = \frac{1}{4}$

302 Now *if* we were to use these relative frequencies of events as the probabilities of the events, we would have:

$P(V) = \frac{90}{200}$ $P(V') = \frac{110}{200}$
$P(X) = \frac{80}{200}$ $P(X') = \frac{120}{200}$
$P(V \cap X) = \frac{20}{200}$ $P(V \cap X') = \frac{70}{200}$
$P(V' \cap X) = \frac{60}{200}$ $P(V' \cap X') = \frac{50}{200}$

Copy these and save.

Have a copy of the probabilities just listed.

303 If you look at the probabilities just listed, you probably will not see anything very interesting. We are trying to find some easier techniques for computing probabilities of more complicated events if we are given or can find probabilities of simpler events, such as finding $P(A \cap B)$ if we know, for example, $P(A)$ and $P(B)$.
Do you, for example, see any interesting relationship between $P(V)$, $P(X)$, and $P(V \cap X)$?

No   (at least, I don't).

304 Nothing has happened so far, then, so let us go bravely onward. An interesting kind of question, and one you probably looked at when you first saw the chart, is, *of the vaccinated hamsters*, how many contracted disease X?

20

305 Of the vaccinated hamsters, 20 contracted disease X. How many of the unvaccinated hamsters contracted disease X?

60

306 But the *numbers* contracting the disease do not tell the whole story. Of course, more unvaccinated hamsters than vaccinated hamsters contracted the disease, but the total number of unvaccinated hamsters (110) was greater than the total number of vaccinated ones (90); so more of the unvaccinated hamsters had a chance to get the disease. A better measure of comparison would be the _____.

relative frequency

307 What we would like to see is the relative frequency of disease X among the vaccinated hamsters compared with the relative frequency of disease X among the unvaccinated hamsters. Note, then, that we are splitting the experiment, and the relative frequencies we are speaking of are *not* computed with respect to the 200 experiments. For example, the relative frequency of disease X among the vaccinated hamsters is given by the number of times X occurred in row 1, where only 90 experiments occurred. Therefore the relative frequency of X among the vaccinated hamsters $= \frac{20}{90}$. Similarly, the relative frequency of X among the unvaccinated hamsters $=$ ___.

$\frac{60}{110}$

308 We need some new notation for such relative frequencies. For example, the relative frequency of X among all 200 hamsters $= 80/200$, but the relative frequency of X among the vaccinated hamsters $=$

▼

20/90. What we mean by the latter relative frequency is the relative frequency of X, given that V has occurred. Similarly, the relative frequency of X, given that V' has occurred = ___.

$\frac{60}{110}$

---

309 Similarly, the relative frequency of X', given that V has occurred, means to find the relative frequency of X' among the vaccinated hamsters. Therefore, relative frequency of X', given that V has occurred = ___.

$\frac{70}{90}$

---

310 The notation: relative frequency of $(A|B)$ will mean the relative frequency of event A, given that event B has occurred. Thus, relative frequency of $(X'|V')$ means the relative frequency of X' among the unvaccinated hamsters, that is, given that event V' has occurred. Therefore, relative frequency of $(X'|V') =$ ___.

$\frac{50}{110}$

---

311 Relative frequency of $(A|B)$ means the relative frequency of event A, given that event B has occurred. For example, 10 rolls of a die produced the following results: 2, 5, 3, 5, 1, 6, 3, 4, 2, 1. Suppose event A is that an even number occurred, then relative frequency of $A = 4/10$. Suppose event B is that a number less than 5 occurred. To find the relative frequency of $(A|B)$ means to find relative frequency of event A, given that B has occurred. That is, find the relative frequency of event A with respect to the number of times that B occurred. Now, B occurred seven times (check). *During those seven times,* **(1)** A occurred _____ times. Therefore, **(2)** relative frequency of $(A|B) =$ ___.

---

(1)   three   (2)   3/7

---

312 So, from the table, relative frequency of $(V|X)$ means the relative frequency of vaccination given that the hamsters contracted disease X. So we are interested in the relative frequency of V *only among the 80 hamsters* contracting the disease. Therefore, relative frequency of $(V|X) =$ ___.

$\frac{20}{80}$

●**313** From the table, relative frequency of $(V'|X) =$ ___.

$\frac{60}{80}$

314 From the table, relative frequency of $(V \mid X') =$ ___.

$\frac{70}{120}$

315 From the table,
(1) Relative frequency of $(V' \mid X') =$ ___
(2) Relative frequency of $(X \mid V) =$ ___

(1) $\frac{50}{120}$ (2) $\frac{20}{90}$

316 From the table,
(1) Relative frequency of $(X' \mid V) =$ ___
(2) Relative frequency of $(X \mid V') =$ ___
(3) Relative frequency of $(X' \mid V') =$ ___

(1) $\frac{70}{90}$ (2) $\frac{60}{110}$ (3) $\frac{50}{110}$

317 Suppose these relative frequencies are used as values for probabilities. We would have among others
$P(X \mid V) = \frac{20}{90}$ $P(X \mid V') =$ ___.

$P(X \mid V') = \frac{60}{110}$

318 Now consider carefully the probabilities listed here and the ones that you have copied from frame 302.
$P(V) = \frac{90}{200}$ $P(X \mid V) = \frac{20}{90}$ $P(V \cap X) = \frac{20}{200}$
$P(V') = \frac{110}{200}$ $P(X \mid V') = \frac{60}{110}$ $P(V' \cap X) = \frac{60}{200}$
Note this relationship:
$P(V \cap X) = \frac{20}{200}$
$P(V) \cdot P(X \mid V) = \frac{90}{200} \cdot \frac{20}{90} = \frac{20}{200}$
$\therefore P(V \cap X) = P(V) \cdot P(X \mid V)$

Show that $P(V' \cap X) = P(V') \cdot P(X \mid V')$.

$P(V' \cap X) = \frac{60}{200}$
$P(V') \cdot P(X \mid V') = \frac{110}{200} \cdot \frac{60}{110}$
$\therefore P(V' \cap X) = P(V') \cdot P(X \mid V')$

319 So we have a conjecture. If the pattern from frame 318 is to continue, then, if A and B are events, $P(A \cap B) = P(A) \cdot P(B \mid A)$. Let us check some others. From the table, (1) $P(X \cap V) =$ ___,
(2) $P(X) =$ ___, (3) $P(V \mid X) =$ ___, (4) Write the relationship which holds with the three expressions: $P(X \cap V) ; P(X) ; P(V \mid X)$.

▼

(5) Show that the relationship in (4) is true by substituting the values you found for (1), (2), and (3).

---

(1) $\frac{20}{200}$ (2) $\frac{80}{200}$ (3) $\frac{20}{80}$
(4) $P(X \cap V) = P(X) \cdot P(V \mid X)$
(5) $P(X \cap V) = \frac{20}{200}$
$P(X) \cdot P(V \mid X) = \frac{80}{200} \cdot \frac{20}{80} = \frac{20}{200}$

$\therefore \ P(X \cap V) = P(X) \cdot P(V \mid X)$

---

320 If you are having trouble, recall that $(X' \cap V)$ means the event X' *and* the event V. $(X' \cap V)$ occurred 70 times out of the 200 trials; so using relative frequency of $(X' \cap V)$ as an approximation of $P(X' \cap V)$, we have $P(X' \cap V) =$ ___.

$\frac{70}{200}$

---

321 Recall also that $(V \mid X')$ means the event V on the condition that event X' has occurred. Therefore, relative frequency of $(V \mid X')$ means the relative frequency of V during the times when X' occurred. Now, X' occurred 120 times; so $n(V \mid X')$, that is, the number of times V occurred during these 120 times that X' occurred, is, from the table, 70; therefore, relative frequency of $(V \mid X') =$ ___.

$\frac{70}{120}$ So, if we use the relative frequency as an approximation,
$P(V \mid X') = \frac{70}{120}$

---

322 We have, from frames 320 and 321, that $P(X' \cap V) = \frac{70}{200}$,
$P(V \mid X') = \frac{70}{120}$, and from the table, $P(X') = \frac{120}{200}$.
Does $P(X' \cap V) = P(X') \cdot P(V \mid X')$?

---

yes

●323 So, using the relative frequencies of events in place of probabilities, we find that the pattern $P(A \cap B) = P(A) \cdot P(B \mid A)$ still holds. Let us check some more.
(1) $P(X' \cap V') =$ ___ (2) $P(X') =$ ___ (3) $P(V' \mid X') =$ ___,
(4) Show that $P(X' \cap V') = P(X') \cdot P(V' \mid X')$.

---

(1) $\frac{50}{200}$ (2) $\frac{120}{200}$ (3) $\frac{50}{120}$
(4) $P(X' \cap V') = \frac{50}{200}$
$P(X') \cdot P(V' \mid X') = \frac{120}{200} \cdot \frac{50}{120} = \frac{50}{200}$

$\therefore \ P(X' \cap V') = P(X') \cdot P(V' \mid X')$

324 Maybe we have something important here. Let us try another example. A die is tossed 100 times with the following results:
The 1 turned up 20 times   The 2 turned up 15 times
The 3 turned up 12 times   The 4 turned up 18 times
The 5 turned up 16 times   The 6 turned up 19 times

Copy this information and save it.
Let A be the event that an even number turned up.
How many times did A occur?

52

325 Since A is the event that an even number turned up and A occurred 52 times out of a total of 100 trials, relative frequency of A = ___.

$\frac{52}{100}$

326 Let B be the event that a number less than 4 appeared. How many times did B occur?

47

327 If B is the event that a number less than 4 appears, the relative frequency of B = ___.

$\frac{47}{100}$

328 Record this information and save it with the results of the experiments.
A is the event that an even number appeared.
B is the event that a number less than 4 appeared.
Note that we will use the relative frequencies of events as values for the probabilities. Thus, for this die, we would let $P(A) = \frac{52}{100}$ and $P(B)$ = ___.

$\frac{47}{100}$

Have a copy of events A and B.

329 Now, suppose you are given that B has occurred, that is, you are considering only those trials which resulted in a number less than 4. Under this condition, how many times did A occur?

15

330 So, given that event B occurred, we are considering only the trials resulting as follows:
The 1 turned up 20 times
The 2 turned up 15 times
The 3 turned up 12 times
So the relative frequency of A on the condition that B has occurred is ___.

$\frac{15}{47}$ (notice the 47)

331 As long as we are using relative frequency for a value of P, $P(A \mid B)$ is exactly that relative frequency just computed, i.e., the ratio of the number of times which event A occurred during those trials resulting in B to the number of times event B occurred. B occurred 47 times, and during those 47 times, A occurred 15 times. Therefore, we have $P(A \mid B) =$ ___.

$\frac{15}{47}$

●**332** Similarly, to find $P(B \mid A)$, we consider only the trials in which A has occurred (52 times). (1) Out of the 52 times which A occurred, how many times did B occur? Therefore, (2) $P(B \mid A) =$ ___.

(1) 15   (2) $\frac{15}{52}$

333 *Definition:* Given two events, say C and D, $P(C \mid D)$ is called the *conditional probability of C given D*. It means the probability of C given the condition that D has occurred. Note that $P(C)$ and $P(C \mid D)$ need not be the same value. For the problem under discussion, (1) $P(A) =$ ___ and (2) $P(A \mid B) =$ ___.

(1) $\frac{52}{100}$ (2) $\frac{15}{47}$ *Note:* $P(A) \neq P(A \mid B)$

334 It will be easier for our work to set up a table in the following manner.
A occurred 52 times. Of these 52 times, B occurred 15 times and B' occurred 37 times. (Remember, B' is the event that B did

▼

not occur.) A' occurred 48 times. Of these 48 times, B occurred 32 times, and B' occurred ___ times. So we have,

	B	B'
A	15	37
A'	32	—

16

	B	B'
A	15	37
A'	32	16

Copy this table and save it.

335 From the table, it is easy to find $P(A)$ since the trials resulting in event A are recorded in row 1.
A occurred 15 + 37 = 52 times. Therefore, we will use $P(A) = \frac{52}{100}$.
Similarly, $P(A') =$ ___.

$\frac{48}{100}$

336 From frame 335 we have $P(A) = \frac{52}{100}$ and $P(A') = \frac{48}{100}$.
$P(A) + P(A') =$ ___

$\frac{100}{100}$ or 1

337 From the table, $P(B)$ is easy to find since the number of trials resulting in B are recorded in the first column. So B occurred 15 + 32 = 47 times. Therefore, we will use $P(B) = \frac{47}{100}$.
Similarly, $P(B') =$ ___.

$\frac{53}{100}$

338 $(A \cap B)$ is the event A and B occur. $P(A \cap B)$ is easy to see from the table since the trials in which event A and event B occurred are recorded in the upper left-hand block. $A \cap B$ occurred 15 times; so we take $P(A \cap B) =$ ___.

$\frac{15}{100}$

339 $A \cap B = B \cap A$; so if $P(A \cap B) = \frac{15}{100}$, $P(B \cap A) =$ ___.

$\frac{15}{100}$

340 From the table, $P(A \cap B') = $ ___ .

$\frac{37}{100}$

341 From the table, $P(A' \cap B) = $ ___ .

$\frac{32}{100}$

342 From the table, $P(A' \cap B') = $ ___ .

$\frac{16}{100}$

343 Now, to find $P(A \mid B)$ from the table, we know that $(A \mid B)$ gives us the condition that B has occurred. Therefore, we are concerned only with the 47 trials recorded in the first column. Of these 47 trials, A occurred 15 times; so $P(A \mid B) = \frac{15}{47}$.
Similarly find $P(B \mid A)$.

$P(B \mid A) = \frac{15}{52}$
Given the condition that A has occurred, we consider only those trials listed in the first row. So we are considering only the 52 trials in which A occurred. Of these, B occurred 15 times.
$\therefore P(B \mid A) = \frac{15}{52}$

344 From the table, find $P(A \mid B')$.

$P(A \mid B') = \frac{37}{53}$
The conditional probability of A given B' means that we are concerned only with those trials in which B' has occurred, that is, with column 2. From this column, we see that A occurred 37 times out of the 53 times that B' occurred.

345 From the table, find $P(B' \mid A)$.

$\frac{37}{52}$

346 From the table, find
(1) $P(A' \mid B)$
(2) $P(B \mid A')$
(3) $P(A' \mid B')$
(4) $P(B' \mid A')$

(1) $\frac{32}{47}$ (2) $\frac{32}{48}$ (3) $\frac{16}{53}$ (4) $\frac{16}{48}$

347 Now, let us check our conjecture. We think possibly that if C and D are events, $P(C \cap D) = P(C) \cdot P(D \mid C)$. From our table, $P(A \cap B) = \frac{15}{100}$, $P(A) = \frac{52}{100}$, $P(B \mid A) = \frac{15}{52}$.
Show by substitution that the conjecture is true for this case.

$P(A \cap B) = \frac{15}{100}$
$P(A) \cdot P(B \mid A) = \frac{52}{100} \cdot \frac{15}{52} = \frac{15}{100}$
$\therefore P(A \cap B) = P(A) \cdot P(B \mid A)$

348 We know $A \cap B = B \cap A$, so $P(A \cap B) = P(B \cap A)$. Using our conjecture, we should find $P(B \cap A) = P(B) \cdot P(A \mid B)$.
Now, from the table, $P(B \cap A) = \frac{15}{100}$, $P(B) = \frac{47}{100}$, $P(A \mid B) = \frac{15}{47}$.
Show by substitution that the conjecture is true for this case.

$P(B \cap A) = \frac{15}{100}$
$P(B) \cdot P(A \mid B) = \frac{47}{100} \cdot \frac{15}{47} = \frac{15}{100}$
$\therefore P(B \cap A) = P(B) \cdot P(A \mid B)$

349 From the table, $P(A \cap B') = \frac{37}{100}$, $P(A) = \frac{52}{100}$, $P(B' \mid A) = \frac{37}{52}$.
$\therefore P(A \cap B') = P(A) \cdot P(B' \mid A)$
Try the following: $P(B' \cap A) = \frac{37}{100}$
(1) $P(B') =$ ___   (2) $P(A \mid B') =$ ___
(3) Show that in this case $P(B' \cap A) = P(B') \cdot P(A \mid B')$.

(1) $\frac{53}{100}$ (2) $\frac{37}{53}$
(3) $P(B' \cap A) = \frac{37}{100}$
$P(B') \cdot P(A \mid B') = \frac{53}{100} \cdot \frac{37}{53} = \frac{37}{100}$
$\therefore P(B' \cap A) = P(B') \cdot P(A \mid B')$

350 From the table,
(1) $P(A' \cap B') =$ ___
(2) $P(A') =$ ___
(3) $P(B' \mid A') =$ ___

(1) $\frac{16}{100}$ (2) $\frac{48}{100}$ (3) $\frac{16}{48}$
Note again, $P(A' \cap B') = P(A') \cdot P(B' \mid A')$

351 From the table,
(1) $P(A' \cap B) =$ ___
(2) $P(A') =$ ___
(3) $P(B \mid A') =$ ___

(1) $\frac{32}{100}$ (2) $\frac{48}{100}$ (3) $\frac{32}{48}$
Once again, $P(A' \cap B) = P(A') \cdot P(B \mid A')$

352 So, our conjecture stands unchallenged (but not proved). Our conjecture is that if X and Y are events, then $P(X \cap Y) = \underline{\hspace{1cm}} \cdot \underline{\hspace{1cm}}$ [Copy the $P(X \cap Y) =$ when you answer.]

$P(X \cap Y) = P(X) \cdot P(Y \mid X)$
or $P(X \cap Y) = P(Y) \cdot P(X \mid Y)$

353 Suppose we try another problem, but instead of using results from an experiment and using the relative frequencies as values for probabilities, let us take a simple experiment and set up a sample space and assign probabilities which appear reasonable. Copy the following.
Experiment: Two coins are tossed.
Let $S = \{e_1, e_2, e_3, e_4\}$ where

$e_1 \leftrightarrow HH \quad e_2 \leftrightarrow HT$
$e_3 \leftrightarrow TH \quad e_4 \leftrightarrow TT$

Have a copy of the experiment and the sample space.

354 We have $S = \{e_1, e_2, e_3, e_4\}$ where

$e_1 \leftrightarrow HH \quad e_2 \leftrightarrow HT$
$e_3 \leftrightarrow TH \quad e_4 \leftrightarrow TT$

It seems reasonable to assign equal probabilities to each element of S; so let $P(e_1) = P(e_2) = P(e_3) = P(e_4) = \underline{\hspace{1cm}}$.

$\frac{1}{4}$

355 Now let A be the event that at least one head turns up. (1) Then $A = \underline{\hspace{1.5cm}}$. Let B be the event that at least one tail turns up. (2) Then $B = \underline{\hspace{1.5cm}}$. (3) Then $A \cap B$ is the event that at least one head and at least one tail turns up, and $A \cap B = \underline{\hspace{1.5cm}}$.

(1) $\{e_1, e_2, e_3\}$ (2) $\{e_2, e_3, e_4\}$ (3) $\{e_2, e_3\}$

356 So from our sample space, $P(A \cap B)$ is easy to compute.
$A \cap B = \{e_2, e_3\}$; so $P(A \cap B) = \underline{\hspace{2cm}}$.

$P(e_2) + P(e_3) = \frac{1}{4} + \frac{1}{4} = \frac{1}{2}$

357 Now, will our conjecture give us the same answer, that is, will $P(A \cap B) = P(A) \cdot P(B \mid A)$?
It is easy to find $P(A)$. A is the event that at least one head turns

▼

up; so (1) $A =$ _____. Therefore (2) $P(A) =$_____.
We will try to find $P(B \mid A)$ in frame 358.

---

(1) $\{e_1, e_2, e_3\}$ (2) $P(e_1) + P(e_2) + P(e_3) = \frac{3}{4}$

---

358 By $P(B \mid A)$ we mean the probability of event B *given that A has occurred*. Now we see that event A occurs only if the two coins turn up *HH, HT,* or *TH*; so, on the condition that A has occurred, we have a new sample space containing only three elements, each of which could reasonably be assigned a probability of $\frac{1}{3}$.
(1) In how many of these elements does B occur?
    (B is that at least one tail appears.)
(2) $P(B \mid A) =$ ___

---

(1) two   (2) $\frac{2}{3}$

---

359 From frames 356, 357, and 358, we have that
$P(A \cap B) = \frac{1}{2}$ $P(A) = \frac{3}{4}$ $P(B \mid A) = \frac{2}{3}$
Show that for this case our conjecture works.

$P(A \cap B) = \frac{1}{2}$
$P(A) \cdot P(B \mid A) = \frac{3}{4} \cdot \frac{2}{3} = \frac{2}{4} = \frac{1}{2}$
$\therefore P(A \cap B) = P(A) \cdot P(B \mid A)$

---

360 Let us try another. Copy the following and save it. A hat contains three black balls and two white balls. Two balls are to be drawn from the hat (one after the other and without replacing the first).
Let A be the event that the first ball is black.
Let B be the event that the second ball is white.

Have a correct description of the experiment and the events.

---

361 We want to compute the probability that the first ball is white *and* the second ball is black, that is, find $P(A \cap B)$ in two ways:
1. Using our old techniques
2. Using our conjecture
To do method 2 first, our conjecture is that $P(A \cap B) =$ _____.

$P(A) \cdot P(B \mid A)$

---

362 So, we need $P(A)$ and $P(B \mid A)$.
First, A is the event that a single ball drawn from the hat is black. Obviously, S for this problem contains five elements.

▼

$e_1 \longleftrightarrow B_1$
$e_2 \longleftrightarrow B_2$ and we would let $P(e_1) = P(e_2) = \cdots = P(e_5) = \frac{1}{5}$
$e_3 \longleftrightarrow B_3$
$e_4 \longleftrightarrow W_1$
$e_5 \longleftrightarrow W_2$

(1) $A =$ _____ ; so (2) $P(A) =$ _____

---

(1) $\{e_1,\ e_2,\ e_3\}$ (2) $P(e_1) + P(e_2) + P(e_3) = \frac{3}{5}$

---

363 Now, to find $P(B \mid A)$.

$P(B \mid A)$ is the conditional probability of B given A; so we work on the assumption that A has occurred. In other words, suppose that only *one* ball has been removed from the hat and that it is *black*. Then, under this condition, the hat now contains only (1) ____ balls, (2) ____ black and (3) ____ white.

---

(1) 4   (2) 2   (3) 2   since, if A has occurred, one of the black balls has been drawn out.

---

364 Therefore, given that A has occurred, the hat now contains two black balls and two white balls. At this point, the sample space for drawing one ball contains four elements:

$e_2 \longleftrightarrow B_2$ $e_3 \longleftrightarrow B_3$ $e_4 \longleftrightarrow W_1$ $e_5 \longleftrightarrow W_2$

each of which has a probability of $\frac{1}{4}$. The ball drawn is white in two of these four elements, e_4, e_5; so $P(B \mid A) = \frac{2}{4} = \frac{1}{2}$. We now have $P(A) = \frac{3}{5}$ and $P(B \mid A) = \frac{1}{2}$; so our conjecture would give $P(A \cap B) =$ _____ .

$P(A) \cdot P(B \mid A) = \frac{3}{5} \cdot \frac{1}{2} = \frac{3}{10}$

---

365 Now let us compute $P(A \cap B)$ using our old techniques. If two balls are drawn, without replacement, from the hat, and since the order of drawing is important, a sample space for this experiment is $S = \{e_1,\ e_2,\ \ldots,\ e_{20}\}$ where

$e_1 \longleftrightarrow B_1 B_2$ $e_2 \longleftrightarrow B_1 B_3$ $e_3 \longleftrightarrow B_1 W_1$ $e_4 \longleftrightarrow B_1 W_2$
$e_5 \longleftrightarrow B_2 B_1$ $e_6 \longleftrightarrow B_2 B_3$ $e_7 \longleftrightarrow B_2 W_1$ $e_8 \longleftrightarrow B_2 W_2$
$e_9 \longleftrightarrow B_3 B_1$ $e_{10} \longleftrightarrow B_3 B_2$ $e_{11} \longleftrightarrow B_3 W_1$ $e_{12} \longleftrightarrow B_3 W_2$
$e_{13} \longleftrightarrow W_1 B_1$ $e_{14} \longleftrightarrow W_1 B_2$ $e_{15} \longleftrightarrow W_1 B_3$ $e_{16} \longleftrightarrow W_1 W_2$
$e_{17} \longleftrightarrow W_2 B_1$ $e_{18} \longleftrightarrow W_2 B_2$ $e_{19} \longleftrightarrow W_2 B_3$ $e_{20} \longleftrightarrow W_2 W_1$

and if we let $P(e_1) = P(e_2) = \cdots = P(e_{20}) = \frac{1}{20}$

▼

(1)　$A \cap B =$ _____
(2)　$P(A \cap B) =$ _____
(3)　How does answer (2) compare with our conjecture in frame 364?

---

(1)　Remember, $A \cap B$ means A and B, that is, that the first ball is black and the second ball is white; so
　　　$A \cap B = \{e_3,\ e_4,\ e_7,\ e_8,\ e_{11},\ e_{12}\}$
(2)　$\frac{6}{20} = \frac{3}{10}$
(3)　The same answer as our conjecture.

366　Perhaps it will be easier to see the worth of formula
$P(A \cap B) = P(A) \cdot P(B \mid A)$ (if it is true) by looking at an experiment with larger numbers.
Suppose a hat contained 50 white balls and 50 black balls and an experiment consists of drawing two balls in succession without replacement. If we wish to find the probability that both balls are white, we would let A be the event that the first ball is white and B be the event that the second ball is white and try to find $P(A \cap B)$.
Now, obviously $P(A) = \frac{50}{100}$ and $P(B \mid A) = \frac{49}{99}$. Since if A occurs, the hat contains only 99 balls, 49 of which are white, and we would have, if our conjecture is correct, $P(A \cap B) =$ _____.
But, if we were to list the sample space for drawing two balls from the hat in succession, we would have 9,900 elements in S.
You would spend a fair amount of time listing them.

$P(A) \cdot P(B \mid A) = \frac{50}{100} \cdot \frac{49}{99} = \frac{49}{198}$

367　Let us go back. Suppose we have two events A and B for a given experiment. Graphically, a general case might be:

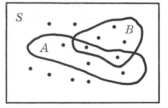

Recall that A', the complement of A, consists of all the elements of S that are not in ___ .

A

368 Suppose S, A, and B look like this:

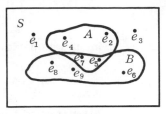

Since A' is the set of all elements of S not in A and B' is the set of all elements of S not in B, then on any trial of the experiment,
If e_1 occurs, then A' and B' occur, that is, $A' \cap B'$ occurs
If e_2 occurs, then A and B' occur, that is, $A \cap B'$ occurs
If e_3 occurs, then A' and B' occur, that is, $A' \cap B'$ occurs
Complete listing the elements of the set (through e_9) in the same manner.

If e_4 occurs, then A and B' occur, that is, $A \cap B'$ occurs
If e_5 occurs, then A and B occur, that is, $A \cap B$ occurs
If e_6 occurs, then A' and B occur, that is, $A' \cap B$ occurs
If e_7 occurs, then A and B occur, that is, $A \cap B$ occurs
If e_8 occurs, then A' and B occur, that is, $A' \cap B$ occurs
If e_9 occurs, then A' and B occur, that is, $A' \cap B$ occurs

369 So, on any trial of an experiment, $A \cap B$, $A \cap B'$, $A' \cap B$, or $A' \cap B'$ occurs.
Suppose an experiment has been performed N times and these results have been recorded:

	B	B'
A	n_1	n_2
A'	n_3	n_4

From the table, $A \cap B$ occurred n_1 times, $A \cap B'$ occurred ___ times.   Copy this table and save it.

n_2

370 From the table, how many times did event A occur?

$n_1 + n_2$

371 From the table, how many times did event B occur?

$n_1 + n_3$

372 Suppose n_1, n_2, n_3, n_4 are values such that the relative frequencies of the events are the probabilities of the events. Then, we would have $P(A) = \dfrac{n_1 + n_2}{N}$

(Remember, the experiment was performed N times.)

$P(B) = $ _____.

$$\dfrac{n_1 + n_3}{N}$$

373 We know from frame 369 that $A \cap B$ occurred n_1 times From the table, if the probabilities are given by the relative frequencies, $P(A \cap B) = $ _____.

$\dfrac{n_1}{N}$,   since A and B occurred n_1 times.

374 The relative frequency of $(B \mid A)$ means the ratio of the number of times B occurred during the trials in which A occurred.

Now, (1) A occurred ___ times, and of these,
     (2) B occurred ___ times.
     (3) If the relative frequencies are used as probabilities,
         $P(B \mid A) = $ ___ .

(1) $n_1 + n_2$ (2) n_1 (3) $\dfrac{n_1}{n_1 + n_2}$

375 We have found from the table in frame 369 that

1. $P(B \mid A) = \dfrac{n_1}{n_1 + n_2}$

2. $P(A) = \dfrac{n_1 + n_2}{N}$

3. $P(A \cap B) = \dfrac{n_1}{N}$

Show that $P(A \cap B) = P(A) \cdot P(B \mid A)$.

$P(A \cap B) = \dfrac{n_1}{N}$

$P(A) \cdot P(B \mid A) = \dfrac{n_1 + n_2}{N} \cdot \dfrac{n_1}{n_1 + n_2} = \dfrac{n_1}{N}$

$\therefore P(A \cap B) = P(A) \cdot P(B \mid A)$

376 (1) $P(B) = $ _____
    (2) $P(A \mid B) = $ _____
    (3) $P(A \cap B) = $ ___

(1) $\dfrac{n_1 + n_3}{N}$ (2) $\dfrac{n_1}{n_1 + n_3}$ (3) $\dfrac{n_1}{N}$

377 Show, by using the correct answers from frame 376 (1), (2), and (3), that $P(A \cap B) = P(B) \cdot P(A \mid B)$.

$$P(A \cap B) = \frac{n_1}{N}$$
$$P(B) \cdot P(A \mid B) = \frac{n_1 + n_3}{N} \cdot \frac{n_1}{n_1 + n_3} = \frac{n_1}{N}$$
$$\therefore P(A \cap B) = P(B) \cdot P(A \mid B)$$

●**378** So, we have the result (assuming that the relative frequencies are equal to the corresponding probabilities): If A and B are events for a given experiment, then the probability that both A and B occur is given by $P(A \cap B) =$ _____.
[Copy $P(A \cap B)$ = when you answer.]

$$P(A \cap B) = P(A) \cdot P(B \mid A)$$
$$\text{or } P(A \cap B) = P(B) \cdot P(A \mid B)$$

comment

It should be noted that the preceding "proof" involves the assumption that the relative frequencies, for some N, are equal to the respective probabilities of the various events. This in itself is a great deal to ask. Moreover, since the relative frequencies are rational numbers, the requirements would be impossible to satisfy if any of the probabilities involved were irrational numbers. Despite these qualifications, this "proof" has been used for its instructional values. An alternative method, used in some books, is simply to define, when $P(B) \neq 0$ then $P(A \mid B) = P(A \cap B)/P(B)$.

From this definition we could obtain the desired results.

379 A carton contains 100 harmonicas, 10 of which are defective. An experiment consists of drawing two items from the 100. We want to find the probability that *both* are defective.
Let A be the event that the first item is defective.
Let B be the event that the second item is defective.
We wish to find $P(A \cap B)$, and will use: $P(A \cap B) = P(A) \cdot P(B \mid A)$.
If a single trial consists of drawing one item from the box, S contains 100 elements, each having a probability of $\frac{1}{100}$. Ten of these will result in event A. Therefore $P(A) =$.
(We will continue in frame 380.)

$$\frac{10}{100} = \frac{1}{10}$$

380 Continuing the experiment in frame 379, to find $P(B \mid A)$, we consider that one item has been drawn from the 100 and that it was defective. Therefore, we have a sample space containing 99 elements, each having a probability of (1) ___. Of these, (2) ___ are defective; so (3) $P(B \mid A)$ = _____.

(1) $\frac{1}{99}$ (2) 9   (3) $\frac{9}{99} = \frac{1}{11}$

381 From frames 379 and 380 we have:
1. $P(A) = \frac{1}{10}$
2. $P(B \mid A) = \frac{1}{11}$
Therefore, $P(A \cap B)$ = _____

$\frac{1}{10} \cdot \frac{1}{11} = \frac{1}{110}$

382 As you have seen in problems of the following type, some probabilities are obvious, and no further discussion of the sample space, etc., will be made.
A hat contains 100 white balls and 50 black balls. A single ball is to be drawn. If A is the event that the ball is white, then
(1) $P(A)$ = ___. After all, it is easy to see that S would contain (2) ___ elements each having probability of (3) ___ and that A contains (4) ___ of these elements.
If at any time such a probability is given with no discussion and you do not see it, then consider the sample space, assign probabilities to the elements, find the event as a subset of the space, and use the original definition of probability.

(1) $\frac{100}{150}$ (2) 150   (3) $\frac{1}{150}$ (4) 100

383 So, the following should be easy to see without setting up the sample space. From a hat containing 50 black balls and 20 white balls, two balls are to be drawn in succession, without replacement. Find the probability that the first ball is black and the second ball is white. Let A be the event that the first ball is black and B be the event that the second ball is white. Then we want
$P(A \cap B)$ and $P(A \cap B) = P(A) \cdot P(B \mid A)$
$$= \frac{50}{70} \cdot \frac{20}{69}$$
$$= \frac{100}{483}$$
Notice, to find $P(B \mid A)$ we assume that A has occurred; so the hat now contains (1) ___ black balls and (2) ___ white balls. Therefore, the probability of getting a white ball (on the condition that a black ball has been drawn) is as given.

(1) 49   (2) 20

384 We have, if A and B are events, that the probability of the occurrence of A and B is equal to the probability of A times the conditional probability of B given A; that is, $P(A \cap B) =$ ___ · ___ .

$P(A)$ · $P(B \mid A)$

385 For a certain experiment with events A and B, we know that $P(A \cap B) = \frac{2}{5}$, $P(A) = \frac{2}{3}$, and $P(B) = \frac{1}{2}$.
(1) Find $P(A \mid B)$.   (2) Find $P(B \mid A)$.

(1) $P(A \cap B) = P(A)$ · $P(B \mid A)$
    $\frac{2}{5} = \frac{2}{3}$ · $P(B \mid A)$
  $\therefore$ $P(B \mid A) = \frac{3}{5}$
(2) $P(A \cap B) = P(B)$ · $P(A \mid B)$
    $\frac{2}{5} = \frac{1}{2}$ $P(A \mid B)$
  $\therefore$ $P(A \mid B) = \frac{4}{5}$

386 Let $S = \{e_1,\ e_2,\ e_3,\ e_4\}$ be a sample space, with $P(e_1) = 0.2$, $P(e_2) = 0.3$, $P(e_3) = 0.4$, $P(e_4) = 0.1$.
Let $A = \{e_1,\ e_2,\ e_3\}$ and $B = \{e_2,\ e_3,\ e_4\}$ be events. Find $P(B \mid A)$.
Suggestion: Find $P(A \cap B)$ and $P(A)$ first.

$P(B \mid A) = \frac{7}{9}$
Detailed work:
1. $A \cap B = \{e_2,\ e_3\}$ $\therefore$ $P(A \cap B) = 0.7$
2. $A = \{e_1,\ e_2,\ e_3\}$ $\therefore$ $P(A) = 0.9$
3. Now $P(A \cap B) = P(A)$ · $P(B \mid A)$ $\therefore$ $0.7 = 0.9\,P(B \mid A)$
                   $P(B \mid A) = \frac{7}{9}$

387 Recall from set theory that intersection of sets is an *associative binary operation;* that is, if $A,\ B,\ C$ are sets, then
$(A \cap B) \cap C = A \cap (B \cap C)$. Therefore, $A \cap B \cap C$ has meaning, since it makes no difference if you find $A \cap (B \cap C)$ or $(A \cap B) \cap C$.
For example, let $A = \{e_1,\ e_3,\ e_5,\ e_7\}$ $B = \{e_1,\ e_2,\ e_3,\ e_4,\ e_5\}$
$C = \{e_2,\ e_3,\ e_5,\ e_7\}$
        (1) $(A \cap B) =$ _____   so (2) $(A \cap B) \cap C =$ _____
also (3) $(B \cap C) =$ _____   so (4) $A \cap (B \cap C) =$ _____

(1) $\{e_1,\ e_3,\ e_5\}$ (2) $\{e_3,\ e_5\}$
(3) $\{e_2,\ e_3,\ e_5\}$ (4) $\{e_3,\ e_5\}$

388 Now, suppose $A,\ B,$ and C are events and we wish to find the probability of the occurrence of all three events, that is, $P(A \cap B \cap C)$. For example, an experiment consists of tossing three coins:

▼

If A is the event that the first coin is a head
If B is the event that the second coin is a head
If C is the event that the third coin is a head
then $A \cap B \cap C$ is the event that all three coins are _____.

heads

389 Suppose $S = \{e_1, e_2, e_3, e_4, e_5, e_6\}$ and $P(e_1) = 0.1$, $P(e_2) = 0.3$,
$P(e_3) = 0.2$, $P(e_4) = 0.1$, $P(e_5) = 0.2$, $P(e_6) = 0.1$
If $A = \{e_1, e_2, e_4, e_5\}$, $B = \{e_2, e_3, e_4, e_6\}$, $C = \{e_2, e_3, e_4, e_5\}$
then (1) $A \cap B \cap C = $ _____ and (2) $P(A \cap B \cap C) = $ _____.

(1) $\{e_2, e_4\}$ (2) $P(e_2) + P(e_4) = 0.3 + 0.1 = 0.4$

●**390** *Experiment:* Three coins are tossed. To find the probability that
all three coins turn up heads, we might let
A be the event that the first coin is a head
B be the event that the second coin is a head
C be the event that the third coin is a head
Then if $S = \{e_1, e_2 \ldots, e_8\}$ where

$e_1 \leftrightarrow HHH$ $e_2 \leftrightarrow HHT$ $e_3 \leftrightarrow HTH$ $e_4 \leftrightarrow THH$
$e_5 \leftrightarrow HTT$ $e_6 \leftrightarrow THT$ $e_7 \leftrightarrow TTH$ $e_8 \leftrightarrow TTT$

and if $P(e_1) = P(e_2) = \cdots = P(e_8) = 1/8$,
then (1) $A = $ _____,   (2) $B = $ _____,   (3) $C = $ _____
(4) $A \cap B \cap C = $ ____ ∴ (5) $P(A \cap B \cap C) = $ ___

(1) $\{e_1, e_2, e_3, e_5\}$
(2) $\{e_1, e_2, e_4, e_6\}$
(3) $\{e_1, e_3, e_4, e_7\}$
(4) $\{e_1\}$
(5) $1/8$

391 Now of course, we would like to have a technique of computing
$P(A \cap B \cap C)$ other than finding $A \cap B \cap C$ in a sample space and
then adding probabilities. It would be easier if we could find
$P(A \cap B \cap C)$ from the simpler probabilities of A, B, and C just
as we found $P(A \cap B) = $ _____.
[Copy the $P(A \cap B) = $ when you answer.]

$P(A \cap B) = P(A) \cdot P(B \mid A)$
or $P(A \cap B) = P(B) \cdot P(A \mid B)$

392 Now, if we are clever, we need not do a great amount of work to
find a technique for computing $P(A \cap B \cap C)$. After all, we have a
technique for finding the probability of the intersection of two events;
so if we can reduce our problem to this form, we have a solution.
But note:

▼

$A \cap B \cap C = (A \cap B) \cap C$
$\therefore \ P(A \cap B \cap C) = P\ [(\underline{}) \cap \underline{}\ ].$
We are on our way.

$A \cap B, \qquad C$

393 We have that $P(A \cap B \cap C) = P[(A \cap B) \cap C]$. Now think of $A \cap B$ as an event (which it is). We know that $P(X \cap Y) = P(X) \cdot P(Y \mid X)$. If we use $(A \cap B) \leftrightarrow X$ and $C \leftrightarrow Y$, we can find $P[(A \cap B) \cap C\ ]$ by substitution.
$P(X \cap Y) = P(X) \cdot P(Y \mid X)$
$P\ [(A \cap B) \cap C\ ] = P(A \cap B) \cdot \underline{}$

$P\ [C \mid (A \cap B)\ ]$

394 We have reached the point that
$P(A \cap B \cap C) = [P(A \cap B) \cap C]$
$\qquad\qquad\quad = P(A \cap B) \cdot P(C \mid A \cap B)$
$\qquad\qquad\quad = \underline{} \cdot \underline{} \cdot P(C \mid A \cap B)$
where the last step is found by using our previous technique on $P(A \cap B)$.

$P(A) \cdot P(B \mid A)$

395 Notice the result we obtained:
$P(A \cap B \cap C) = P(A) \cdot P(B \mid A) \cdot P(C \mid A \cap B)$
The pattern is to multiply the probabilities of each event in succession, but each successive probability is a conditional probability given that the previous events have occurred. If the pattern were to continue in this manner, we would have: if $A, B, C,$ and D are events, then
$P(A \cap B \cap C \cap D) = P(A) \cdot P(B \mid A) \cdot P(C \mid A \cap B) \cdot P(D \mid \underline{})$
In fact, it can be established that this result and similar results for a larger number of events are true.

$A \cap B \cap C$

396 As a simple example, suppose a hat contains 10 black balls and two white balls. One ball at a time is to be drawn from the hat until a white ball is drawn. To find the probability that a white ball will not occur until the sixth ball is drawn, we would think of the events:
A is the event that the first ball is black
B is the event that the second ball is black
C is the event that the third ball is black
D is the event that the fourth ball is black
E is the event that the fifth ball is black
F is the event that the sixth ball is *white*

▼

We want $P(A \cap B \cap C \cap D \cap E \cap F)$.

$\therefore P(A \cap B \cap C \cap D \cap E \cap F) = \frac{10}{12} \cdot \frac{9}{11} \cdot \frac{8}{10} \cdot \underline{\hspace{1cm}} \cdot \underline{\hspace{1cm}} \cdot \underline{\hspace{1cm}}$

where each succeeding factor is computed on the condition that the preceding events have occurred.

(Be careful, we want the last ball to be white. Consider the number of white balls in the hat.)

$\frac{7}{9} \cdot \frac{6}{8} \cdot \frac{2}{7}$

(Note: After five black balls have been drawn, the hat contains five black balls and two white ones, and we want the probability that a white one is drawn on the sixth drawing.)

397 An ordinary deck of playing cards contains 52 cards, four of which are aces. If four cards are drawn at random,

The probability that the first card drawn is an ace is $\frac{4}{52}$

If the first card drawn is an ace, the probability that the second card drawn is an ace is $\frac{3}{51}$

If the first two cards drawn are aces, the probability that the third card drawn is an ace is (1)

If the first three cards drawn are aces, the probability that the fourth card drawn is an ace is (2)

Here again, each succeeding factor is computed on the condition that the preceding events have occurred.

(1) $\frac{2}{50}$ (2) $\frac{1}{49}$

398 A coin is tossed twice. If we wish to use our new theorem to find the probability that heads appear on both tosses, we let A be the event that the first toss turns up heads and B be the event that the second toss turns up heads. Then we wish to find $P(A \cap B)$, and our theorem says that $P(A \cap B) = P(A) \cdot \underline{\hspace{1cm}}$. We will continue in frame 399.

$P(B \mid A)$

399 A coin is tossed twice. If A is the event that on the first toss, a head appears—since we are only concerned with the first toss—we might just as well consider that $S = \{e_1, e_2\}$ where $e_1 \leftrightarrow H; e_2 \leftrightarrow T$; so $A = \{e_1\}$ and $P(A) = \underline{\hspace{1cm}}$.

$P(e_1) = \frac{1}{2}$

400 With the same experiment as in frames 398 and 399, if A is the event that the first toss comes up heads and B is the event that the second toss comes up heads, then to find $P(B \mid A)$ we have that A *has occurred.* Therefore, the sample space contains only two ele-

▼

ments: $e_1 \leftrightarrow HH$ and $e_2 \leftrightarrow HT$. If we assign $P(e_1) = \frac{1}{2}$ and $P(e_2) = \frac{1}{2}$, we have that $P(B \mid A) = \{e_1\}$ ∴ $P(B \mid A) =$ ___

$\frac{1}{2}$

---

401 Continuing the problem that we began in frame 398:
$P(A \cap B = P(A) \cdot P(B \mid A) = \frac{1}{2} \cdot \frac{1}{2} = \frac{1}{4}$
Now note an important fact in this problem: If a coin is tossed twice, and B is the event that the second toss comes up heads, find $P(B)$. $S = \{e_1, e_2, e_3, e_4\}$ where

$e_1 \leftrightarrow HH \quad e_2 \leftrightarrow HT \quad e_3 \leftrightarrow TH \quad e_4 \leftrightarrow TT$

$P(e_1) = P(e_2) = P(e_3) = P(e_4) = \frac{1}{4}$
(1) $B =$ _____ so (2) $P(B) =$ ___

---

(1) $\{e_1, e_3\}$ (2) $\frac{1}{2}$

---

402 So, in the problem in frames 398 to 402 $P(B \mid A) = P(B)$, and this was the feature of those isolated problems at the beginning of this work on probabilities of intersections in which
$P(A \cap B) = P(A) \cdot P(B)$. You recall that this equation worked for some problems and did not work for other problems. You see now that if C and D are events, then $P(C \cap D) = P(C) \cdot P(D \mid C)$, but if ___ = _____, then $P(C \cap D) = P(C) \cdot P(D)$.

$P(D) = P(D \mid C)$

---

403 Sometimes, two events, say A and B, are so related that $P(B) = P(B \mid A)$; that is, the probability of B is the same as the conditional probability of B given A. In other words, the occurrence of A has no effect on the probability of the occurrence of B. For example, in the last problem, a coin was to be tossed twice, A is the event that the first toss is heads and B is the event that the second toss is heads. Without knowing whether or not A has occurred, (1) $P(B) =$ ___. Suppose A has occurred; then (2) $P(B \mid A) =$ ___.

---

(1) $\frac{1}{2}$ (2) $\frac{1}{2}$

---

404 Take another example. A hat contains two red balls and one white ball. A ball is to be drawn from the hat, its color noted, *returned to the hat*, and then a second ball chosen and its color noted. Suppose B is the event that the second ball chosen is red. $S = \{e_1, e_2, e_3, \ldots, e_9\}$ where

$e_1 \leftrightarrow R_1R_1 \quad e_2 \leftrightarrow R_1R_2 \quad e_3 \leftrightarrow R_1W$
$e_4 \leftrightarrow R_2R_1 \quad e_5 \leftrightarrow R_2R_2 \quad e_6 \leftrightarrow R_2W$
$e_7 \leftrightarrow WR_1 \quad e_8 \leftrightarrow WR_2 \quad e_9 \leftrightarrow WW$

and we let $P(e_1) = P(e_2) = \cdots = P(e_9) = \frac{1}{9}$. Then (1) $B =$ _____,
(2) $P(B) =$ ___.

▼

Now suppose A is the event that the first ball is white. To find
$P(B \mid A)$ we assume that A has occurred. Then our sample space
S contains only three elements $f_1 \leftrightarrow WR_1$, $f_2 \leftrightarrow WR_2$, $f_3 \leftrightarrow WW$,
each having a probability of $\frac{1}{3}$, and (3) $(B \mid A) =$ _____; so
(4) $P(B \mid A) =$ ___.

(1) $\{e_1,\ e_2,\ e_4,\ e_5,\ e_7,\ e_8\}$
(2) $\frac{2}{3}$ (3) $\{f_1,\ f_2\}$ (4) $\frac{2}{3}$

405 After all, in the experiment in frame 404 the first ball drawn was
replaced and then the second ball was drawn. It seems obvious that
if B is the event that the second ball drawn is red, the probability
of B will not be affected by whether or not A has occurred. It does
not matter what color the first ball was *as long as it was replaced*.
Suppose a hat contains two red balls and 20 white balls. Fifteen
balls are drawn from the hat and replaced. If E is the event that
the sixteenth ball drawn is red, (1) $P(E) =$ _____. Suppose A is
the event that the first 15 balls were white, and suppose A occurred.
Then (2) $P(B \mid A) =$ _____.

(1) $\frac{2}{22} = \frac{1}{11}$ (2) $\frac{2}{22} = \frac{1}{11}$

406 For some experiments and events, say A and B, the fact that
$P(B \mid A) = P(B)$ is obvious; that is, it hardly needs any proof to
show that the occurrence of A has no effect on the probability of B.
But if a proof is desired, you need only set up the sample spaces
involved and compute $P(B)$ and $P(B \mid A)$. For example, let an experiment consist of rolling a die twice. Let A be the event that the
first roll turns up a 2 or a 4 and B be the event that a number
greater than 4 appears on the second roll.
Now, it should be obvious that the occurrence of A will have no
effect upon the probability of the occurrence of B; that is,
$P(B) = P(B \mid A)$. But suppose we want to prove it. To find $P(B)$,
(1) set up the sample space S, (2) assign equal probabilities,
(3) determine B, and thus (4) find $P(B)$. (There are 36 elements
in S.)

(1) $S = \{e_1,\ e_2,\ \ldots,\ e_{36}\}$ where $e_1 \leftrightarrow (1,1)$, $e_2 \leftrightarrow (1,2)$, etc., as on
Panel 1, with the first number indicating the first roll and the
second number indicating the second roll.
(2) Let $P(e_1) = P(e_2) = \cdots = P(e_{36}) = \frac{1}{36}$
(3) $B = \{e_5,\ e_6,\ e_{11},\ e_{12},\ e_{17},\ e_{18},\ e_{23},\ e_{24},\ e_{29},\ e_{30},\ e_{35},\ e_{36}\}$
(4) $P(B) = \frac{12}{36} = \frac{1}{3}$

407 We continue the experiment that we began in frame 406. To find
$P(B \mid A)$, the conditional probability of B given A, we work with the
understanding that A has occurred.

▼

Then the sample space for this event is
$S = \{e_1, e_2, \ldots, e_{12}\}$ where

$e_1 \leftrightarrow (2,1)$ $e_2 \leftrightarrow (2,2)$ $e_3 \leftrightarrow (2,3)$ $e_4 \leftrightarrow (2,4)$
$e_5 \leftrightarrow (2,5)$ $e_6 \leftrightarrow (2,6)$ $e_7 \leftrightarrow (4,1)$ $e_8 \leftrightarrow (4,2)$
$e_9 \leftrightarrow (4,3)$ $e_{10} \leftrightarrow (4,4)$ $e_{11} \leftrightarrow (4,5)$ $e_{12} \leftrightarrow (4,6)$

and we let $P(e_1) = P(e_2) = \cdots = P(e_{12}) = \frac{1}{12}$.
Then the elements of B in this sample space are **(1)** _____;
so **(2)** $P(B \mid A) =$ _____.

---

(1) $e_5,\ e_6,\ e_{11},\ e_{12}$ **(2)** $\frac{4}{12} = \frac{1}{3}$

---

408 We found in the experiment from frames 406 and 407 that $P(B) = \frac{1}{3}$
and $P(B \mid A) = \frac{1}{3}$.
Definition: Two events C and D are *independent* if and only if
$P(C) = P(C \mid D)$ and are *dependent* if and only if $P(C) \neq P(C \mid D)$.
Thus, for the last experiment, A and B are _____ events, since
we found $P(B) = \frac{1}{3}$ and $P(B \mid A) = \frac{1}{3}$.

---

independent

Self-test IV

1 For a given experiment
$S = \{e_1, e_2, e_3, e_4, e_5, e_6, e_7\}$
$A = \{e_2, e_4, e_5, e_6\}$
$B = \{e_5, e_6, e_7\}$
$A \cap B =$ _____

2 Look at Panel 1. Suppose A is the event that the sum of the dots
is more than 10. **(1)** Then $A =$ _____. Suppose B is the
event that the first die and the second die turn up the same number. **(2)** Then $B =$ _____. Suppose the outcome corresponding to e_{15} occurs on a trial of the experiment. **(3)** Has A occurred?
(4) Has B occurred?

3 Graphically, let a sample space S and events A and B for a given
experiment be as shown:

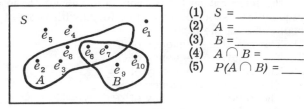

(1) $S =$ _____
(2) $A =$ _____
(3) $B =$ _____
(4) $A \cap B =$ _____
(5) $P(A \cap B) =$ ___

and $P(e_1) = P(e_2) = \cdots = P(e_{10}) = \frac{1}{10}$

4 Suppose a sample space S and events A and B are shown graphically:

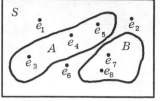

$P(e_1) = P(e_2) = \cdots = P(e_8) = \frac{1}{8}$

(1) $S =$ _____

(2) $A =$ _____

(3) $B =$ _____

(4) $A \cap B =$ ____

(5) $P(A \cap B) =$ ____

(6) A and B are _____ events.

5 A teacher performed the following experiment: A student is chosen and a coin is tossed.
1. If the coin turned up heads, the student was given a programmed textbook in probability (H).
2. If the coin turned up tails, the student was given a regular textbook in probability (H').
After a certain number of weeks, both groups of students were tested on the material they studied. S was recorded if the student got a score of 80 or higher. S' was recorded if the student got a score of less than 80. One hundred trials of the experiment produced the following results:

	S	S'
H	35	10
H'	25	30

$H \leftrightarrow$ students using programmed material
$H' \leftrightarrow$ students using regular text material
$S \leftrightarrow$ students who got a score of 80 or higher on test
$S' \leftrightarrow$ students who got a score of less than 80

From the table we see that of the **(1)** ____ students who used a program, **(2)** ____ students got a score of 80 or higher. Of the **(3)** ____ students who used a regular text, **(4)** ____ students got a score of less than 80. **(5)** $n(H) =$ ____, **(6)** $n(H') =$ ____, **(7)** $n(S) =$ ____, **(8)** $n(S') =$ ____ .

6 Use the information from Prob. 5 to answer these questions. The frequencies asked for should be found with respect to the hundred trials. From the table:
(1) The relative frequency of $H =$ ____
(2) The relative frequency of $H' =$ ____
(3) The relative frequency of $S =$ ____
(4) The relative frequency of $S' =$ ____
(5) The relative frequency of $(H \cap S) =$ ____
(6) The relative frequency of $(H \cap S') =$ ____

(7) The relative frequency of $(H' \cap S) =$ ___
(8) The relative frequency of $(H' \cap S') =$ ___

7 Use the information from Prob. 5 to answer these questions.
From the table:
(1) The relative frequency of $(S \mid H) =$ ___
(2) The relative frequency of $(S \mid H') =$ ___
(3) The relative frequency of $(S' \mid H) =$ ___
(4) The relative frequency of $(S' \mid H') =$ ___

8 If A and B are events, write the relationship which always exists among $P(A)$, $P(B \mid A)$, $P(A \cap B)$.

9 A hat contains 12 balls, seven black balls and five red balls. If two balls are drawn from the hat, one right after the other without replacing the first, what is the probability that both are red?

10 *Experiment:* Three cards, all aces, are tossed into the air. We want to find the probability that all three cards come to rest face side up (designated by X). Cards that come to rest face side down will be designated by Y.
Let A be the event that the first card is face side up
Let B be the event that the second card is face side up
Let C be the event that the third card is face side up
Then $S = \{e_1, e_2, \ldots, e_8\}$ where

$e_1 \leftrightarrow XXX$ $e_2 \leftrightarrow XXY$
$e_3 \leftrightarrow XYX$ $e_4 \leftrightarrow YXX$
$e_5 \leftrightarrow XYY$ $e_6 \leftrightarrow YXY$
$e_7 \leftrightarrow YYX$ $e_8 \leftrightarrow YYY$

and if $P(e_1) = P(e_2) = \cdots = P(e_8) = \frac{1}{8}$,
then (1) $A =$ _____ (2) $B =$ _____ (3) $C =$ _____
(4) $A \cap B \cap C =$ ___ $\therefore$ (5) $P(A \cap B \cap C) =$ ___

2. Dependent and Independent Events

409 Precisely, two events A and B are independent if $P(B) = P(B \mid A)$.
Roughly speaking, two events are independent if the occurrence of the one has no effect on the probability of the occurrence of the other. Let an experiment consist of rolling two dice, one after the other. Let A be the event that the first die comes up an even number and B be the event that the sum of the spots is 4.
(1) Find $P(B)$ and $P(B \mid A)$. (2) Are A and B independent?

(1) $P(B) = \frac{1}{12}$ $P(B \mid A) = \frac{1}{18}$
(2) no $P(B) \neq P(B \mid A)$; therefore A and B are dependent events.
If your answer is correct, skip to frame 412. If your answer is not correct, go on to frame 410.

410 To get $P(B)$ for the experiment in frame 409: The experiment consisted of rolling a pair of dice, one after the other, B is the event that the sum of the spots is 4. S is given in Panel 1.
   (1) $B =$ _____
$\therefore$ **(2)** $P(B) =$ _____

   (1) $\{e_3,\ e_8,\ e_{13}\}$
   (2) $P(e_3) + P(e_8) + P(e_{13}) = \frac{3}{36} = \frac{1}{12}$

411 To get $P(B \mid A)$ for the experiment in frames 409 and 410: the experiment consisted of rolling a pair of dice, one after another. B is the event that the sum of the spots is 4. A is the event that the first die turns up even. $P(B \mid A)$ is the conditional probability of B, given A. Therefore we assume that A has occurred; so our sample space contains only 18 elements, namely:

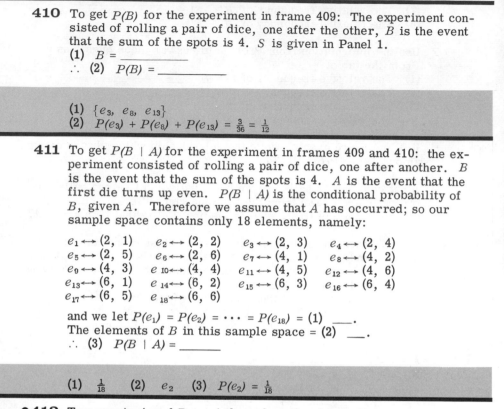

$e_1 \leftrightarrow (2,\ 1)$ $e_2 \leftrightarrow (2,\ 2)$ $e_3 \leftrightarrow (2,\ 3)$ $e_4 \leftrightarrow (2,\ 4)$
$e_5 \leftrightarrow (2,\ 5)$ $e_6 \leftrightarrow (2,\ 6)$ $e_7 \leftrightarrow (4,\ 1)$ $e_8 \leftrightarrow (4,\ 2)$
$e_9 \leftrightarrow (4,\ 3)$ $e_{10} \leftrightarrow (4,\ 4)$ $e_{11} \leftrightarrow (4,\ 5)$ $e_{12} \leftrightarrow (4,\ 6)$
$e_{13} \leftrightarrow (6,\ 1)$ $e_{14} \leftrightarrow (6,\ 2)$ $e_{15} \leftrightarrow (6,\ 3)$ $e_{16} \leftrightarrow (6,\ 4)$
$e_{17} \leftrightarrow (6,\ 5)$ $e_{18} \leftrightarrow (6,\ 6)$

and we let $P(e_1) = P(e_2) = \cdots = P(e_{18}) =$ **(1)** ___.
The elements of B in this sample space = **(2)** ___.
$\therefore$ **(3)** $P(B \mid A) =$ _____

   (1) $\frac{1}{18}$ **(2)** e_2 **(3)** $P(e_2) = \frac{1}{18}$

●**412** Two events A and B are independent if and only if _____.

   $P(B) = P(B \mid A)$ or $P(A) = P(A \mid B)$
   Note: We will prove later that if $P(A) = P(A \mid B)$, then
   $P(B) = P(B \mid A)$.

413 Given two events A and B, if $P(A) \neq P(A \mid B)$, then A and B are _____ *(dependent, independent)*.

   dependent

414 Let a sample space S and events A and B be as shown.

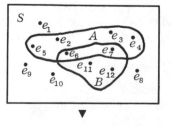

▼

Copy this drawing and use it for frames 415 to 419. If we assign equal probabilities to each element of S, then $P(e_1) = P(e_2) = \cdots = P(e_{12}) = $ ___ .

$\frac{1}{12}$

415 From the drawing, (1) $A = $ _____ . $\therefore$ (2) $P(A) = $ _____ .

(1) $\{e_2,\ e_3,\ e_4,\ e_5,\ e_6,\ e_7\}$
(2) $P(e_2) + P(e_3) + P(e_4) + P(e_5) + P(e_6) + P(e_7) = \frac{6}{12} = \frac{1}{2}$

416 From the drawing, (1) $B = $ _____ . $\therefore$ (2) $P(B) = $ _____ .

(1) $\{e_6,\ e_7,\ e_{11},\ e_{12}\}$
(2) $P(e_6) + P(e_7) + P(e_{11}) + P(e_{12}) = 4/12 = \frac{1}{3}$

417 From the drawing, to find $P(B \mid A)$, the conditional probability of B given A, *we assume that A has occurred.* The sample space to compute $P(B \mid A)$ contains only $A = \{e_2,\ e_3,\ e_4,\ e_5,\ e_6,\ e_7\}$, and if we let $P(e_2) = P(e_3) = \cdots = P(e_7) = \frac{1}{6}$, then the elements of B in this reduced sample space are e_6 and e_7. $\therefore$ $P(B \mid A) = $ _____ .

$\frac{2}{6} = \frac{1}{3}$

•**418** So, if the elements of S are given equal probabilities, we find that $P(B) = 1/3$ and $P(B \mid A) = 1/3$. Therefore, under these conditions, A and B are _____ events.

independent

419 We might also check whether $P(A) = P(A \mid B)$ in this situation. (If not, we are in trouble.) We found that $P(A) = \frac{1}{2}$. To find $P(A \mid B)$ we assume that B has occurred, so the sample space contains only $e_6,\ e_7,\ e_{11},\ e_{12}$, and if we let $P(e_6) = P(e_7) = P(e_{11}) = P(e_{12}) = \frac{1}{4}$ then from this sample space, the elements of A are
(1) ___ . (2) $P(A \mid B) = $ _____ .

(1) $e_6,\ e_7$ (2) $P(e_6) + P(e_7) = \frac{2}{4} = \frac{1}{2}$

420 Let a sample space S and events A and B be as shown:

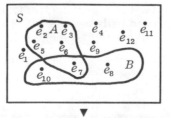

▼

Copy this drawing and use it for frames 421 to 424. If we let each element of S have equal probabilities, then
$P(e_1) = P(e_2) = \cdots = P(e_{12}) =$ ___ .

$\frac{1}{12}$

421 From the drawing, (1) $B =$ _____ .
∴ (2) $P(B) =$ _____ .

(1) $\{e_7, e_8, e_{10}\}$ (2) $\frac{3}{12} = \frac{1}{4}$

422 From the drawing, to find $P(B \mid A)$ we assume A has occurred. Therefore, the sample space to find $P(B \mid A)$ contains only the elements _____ .

$e_2, \; e_3, \; e_5, \; e_6, \; e_7$

423 From the drawing, to find $P(B \mid A)$ we find that, assuming A has occurred, the sample space consists of $e_2, \; e_3, \; e_5, \; e_6, \; e_7$. Let $P(e_2) = P(e_3) = \cdots = P(e_7) = \frac{1}{5}$. In this sample space, the element(s) of B is/are (1) ___ . ∴ (2) $P(B \mid A) =$ ___ .

(1) e_7 (This is the only element of B which is contained in the reduced sample space.)

(2) $\frac{1}{5}$

●**424** In frames 420 to 423, we found that $P(B) = \frac{1}{4}$ and $P(B \mid A) = \frac{1}{5}$. Therefore, A and B are _____ events.

dependent

425 A hat contains two red balls and one white ball. Two balls are to be drawn from the hat, one after the other, *without replacement*. Let B be the event that the second ball drawn is white. Let A be the event that the first ball drawn is red. Find (1) $P(B)$ and (2) $P(B \mid A)$.

(1) $P(B) = \frac{1}{3}$ (2) $P(B \mid A) = \frac{1}{2}$
If your answer is correct, skip to frame 429.
If your answer is not correct, go on to frame 426.

426 To find $P(B)$ for the experiment in frame 425, recall that the hat contained two red balls and one white ball. Two balls are drawn in succession, without replacement. Set up a sample space.

$S = \{e_1, \; e_2, \; \ldots, \; e_6\}$ where

$e_1 \leftrightarrow R_1R_2$ $e_2 \leftrightarrow R_1W$ $e_3 \leftrightarrow R_2R_1$
$e_4 \leftrightarrow R_2W$ $e_5 \leftrightarrow WR_1$ $e_6 \leftrightarrow WR_2$

427 Use the sample space from frame 426 and $P(e_1) = P(e_2) = \cdots = P(e_6) = \frac{1}{6}$. B is the event that the second ball drawn is white. Find (1) B and (2) $P(B)$.

(1) $B = \{e_2, e_4\}$ (2) $P(B) = \frac{2}{6} = \frac{1}{3}$

428 Use the same experiment as in frames 426 and 427. A is the event that the first ball is red. To find $P(B \mid A)$, we are given that A has occurred. Therefore, the sample space contains only:

$$e_1 \leftrightarrow R_1 R_2 \quad e_2 \leftrightarrow R_1 W \quad e_3 \leftrightarrow R_2 R_1 \quad e_4 \leftrightarrow R_2 W$$

If we let $P(e_1) = P(e_2) = P(e_3) = P(e_4) = \frac{1}{4}$, in this sample space, the elements of B are (1) ___.   (2) $P(B \mid A) =$ _____.

(1) e_2, e_4 (2) $\frac{2}{4} = \frac{1}{2}$

429 From frames 426 to 428, we have found that $P(B) = \frac{1}{3}$ and $P(B \mid A) = \frac{1}{2}$; so $P(B) \neq P(B \mid A)$. Therefore, A and B are _____ events.

dependent

430 For problems similar to the ones in frames 425 to 429, $P(B \mid A)$ is usually found, without any rigor, in the following manner. If a hat contains two red balls and one white ball, and two balls are drawn, in succession, without replacement, and if A is the event that the first ball is red and B is the event that the second ball is white, to find $P(B \mid A)$ we say: If A has occurred (the first ball is R) then, before the second ball is drawn, the hat contains only one red ball and one white ball; so obviously, the probability of drawing the white ball is (1) ___. $\therefore$ (2) $P(B \mid A) =$ ___.

(1) $\frac{1}{2}$ (2) $\frac{1}{2}$

431 Similarly, if a hat contains 10 red balls and five white balls and if five balls are to be chosen one after another without replacement, and if A is the event that the first ball is red, B is the event that the second ball is red, and C is the event that the third ball is white, to find $P(C \mid A \cap B)$ we assume A and B have already occurred. Therefore, the hat would contain only 13 balls, eight red and five white. Obviously then, the probability of drawing a white ball is ___.

$\frac{5}{13}$ $\therefore$ $P(C \mid A \cap B) = \frac{5}{13}$

432 Out of 500 times that Slugger McGurk was at bat last season, he got 150 hits. Of the 500 times he was at bat, 200 of them occurred with at least one man on base. *Out of these 200 times at bat,* he got 75 hits. Using relative frequencies as estimates of probabilities, if B is the event that McGurk gets a hit and A is the event that a man is on base when McGurk is at bat, (1) $P(B) = $_____, (2) $P(B \mid A) = $_____. (3) Are A and B independent? Why?

    (1) $\frac{150}{500} = \frac{3}{10}$ (2) $\frac{75}{200} = \frac{3}{8}$
    (3)   No, because $P(B) \neq P(B \mid A)$

433 Precisely, two events A and B are independent if and only if _____. Less precisely, A and B are independent if and only if, for a large number of trials, B occurs with the same relative frequency in A as it does in S. That is, if, for example, B occurs about $\frac{1}{10}$ of the time for all N trials, and if out of the times A occurred, B also occurred in $\frac{1}{10}$ of these, then A and B are independent.

    $P(B) = P(B \mid A)$ [or $P(A) = P(A \mid B)$]

434 A given experiment has been performed a certain number of times and the results, with respect to events A and B, are as shown:

	B	B'
A	10	20
A'	30	40

Copy this table and use it for frames 435 to 439. From the table, $N = $ ___

    100

435 From the table, (1) $n(A) = $ ___.   (2) $n(B) = $ ___.

    (1) 30   (2) 40

436 From the table, using relative frequencies as values for probabilities (1) $P(A) = $_____,   (2) $P(B) = $_____.

    (1) $\frac{30}{100} = \frac{3}{10}$ or 0.3   (2) $\frac{40}{100} = \frac{2}{5}$ or 0.4

437 (1)   From the table, we see that B occurred 0.4 of the time out of the 100 trials. Out of the 30 trials in which A occurred, how many times did B occur?

                       ▼

(2)   What is the relative frequency of the occurrence of B out of the 30 trials in which A occurred?

(1) 10   **(2)** $\frac{10}{30} = \frac{1}{3}$

438   So we see that B occurred 0.4 of the time in *all the trials,* but B occurred only $\frac{1}{3}$ of the time in those trials in which A had occurred. Using relative frequencies as values for probabilities, we have that **(1)** $P(B) =$ ___ and **(2)** $P(B \mid A) =$ ___.

(1)   0.4   **(2)** $\frac{1}{3}$

439   So, in the experiment represented by the table, the occurrence of A does affect the probability of the occurrence of B. Apparently, B is less likely to occur in the trials in which A has occurred. Since $P(B) \neq P(B \mid A)$, we say that A and B are _____ events.

dependent

440   Now copy this table and use it for frames 441 to 443.

	B	B'
A	10	30
A'	15	45

From the table, out of *all* the trials of the experiment, what is the relative frequency of B?

$\frac{25}{100} = \frac{1}{4}$

441   From the table, out of the trials in which A occurred, with what relative frequency did B occur?

$\frac{10}{40} = \frac{1}{4}$

442   In other words, B occurs with the same relative frequency in the trials in which A has occurred as its relative frequency in all trials. Using relative frequencies as values for the probabilities involved, we have that $P(B) = P(B \mid A)$. Therefore, A and B are _____ events.

independent

443 Note also, in the table in frame 440 the relative frequency of
$A = \frac{40}{100} = \frac{2}{5}$. Out of the 25 trials resulting in B, A occurred **(1)** ___
times; so given the occurrence of B, the relative frequency of A is
(2) ___.

(1) 10   **(2)** $\frac{10}{25} = \frac{2}{5}$

comment

So we see also that, using relative frequencies from the table in
frame 440 as values for probabilities, $P(A) = P(A \mid B)$. Note that
we had already said that A and B are independent; so if this result
had not been obtained, we would have been in trouble.

444 For a given experiment, let A and B be two events. Suppose the
experiment was performed N times and the relative frequencies of
A, B, A', B' were equal to the probabilities of A, B, A', and B'.

	B	B'
A	n_1	n_2
A'	n_3	n_4

Copy this table and use it for frames 445 to 451. From the table,
since the experiment was performed N times, using relative frequencies, **(1)** $n(A) =$ _____. $\therefore$ **(2)** $P(A) =$ _____.

(1) $n_1 + n_2$ **(2)** $\frac{n_1 + n_2}{N}$

445 From the table, using relative frequencies as values for the probabilities, **(1)** $n(B) =$ _____. $\therefore$ **(2)** $P(B) =$ _____.

(1) $n_1 + n_3$ **(2)** $\frac{n_1 + n_3}{N}$

446 From the table, using relative frequencies for probabilities, we see
that $P(A \mid B) = n_1/(n_1 + n_3)$. Similarly, $P(B \mid A) =$ _____.

$\frac{n_1}{n_1 + n_2}$

447 From the table, using relative frequencies, we want to prove that if
$P(A) = P(A \mid B)$, then A and B are independent; that is, $P(B) =$ ___.

$P(B \mid A)$

448 From the table, if $P(A) = P(A \mid B)$, then $(n_1 + n_2)/N = $ _____.

$$\frac{n_1}{n_1 + n_3}$$

449 So, if $P(A) = P(A \mid B)$, then $\frac{n_1 + n_2}{N} = \frac{n_1}{n_1 + n_3}$

$\therefore \; \frac{n_1 + n_3}{N} = \frac{n_1}{n_1 + n_2}$

$\therefore \; P(B) = P(B \mid A)$ so A and B are _____ events.

independent

450 Also, obviously, if $P(B) = P(B \mid A)$, then $\frac{n_1 + n_3}{N} = $ _____.

$$\frac{n_1}{n_1 + n_2}$$

451 So, if $P(B) = P(B \mid A)$, then $\frac{n_1 + n_3}{N} = \frac{n_1}{n_1 + n_2}$

$\therefore \; \frac{n_1 + n_2}{N} = \frac{n_1}{n_1 + n_3}$; thus, $P(A) = $ _____.

$P(A \mid B)$

●**452** So we have finally that two events A and B are independent if and only if **(1)** _____ or **(2)** _____.

(1) $P(B) = P(B \mid A)$ **(2)** $P(A) = P(A \mid B)$

453 Recall that, if A and B are events, then
$P(A \cap B) = $ **(1)** $P(A) \cdot$ _____ or
$\qquad\qquad = $ **(2)** $P(B) \cdot$ _____

(1) $P(B \mid A)$ **(2)** $P(A \mid B)$

454 You know that $P(A \cap B) = P(A) \cdot P(B \mid A)$. Moreover, if A and B are independent events, $P(B \mid A) = P(B)$; so in this case,
$P(A \cap B) = P(A) \cdot$ ___.
[Copy $P(A \cap B) = P(A) \cdot$ when you answer.]

$P(A \cap B) = P(A) \cdot P(B)$

455 For two events A and B, A and B are mutually exclusive, if and only if $A \cap B =$ ___ .

∅

456 Suppose A and B are mutually exclusive events and B is an event which can occur. Then $P(B) \neq 0$. But if A and B are mutually exclusive, then if one of them occurs, the other cannot occur since $A \cap B = \emptyset$. $\therefore$ $P(B \mid A) =$ ___ .

0

457 So, if A and B are mutually exclusive events and $P(B) \neq 0$, then $P(B \mid A) = 0$. Therefore $P(B) \neq P(B \mid A)$; so A and B are _____ events.

dependent

3. Review and Further Discussion of Sample Spaces, with Emphasis on Independent Events

458 We have been concerned with experiments of a type which could be performed a large number of times under essentially the same conditions given enough time and money. If A is an outcome of an experiment and if the experiment is performed N times during which A occurs $N(A)$ times, then $n(A)/N$ is called the _____ .

relative frequency of event A

459 For example, let an experiment consist of rolling a single die and observing the number of spots on the upper face. Suppose event A is that the number of spots appearing is either a 2 or a 5. Each trial of the experiment will be such that, on observing the die, either 1. a 2 or a 5 will appear, in which case we say that event A has occurred, or 2. a 2 or a 5 will not appear, in which case we say that event A has not occurred. Suppose after 500 trials we find that A has occurred 180 times; that is, $n(A) = 180$. Then the relative frequency of event $A =$ _____ .

$\frac{180}{500} = \frac{9}{25}$

460 It seems reasonable (and has been verified by experiment) that, for this type of experiment, as the number of trials becomes large, the relative frequency of event A will not vary appreciably from some fixed value. We assume that there is some "ideal number" whose value we approximate when we find the relative frequency of event A for a large N. This value is called the _____.

probability of event A

461 So, for example, when we say that for a certain experiment the probability of event $A = \frac{1}{3}$ we mean that, if the experiment is performed a large number of times, the relative frequency of event A should ultimately become very close to ___.

$\frac{1}{3}$

462 For fairly uncomplicated outcomes of simple events, we can often agree on the probabilities because of some inherent symmetry involved in the experiment. For example, most people will offer no argument if it is claimed that in an honest toss of an honest coin, if A is the event that a head will occur, then $P(A) =$ ___.

$\frac{1}{2}$

463 For other events, although fairly simple, probabilities will have to be approximated by actually performing the experiment a large number of times and using the relative frequency of event A as the value of $P(A)$. For example, suppose an experiment consists of measuring the precipitation during a 24-hour period during May in Squall Valley and event A is that some precipitation occurred. If someone were to say, either A occurs or it does not so $P(A) = \frac{1}{2}$, we might get an argument, especially if local residents were to point out that during the last 10 years, for the 310 May days, it had rained during 290 of them. On the basis of these records, we would be more apt to admit that $P(A)$ is closer to

_____.

$\frac{290}{310}$ or $\frac{29}{31}$

464 In any event, we are searching for techniques which will enable us to compute probabilities of complicated events, assuming that the probabilities of simpler events can be agreed upon in some way or another. Our method is to build a theoretical model of the experiment under consideration, using as clues the events and relative frequencies of the actual experiment.

▼

Our first discovery is that, if A is any outcome of an experiment, and if N trials of the experiment are performed, then;
(1)   The smallest number of times which A could occur is ___.
(2)   The greatest number of times which A could occur is ___.

(1) 0   (2) N

465 Therefore, if A is any outcome of an experiment:
(1)   The smallest possible value for the relative frequency of event A is ___.
(2)   The largest possible value for the relative frequency of event A is ___.

(1) 0   (2) 1

466 Using the results in frames 464 and 465 as clues, in building our mathematical model, if A is the part of the model corresponding to the outcome A of the experiment, then the probability value assigned to A should have the same restrictions as the relative frequency of event A in the experiment; that is, ___ $\leq P(A) \leq$ ___.   [Copy the $\leq P(A) \leq$ when you answer.]

$0 \leq P(A) \leq 1$

467 Furthermore, if we list a number of possible outcomes, say $A_1, A_2, \ldots, A_i$, of an experiment in such a way that any single trial of an experiment can result in one and only one of these outcomes then, if the experiment is performed N times, $n(A_1) + n(A_2) + \cdots + n(A_i) =$ ___.

N

468 For example, let an experiment consist of tossing a die. If A is the event that an even number turns up, B is the event that a 1 turns up, and C is the event that a 3 or a 5 turns up, then if the experiment is performed once, exactly one of these events will occur. If the experiment is performed 100 times, then $n(A) + n(B) + n(C) =$ ___.

100

469 Now, for a given experiment, if outcomes $A_1, A_2, \ldots, A_i$ are considered and are such that each trial of the experiment will result in exactly one of these outcomes, then relative frequency of

▼

A_1 + relative frequency of A_2 + $\cdots$ + relative frequency of A_i =

$$\frac{n(A_1)}{N} + \frac{n(A_2)}{N} + \cdots + \frac{n(A_i)}{N} = \frac{n(A_1) + n(A_2) + \cdots + n(A_i)}{N} = \underline{\hspace{2cm}}$$

$\frac{N}{N} = 1$

470 So, for our model, we construct a set of elements in a 1-to-1 correspondence with the outcomes A_1, A_2, $\ldots$, A_i and assign probabilities in one manner or another to these elements. But using as a clue that the sum of the relative frequencies of the events A_1, $\ldots$, A_i is 1, we decide to impose the restriction in our model that the sum of the probabilities of the elements in the model must equal ___.

1

471 The set of elements in the mathematical model of the experiment is called _____ for the experiment.

sample space

472 Note that for a given experiment a great number of sample spaces may be constructed. For example, suppose an experiment consists of rolling a die. We might consider event A is that an even number turns up and event B is that an odd number turns up. Then a sample space for the experiment would be $S_1 = \{e_1, e_2\}$ where $e_1 \leftrightarrow A$ and $e_2 \leftrightarrow B$. Or we could just as well consider a sample space
$S_2 = \{f_1, f_2, f_3\}$ where $f_1 \leftrightarrow$ a 1 or 2 turns up
$f_2 \leftrightarrow$ a 3 or 4 turns up
$f_3 \leftrightarrow$ _____

a 5 or 6 turns up

473 Similarly, if an experiment consists of tossing two coins, we might set up a model, having a sample space
$S = \{e_1, e_2, e_3\}$ where $e_1 \leftrightarrow$ both coins are heads
$e_2 \leftrightarrow$ exactly one head occurs
$e_3 \leftrightarrow$ _____

no heads appear (or both coins are tails)

474 Although a large number of sample spaces can be constructed for a given experiment, one important restriction to keep in mind is that the outcomes corresponding to the elements of a given sample space S must be such that *each trial of the experiment will result in exactly one of the outcomes.* Suppose an experiment consists

▼

of tossing a die. Would $S = \{e_1,\ e_2,\ e_3\}$ where $e_1 \leftrightarrow$ a number less than 3 occurs, $e_2 \leftrightarrow$ a 3 occurs, $e_3 \leftrightarrow$ a number greater than 3 occurs be an acceptable sample space?

Yes. Any trial of the experiment will result in exactly one of these outcomes.

●**475** Suppose an experiment consists of tossing two coins and $S = \{e_1,\ e_2\}$ where $e_1 \leftrightarrow$ two heads appear, $e_2 \leftrightarrow$ one head appears. Is S an acceptable space?

No. What if no heads appear? None of the outcomes has occurred.

●**476** Suppose an experiment consists of tossing two coins and we let $S = \{e_1,\ e_2,\ e_3,\ e_4\}$ where $e_1 \leftrightarrow$ exactly two heads appear, $e_2 \leftrightarrow$ no heads appear, $e_3 \leftrightarrow$ one head appears, $e_4 \leftrightarrow$ one tail appears. Would S be an acceptable sample space?

No. If one head and one tail appear on a trial, then two of the outcomes listed have occurred.

477 An important feature of a sample space S is that the outcomes corresponding to the elements of S are such that any trial of the experiment will result in exactly one of the outcomes. In so doing, we know that if the experiment is performed N times then the sum of the relative frequencies = 1; so in our model we feel that it is reasonable to assign probabilities to the elements of S in such a way that the sum of the probabilities = ___.

1

478 So more than one sample space might be constructed for a given experiment. The important restriction is that the outcomes corresponding to elements of S be such that any trial of the experiment will result in exactly one of the outcomes. If an experiment consists of drawing two balls, without replacement, from a hat containing 50 red balls, 50 white balls, and 50 black balls, and we let $S = \{e_1,\ e_2,\ e_3\}$ where $e_1 \leftrightarrow$ both balls are black, $e_2 \leftrightarrow$ one ball is black, $e_3 \leftrightarrow$ neither ball is black, is S an acceptable sample space?

Yes. Every trial of the experiment will result in exactly one of the outcomes.

479 An experiment consists of drawing a single card from a deck of cards.
1. Let $S_1 = \{e_1,\ e_2,\ e_3,\ e_4\}$ where $e_1 \leftrightarrow$ the card is a spade, $e_2 \leftrightarrow$ the card is a diamond, $e_3 \leftrightarrow$ the card is a heart, $e_4 \leftrightarrow$ the card is a club.

▼

2. Let $S_2 = \{f_1, f_2\}$ where $f_1 \leftrightarrow$ the card is an ace, $f_2 \leftrightarrow$ the card is not an ace.
3. Let $S_3 = \{g_1, g_2, g_3\}$ where $g_1 \leftrightarrow$ the card is a club, $g_2 \leftrightarrow$ the card is a spade, $g_3 \leftrightarrow$ the card is a diamond or a heart.
(1) Is S_1 an acceptable sample space? (2) Is S_2 an acceptable sample space? (3) Is S_3 an acceptable sample space?

(1) yes   (2) yes   (3) yes

comment

In building a model, you have a choice of sample spaces to construct. One of the considerations to keep in mind is that you are ultimately going to have to assign probabilities to the elements of S, so that a chosen sample space would not be of any use if you were unable to assign reasonable probabilities.

●480   Consider the following experiment: A hat contains two red balls, two white balls, and one black ball. Two balls are to be drawn in succession, without replacement. You might decide to let
$S_1 = \{e_1, e_2, e_3\}$ where $e_1 \leftrightarrow$ both balls are red
$e_2 \leftrightarrow$ one ball is red
$e_3 \leftrightarrow$ neither ball is red
Could you reasonably let $P(e_1) = P(e_2) = P(e_3)$?

No; they are not equal.

481   Consider again the experiment in frame 480. Perhaps next you would decide to let $S = \{f_1, f_2, f_3, f_4, f_5\}$ where

$f_1 \leftrightarrow RR$ $f_2 \leftrightarrow RW$ $f_3 \leftrightarrow RB$
$f_4 \leftrightarrow$ (1) _____ $f_5 \leftrightarrow$ (2) _____
where no care is taken about the order in which the balls were drawn. (RW means that one ball was red and the other white, regardless of the order in which they were drawn.)

(1) WW (2) WB

482   Consider the sample space in frame 481. You will still probably have difficulty in assigning values to $P(f_1)$, $P(f_2)$, etc., since it would seem, for example, that RW would occur more often than RB, since there are more white balls than black balls. Therefore, you would not be reasonable in letting $P(f_1) = P(f_2) = \cdots = P(f_5)$. Another sample space might be to consider the balls to be numbers R_1, R_2, W_1, W_2, and B.

▼

Let $S_3 = \{g_1, g_2, \ldots, g_{10}\}$ where $g_1 \leftrightarrow R_1 R_2$, $g_2 \leftrightarrow R_1 W_1$ where again the order in which the balls are drawn is not indicated. Complete listing $g_3, \ldots, g_{10}$.

$g_3 \leftrightarrow R_1 W_2$ $g_4 \leftrightarrow R_1 B$ $g_5 \leftrightarrow R_2 W_1$ $g_6 \leftrightarrow R_2 W_2$
$g_7 \leftrightarrow R_2 B$ $g_8 \leftrightarrow W_1 W_2$ $g_9 \leftrightarrow W_1 B$ $g_{10} \leftrightarrow W_2 B$

(Notice that since we are not concerned with order, we do not list BW_2, BW_1, etc., as separate outcomes.)

483 For S_3 in frame 482, it appears reasonable that one outcome is just as likely to occur as any other outcome, and you would get very little argument from anyone if you assigned equal probabilities to each element of S_3. So, you would let $P(g_1) = P(g_2) = \cdots = P(g_{10}) = $ ___ .

$\frac{1}{10}$

484 So, one consideration in deciding upon a sample space is whether or not we can assign reasonable probability values to the elements. Of course, if we have time and money, we might decide on some sample space whose probabilities cannot be determined by reflection and instead perform the experiment a large number of times and use the _____ of the outcomes corresponding to elements of the sample space as values for the probabilities of the elements of S.

relative frequencies

485 However, for the experiment under discussion in frames 480 to 483 we think our problems are over since we found an S_3 such that we were satisfied with the probabilities assigned. However, suppose we are asked, what is the probability that the second ball drawn is black? We suddenly realize that our outcomes did not take into consideration the order in which the balls were drawn. So, for a problem of this type, a more fundamental sample space would have to be constructed.
Let $S_4 = \{h_1, h_2, \ldots, h_{20}\}$ where

$h_1 \leftrightarrow R_1 R_2$ $h_2 \leftrightarrow R_1 W_1$ $h_3 \leftrightarrow R_1 W_2$ $h_4 \leftrightarrow R_1 B$ $h_5 \leftrightarrow R_2 R_1$

Complete by indicating $h_6, \ldots, h_{20}$.
Remember that order *is* important.

$h_6 \leftrightarrow R_2 W_1$ $h_7 \leftrightarrow R_2 W_2$ $h_8 \leftrightarrow R_2 B$ $h_9 \leftrightarrow W_1 R_1$
$h_{10} \leftrightarrow W_1 R_2$ $h_{11} \leftrightarrow W_1 W_2$ $h_{12} \leftrightarrow W_1 B$ $h_{13} \leftrightarrow W_2 R_1$
$h_{14} \leftrightarrow W_2 R_2$ $h_{15} \leftrightarrow W_2 W_1$ $h_{16} \leftrightarrow W_2 B$ $h_{17} \leftrightarrow BR_1$
$h_{18} \leftrightarrow BR_2$ $h_{19} \leftrightarrow BW_1$ $h_{20} \leftrightarrow BW_2$

●**486** Your choice of a sample space for a given experiment should be influenced by:
   (1) Your ability to form a sample space so that each trial of the experiment results in exactly _____ of the outcomes in the sample space.
   (2) Your ability to assign _____ to each outcome in the sample space.

(1) one   (2) probabilities

487 After a sample space $S = \{e_1, e_2, \ldots, e_n\}$ has been selected, your freedom in assigning probabilities is restricted in the following ways:
   1. The probabilities should be reasonable; that is, they should reflect the physical situation of the experiment as much as possible.
   2. For each $e_i \in S$, (1) ___ $\leq P(e_i) \leq$ ___. [Copy the $\leq P(e_i) \leq$ when you answer.]
   3. $P(e_1) + P(e_2) + \cdots + P(e_n) = $ (2) ___

(1) $0 \leq P(e_i) \leq 1$ (2) 1

488 Consider an experiment in which 1,000 coins are tossed.
   Let $S = \{e_1, e_2\}$ where $e_1 \leftrightarrow$ all 1,000 coins are heads
                              $e_2 \leftrightarrow$ at least one tail appears
   Let $P(e_1) = P(e_2) = \frac{1}{2}$.
   (1) Are the outcomes corresponding to e_1 and e_2 such that any trial of the experiment will result in exactly one of them?
   (2) (a) Is $0 \leq P(e_1) \leq 1$?   (b) Is $0 \leq P(e_2) \leq 1$?
   (3) Does $P(e_1) + P(e_2) = 1$?

(1) yes   (2) (a) yes   (b) yes   (3) yes

489 So, technically, the model of the experiment in frame 488 is acceptable. But it is unreasonable to expect that the outcome corresponding to e_1 will occur just as often as the outcome corresponding to e_2. So what part of the model set up in the last experiment would you consider unreasonable?

To let $P(e_1) = P(e_2) = \frac{1}{2}$

490 Technically, then, a model consists of a sample space $S = \{e_1, e_2, \ldots, e_n\}$, and to each element e_i of S there is assigned a value $P(e_i)$ called the (1) ___ of e_i such that (2) ___ $\leq P(e_i) \leq$ ___ for $i = 1, 2, \ldots, n$ and

▼

$P(e_1) + P(e_2) + \cdots + P(e_n) = (3)$ ___
[Copy $\leq P(e_i) \leq$ when you answer (2).]

---

(1) probability   (2) $0 \leq P(e_i) \leq 1$ (3) 1

---

comment

One other point, (1) *if* a sample space S having probabilities satisfying the restrictions listed in frame 490 is set up, and (2) *if* this
model is used for a given experiment by associating each element
of S with an outcome of the experiment in such a way that each trial
of the experiment must result in exactly one of these outcomes, and
(3) *if* the results correctly obtained are not reasonable, then it is
not the mathematics which is at fault but simply that the model is
not a good one for this experiment. Another choice of model must
be made.

A good deal of thought then should be given to the sample space and
probabilities assigned to its elements when constructing a model
for a particular experiment. Once these have been determined, the
techniques for computing probabilities of complicated outcomes are
not too difficult and the results obtained (by proper techniques) are
unassailable mathematically. The most vulnerable part of your
work is whether the model you have constructed is a good one for
the experiment.

---

491 Copy the following model:
Let $S = \{e_1,\ e_2,\ e_3\}$ and $P(e_1) = \frac{1}{4}$, $P(e_2) = \frac{1}{2}$, $P(e_3) = \frac{1}{4}$.
Technically, is there anything wrong with the sample space and
probabilities?

No
Have a copy of the sample space and probabilities.

---

492 Now we have defined an *event* to be any subset of a sample space.
So, if $A = \{e_1,\ e_3\}$ for the last item, A is a subset of S; therefore
A is an _____.

---

event

---

493 Moreover, we have defined the following: If A is an event, then
$P(A)$, called the probability of A, is equal to the sum of the probabilities of the elements of A. So, from the model we are working
on in frame 491, if $A = \{e_1,\ e_3\}$, then $P(A) =$ _____.

$P(e_1) + P(e_3) = \frac{1}{4} + \frac{1}{4} = \frac{2}{4} = \frac{1}{2}$

494 Now consider the following experiment: A hat contains one red ball, two white balls, and one blue ball. A single ball is drawn from the hat and its color noted. If we let our model correspond to the experiment in the following way, $e_1 \leftrightarrow$ the ball is red, $e_2 \leftrightarrow$ the ball is white, $e_3 \leftrightarrow$ the ball is blue, then $A = \{e_1, e_3\}$ corresponds to the outcome of the experiment that the ball is (1) _____ or the ball is (2) _____.

(1) red   (2) blue   (Any order is correct.)

495 Consider an experiment in which two coins are tossed and the number of heads is recorded. If we let our model correspond to this experiment in the following way: $e_1 \leftrightarrow$ two heads appear, $e_2 \leftrightarrow$ one head appears, $e_3 \leftrightarrow$ no heads appear, then $P(A)$, which we found to be ___, can be interpreted as the probability that both coins turn up the same way, either both heads or both tails. You will find that the results obtained are consistent with actual performance of the experiment.

$\frac{1}{2}$

496 You will find that $P(A) = \frac{1}{2}$ from the model in frame 491 is consistent with and represents correctly the results obtained by actually performing the experiment a large number of times. That is, the model is good for this experiment. Now, suppose the hat contains 500 red balls, 10 white balls, and 500 blue balls, and we let $e_1 \leftrightarrow$ the ball is red, $e_2 \leftrightarrow$ the ball is white, $e_3 \leftrightarrow$ the ball is blue. Now A still corresponds to the outcome that the ball drawn is either red or blue, and $P(A) = \frac{1}{2}$ is still correct, but do you feel that this model should be used for this experiment?

No, the model does not match reality to any extent.

497 The point is that there was nothing wrong with the mathematics of the model. We simply used the model for an experiment it did not fit. If $S = \{e_1, e_2, e_3\}$ and $P(e_1) = \frac{1}{4}$, $P(e_2) = \frac{1}{2}$, $P(e_3) = \frac{1}{4}$, and $A = \{e_1, e_3\}$, then $P(A) =$ ___ no matter what experiment we might be attempting to fit the model to.

$\frac{1}{2}$

498 Let us take a simple experiment and illustrate various sample spaces which might be used as models for the experiment. *Note:* An ordinary deck of playing cards contains 52 cards. Of the 52, 13 are marked spades, 13 are marked diamonds, 13 are marked clubs, and 13 are marked hearts. These four markings, spades, diamonds, clubs, and hearts, are called suits. In each suit there is a 2, 3, 4, 5, 6, 7, 8, 9, 10, jack, queen, king, and

▼

ace. Thus, for example, there are ___ sevens in the deck, a seven of spades, a seven of diamonds, a seven of clubs, and a seven of hearts. Copy this description if you do not know it.

---

four
Have the description of a deck of cards if you are not familiar with it.

---

499 In describing the experiments with a deck of cards, it is always understood that the cards have been well mixed or shuffled before each trial of the experiment and that any cards drawn are drawn at random. Copy the following experiment and events:
A single card is to be drawn from a deck of cards. Let event A be that the card is a club, let event B be that the card is a jack or a king, let event C be that the card is a jack or a club (or both). Now let us see about constructing sample spaces for the experiment. Looking forward to event A, we see that the important feature of event A is the suit. So we might construct a sample space as follows:
Let $S = \{e_1,\ e_2,\ e_3,\ e_4\}$ where $e_1 \leftrightarrow$ the card drawn is a spade, $e_2 \leftrightarrow$ the card drawn is a diamond, $e_3 \leftrightarrow$ the card drawn is a club, $e_4 \leftrightarrow$ the card drawn is a heart. Will each trial of the experiment result in exactly one of the outcomes corresponding to $e_1,\ e_2,\ e_3,$ or e_4?

Yes. Each card in the deck is marked with exactly *one* of the suits. Have a correct copy of the experiment and the events.

---

500 Now, it seems reasonable, because of the symmetry of the deck (each suit has 13 cards), that we assign equal probabilities to the elements of S.
$\therefore\ P(e_1) = P(e_2) = P(e_3) = P(e_4) =$ ___ .

$\frac{1}{4}$

---

501 We have then, for an experiment of drawing a single card from a deck of cards, a sample space $S = \{e_1,\ e_2,\ e_3,\ e_4\}$ where $e_1 \leftrightarrow$ the card is a spade, $e_2 \leftrightarrow$ the card is a diamond, $e_3 \leftrightarrow$ the card is a club, $e_4 \leftrightarrow$ the card is a heart, and $P(e_1) = P(e_2) = P(e_3) = P(e_4) = \frac{1}{4}$. Copy this sample space and its probabilities.
Note carefully that the model is technically satisfactory, that is,
(1) Each trial of the experiment can result in exactly _____ outcome(s) corresponding to an element of S.
(2) ___ $\leq P(e_i) \leq$ ___ for $i = 1, 2, 3, 4$.
(3) $P(e_1) + P(e_2) + P(e_3) + P(e_4) =$ ___ .
[Copy the $\leq P(e_i) \leq$ when you answer (2).]

---

(1) one   (2) $0 \leq P(e_i) \leq 1$ (3) 1
Have a correct copy of the sample space and its probabilities.

502 Note also that the only reason we feel secure about the probabilities assigned is that each suit contains the same number of cards, and we feel intuitively that each suit has the same chance of being chosen. (If the deck were incomplete, say five of the spades were missing, we would not have been so fortunate.) Even so, the assignment of probabilities is an important step; think carefully before you do it. Now, of course, event A is simple. From our sample space, (1) $A =$___ ; so (2) $P(A) =$ _____ .

(1) $\{e_3\}$ (2) $P(e_3) = \frac{1}{4}$

503 Now look at B. As far as S is concerned, B is not even an event. The sample space S is not satisfactory for computing $P(B)$, even though S is a mathematically correct sample space. So, back to the sample-space factory we go. Event B is concerned with face values of the cards, not the suits; so suppose we let $S_1 = \{f_1, f_2, \ldots, f_{13}\}$ where $f_1 \leftrightarrow$ the card drawn is a 2, $f_2 \leftrightarrow$ the card drawn is a 3, $f_3 \leftrightarrow$ the card drawn is a 4. Copy this part of S_1; complete and save it.

$S_1 = \{f_1, f_2, f_3, \ldots, f_{13}\}$

$f_1 \leftrightarrow$ the card is a 2 $\quad$ $f_2 \leftrightarrow$ the card is a 3
$f_3 \leftrightarrow$ the card is a 4 $\quad$ $f_4 \leftrightarrow$ the card is a 5
$f_5 \leftrightarrow$ the card is a 6 $\quad$ $f_6 \leftrightarrow$ the card is a 7
$f_7 \leftrightarrow$ the card is an 8 $\quad$ $f_8 \leftrightarrow$ the card is a 9
$f_9 \leftrightarrow$ the card is a 10 $\quad$ $f_{10} \leftrightarrow$ the card is a jack
$f_{11} \leftrightarrow$ the card is a queen $\quad$ $f_{12} \leftrightarrow$ the card is a king
$f_{13} \leftrightarrow$ the card is an ace

504 It seems reasonable, because of the symmetry in the deck, to let $P(f_1) = P(f_2) = \cdots = P(f_{13}) =$___ . After all, there are exactly four cards of each face value; so it seems reasonable that there is just as much chance that an ace be chosen as a 2 or a 4, etc.

$\frac{1}{13}$

505 Look at S_1. Add to it the information that
$P(f_1) = P(f_2) = P(f_{13}) = \frac{1}{13}$.
S_1 is technically correct as a model; that is,
(1) Each trial of the experiment will result in exactly one of the _____ corresponding to the elements of S_1.
(2) ___ $\leq P(f_i) \leq$ ___ for $i = 1, 2, \ldots, 13$.
(3) $P(f_1) + P(f_2) + \cdots + P(f_{13}) =$___ .
[Copy $\leq P(f_i) \leq$ when you answer (2).]

(1) outcomes (2) $0 \leq P(f_i) \leq 1$ (3) 1

506 Now, with respect to S_1, (1) $B =$ _____; so (2) $P(B) =$ _____ .

(1) $\{f_{10}, f_{12}\}$ (2) $P(f_{10}) + P(f_{12}) = \frac{2}{13}$

507 Look at event C. As far as S and S_1 are concerned, C is not even an event (it is not a subset of S or S_1). Back to the sample-space factory. Event C is concerned with both suit and face value; so we let $S_2 = \{g_1, g_2, \ldots, g_{52}\}$ where

$g_1 \leftrightarrow$ 2 of spades	$g_2 \leftrightarrow$ 3 of spades
$g_3 \leftrightarrow$ 4 of spades	$g_{14} \leftrightarrow$ 2 of diamonds
$g_{15} \leftrightarrow$ 3 of diamonds	$g_{16} \leftrightarrow$ 4 of diamonds
$g_{27} \leftrightarrow$ 2 of clubs	$g_{28} \leftrightarrow$ 3 of clubs
$g_{29} \leftrightarrow$ 4 of clubs	$g_{40} \leftrightarrow$ 2 of hearts
$g_{41} \leftrightarrow$ 3 of hearts	$g_{42} \leftrightarrow$ 4 of hearts

Complete this sample space and save it.

$S_2 = \{g_1, g_2, \ldots, g_{52}\}$ where

Spades	Clubs
$g_1 \leftrightarrow$ 2 of spades	$g_{27} \leftrightarrow$ 2 of clubs
$g_2 \leftrightarrow$ 3 of spades	$g_{28} \leftrightarrow$ 3 of clubs
$g_3 \leftrightarrow$ 4 of spades	$g_{29} \leftrightarrow$ 4 of clubs
$g_4 \leftrightarrow$ 5 of spades	$g_{30} \leftrightarrow$ 5 of clubs
$g_5 \leftrightarrow$ 6 of spades	$g_{31} \leftrightarrow$ 6 of clubs
$g_6 \leftrightarrow$ 7 of spades	$g_{32} \leftrightarrow$ 7 of clubs
$g_7 \leftrightarrow$ 8 of spades	$g_{33} \leftrightarrow$ 8 of clubs
$g_8 \leftrightarrow$ 9 of spades	$g_{34} \leftrightarrow$ 9 of clubs
$g_9 \leftrightarrow$ 10 of spades	$g_{35} \leftrightarrow$ 10 of clubs
$g_{10} \leftrightarrow$ jack of spades	$g_{36} \leftrightarrow$ jack of clubs
$g_{11} \leftrightarrow$ queen of spades	$g_{37} \leftrightarrow$ queen of clubs
$g_{12} \leftrightarrow$ king of spades	$g_{38} \leftrightarrow$ king of clubs
$g_{13} \leftrightarrow$ ace of spades	$g_{39} \leftrightarrow$ ace of clubs

Diamonds	Hearts
$g_{14} \leftrightarrow$ 2 of diamonds	$g_{40} \leftrightarrow$ 2 of hearts
$g_{15} \leftrightarrow$ 3 of diamonds	$g_{41} \leftrightarrow$ 3 of hearts
$g_{16} \leftrightarrow$ 4 of diamonds	$g_{42} \leftrightarrow$ 4 of hearts
$g_{17} \leftrightarrow$ 5 of diamonds	$g_{43} \leftrightarrow$ 5 of hearts
$g_{18} \leftrightarrow$ 6 of diamonds	$g_{44} \leftrightarrow$ 6 of hearts
$g_{19} \leftrightarrow$ 7 of diamonds	$g_{45} \leftrightarrow$ 7 of hearts
$g_{20} \leftrightarrow$ 8 of diamonds	$g_{46} \leftrightarrow$ 8 of hearts
$g_{21} \leftrightarrow$ 9 of diamonds	$g_{47} \leftrightarrow$ 9 of hearts
$g_{22} \leftrightarrow$ 10 of diamonds	$g_{48} \leftrightarrow$ 10 of hearts
$g_{23} \leftrightarrow$ jack of diamonds	$g_{49} \leftrightarrow$ jack of hearts
$g_{24} \leftrightarrow$ queen of diamonds	$g_{50} \leftrightarrow$ queen of hearts
$g_{25} \leftrightarrow$ king of diamonds	$g_{51} \leftrightarrow$ king of hearts
$g_{26} \leftrightarrow$ ace of diamonds	$g_{52} \leftrightarrow$ ace of hearts

508 Moreover, it seems quite reasonable to let
$P(g_1) = P(g_2) = \cdots = P(g_{52}) =$ ___ .

$\frac{1}{52}$

Add this to the information you have from frame 507.

509 Note for S_2:
  (1) Each trial of the experiment must result in exactly one out-
        come corresponding to an _____ of S_2.
  (2) ___ $\leq P(g_i) \leq$ ___ for $i = 1, 2, \ldots, 52$.
  (3) $P(g_1) + P(g_2) + \cdots + P(g_{52}) =$ ___ .
  [Copy $\leq P(g_i) \leq$ when you answer (2).]

  (1) element   (2) $0 \leq P(g_i) \leq 1$ (3) 1

510 Now, with respect to S_2, (1) $C =$ _____ ; so (2) $P(C) =$ _____ .

  (1) $\{g_{10}, g_{23}, g_{36}, g_{49}, g_{27}, g_{28}, g_{29}, g_{30}, g_{31}, g_{32}, g_{33}, g_{34}, g_{35},$
        $g_{37}, g_{38}, g_{39}\}$
  (2) Note that g_{36} is not included twice in the listing;
        $\therefore P(C) = \frac{16}{52} = \frac{4}{13}$

511 Note that $A \subset S_2$, in fact, with respect to S_2,
  (1) $A =$ _____ ; so (2) $P(A) =$ _____ .

  (1) $\{g_{27}, g_{28}, g_{29}, \ldots, g_{39}\}$
  (2) $P(g_{27}) + P(g_{28}) + \cdots + P(g_{39}) = \frac{13}{52} = \frac{1}{4}$

512 You saw in frame 511 that $P(A) = \frac{1}{4}$. Is this the same answer
obtained when using sample space S in frame 502?

  yes

513 Note also that $B \subset S_2$, in fact, with respect to
S_2, (1) $B =$ _____ $\therefore$ (2) $P(B) =$ _____ .

  (1) $g_{10}, g_{23}, g_{36}, g_{49}, g_{12}, g_{25}, g_{38}, g_{51}$
  (2) $P(g_{10}) + P(g_{23}) + \cdots = \frac{8}{52} = \frac{2}{13}$

514 You saw in frame 513 that $P(B) = \frac{2}{13}$. Is this the same answer
obtained when using sample space S_1 in frame 506?

  yes

515 S_2 is a more fundamental sample space than S or S_1 since it contains more information. Note that S_2 is also more difficult to write out completely. For a given problem, the thing to do is to use the easiest sample space possible to construct for which (1) it is possible to assign reasonable (1) _____ and (2) the events whose probabilities you wish to compute are (2) _____ of S. Of course, if you construct a more fundamental sample space than necessary, you probably will still be able to get your answers, you will just do extra work.

(1) probabilities   (2) subsets
Continue to save S, S_1, and S_2 for future reference.

comment

When we have developed some of our techniques for computing probabilities of more complicated events where probabilities of simpler events are known or can be found, you will find that you need not construct the most fundamental sample space needed for the event with which you are concerned. For example, later you will be able to find $P(C)$ from sample space S and S_1 by expressing C as combinations of events contained in S and S_1 and using some later theorems. Here is a preview of how it can be done.
Let D be that the card is a jack.
Let E be that the card is a club.
We will see that $C = (D \cup E)$ and $P(C) = P(D \cup E)$.
Later we will prove that
$$P(D \cup E) = P(D) + P(E) - P(D \cap E)$$
$$\therefore\ P(D \cup E) = P(D) + P(E) - P(D) \cdot P(E \mid D)$$
From S_1, $P(D) = \frac{1}{13}$. From S, $P(E) = \frac{1}{4}$ and $P(E \mid D) = \frac{1}{4}$;
so $P(D \cup E) = \frac{1}{13} + \frac{1}{4} - \frac{1}{13} \cdot \frac{1}{4}$
$$= \frac{1}{13} + \frac{1}{4} - \frac{1}{52}$$
$$= \frac{4 + 13 - 1}{52} = \frac{16}{52} = \frac{4}{13}$$
This is the same answer that you obtained for $P(C)$ using S_2 in frame 510.

One other simple experiment should convince you of the need for techniques other than counting points in a sample space. Suppose five cards are to be drawn without replacement from a deck of cards. We are interested in finding the probability of an event which involves both face value and suit. A sample space comparable to S_2 would contain $(52 \cdot 51 \cdot 50 \cdot 49 \cdot 48)/(1 \cdot 2 \cdot 3 \cdot 4 \cdot 5)$ elements. (Multiply it out, if you are interested.)

Moreover, if the event involved the order in which the cards are drawn, the denominator would not be there. The thought of listing such a sample space should motivate you in the study of techniques for finding probabilities of complicated events.

516 From a viewpoint of sets, if $A = \{e_1, e_2, e_5, e_8, e_{10}\}$ and $B = \{e_1, e_3, e_4, e_6, e_8\}$, then $A \cap B = $ _____

$\{e_1, e_8\}$

517 From the drawing, $A \cap B = $ _____ .

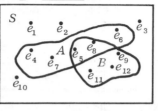

$\{e_5, e_8\}$

518 From the viewpoint of outcomes, if A is an event corresponding to some outcome A of the experiment and B is an event corresponding to some outcome B of the experiment, then $A \cap B$ is an event corresponding to the outcome of A *and* B. For example, look at S_2 of the card experiment in frame 507. Let H be the event that the card is a king. Then **(1)** $H = $ _____ . Let J be the event that the card is a club. Then **(2)** $J = $ _____ .
(3) $H \cap J = $ ___ , and this element corresponds to the outcome that the card is a king *and* a club.

(1) $\{g_{12}, g_{25}, g_{...}, g_{51}\}$
(2) $\{g_{27}, g_{28}, g_{29}, \cdots, g_{39}\}$
(3) $\{g_{38}\}$

519 *Experiment:* Two cards are to be drawn in succession without replacement from a deck of cards. Event A is that the first card is an ace and the second card is a club. If we are asked to compute $P(A)$, rather than listing a sample space fundamental enough to contain A (there would be 2,652 elements in it), we might let B be the event that the first card is an ace, C be the event that the second card is a club. Then, symbolically, we would have $A = $ _____ .

$B \cap C$
Note that B and C are simpler events and $P(B \cap C)$ might be found from smaller sample spaces.

520 With relative frequencies as a guide, we established that if A and B are events, then $P(A \cap B) = $ _____ . [Copy $P(A \cap B) = $ when you answer.]

$P(A \cap B) = P(A) \cdot P(B \mid A)$
or $P(A \cap B) = P(B) \cdot P(A \mid B)$

521 Recall that, if A and B are events, $P(B \mid A)$ *is the* _____ *probability of B given A*; that is, it is the probability of B on the assumption that A has occurred. You should realize that for certain experiments and events, $P(B)$ and $P(B \mid A)$ need not have the same values. For example, let an experiment consist of drawing a single card from a deck of cards. A is the event that the card is higher in face value than a jack (that is, that it is a queen, king, or ace). Let B be the event that the card is the ace of clubs. Copy this experiment and events A and B.

conditional
Have a copy of the experiment and events A and B.

522 We want to see, for the experiment in frame 521, if $P(B)$ and $P(B \mid A)$ have the same values. From S_2 (from the earlier card experiment in frame 507), (1) $B =$ ___; so (2) $P(B) =$ ___.

(1) $\{g_{39}\}$ (2) $\frac{1}{52}$

523 Now, to find $P(B \mid A)$ we work on the assumption that A has occurred, that is, that the card drawn has a face value greater than a jack. Therefore, the sample space needed to find $P(B \mid A)$ contains only the elements of A from S_2; that is, we have a sample space, using the notation from S_2,
$S_3 = \{g_{11}, g_{12}, g_{13}, g_{24}, g_{25}, g_{26}, g_{37}, g_{38}, g_{39}, g_{50}, g_{51}, g_{52}\}$ and we let $P(g_{11}) = P(g_{12}) = \cdots = P(g_{52}) = \frac{1}{12}$. Now in S_3, $B = \{e_{39}\}$; so $P(B \mid A) =$ ___.

$\frac{1}{12}$

524 So we have in this case that $P(B) \neq P(B \mid A)$. Note also for this experiment, from S_2,
$A = \{g_{11}, g_{12}, g_{13}, g_{24}, g_{25}, g_{26}, g_{37}, g_{38}, g_{39}, g_{50}, g_{51}, g_{52}\}$ so $P(A) = \frac{12}{52} = \frac{3}{13}$. Now to find $P(A \mid B)$ we assume that B has occurred. But obviously, if B has occurred, $P(A \mid B) =$ ___, because B is the event that the card is the ace of clubs.

1
You can set up the sample space if you want, but obviously, if B has occurred, then the card drawn is the ace of clubs, and the probability that the card is a queen, king, or ace is now obviously 1. So we have in this case $P(A) \neq P(A \mid B)$.

●**525** Let an experiment consist of drawing a single card from a deck of cards. Let A be the event that the card is a king. Let B be the event that the card is a club. (1) Find $P(B)$. (2) Find $P(B \mid A)$.

(1) $P(B) = \frac{1}{4}$
(2) $P(B \mid A) = \frac{1}{4}$
Note in this case, $P(B) = P(B \mid A)$. If your answer is correct, skip to frame 529. If your answer is not correct, go on to frame 526.

526 To find $P(B)$ use either sample space S in frame 499 or S_2 in frame 507. In S, $B = \{e_3\}$; so $P(B) = P(e_3) = \frac{1}{4}$.
In S_2, (1) $B = $ _____ ; so (2) $P(B) = $ _____ .

(1) $\{g_{27}, g_{28}, g_{29}, \ldots, g_{39}\}$
(2) $P(g_{27}) + P(g_{28}) + P(g_{29}) + \cdots + P(g_{39}) = \frac{13}{52} = \frac{1}{4}$

527 Now to find $P(B \mid A)$, the conditional probability of B given A, we assume A has occurred, that is, that the card drawn is a king. Therefore, the sample space needed to find $P(B \mid A)$ has only four elements; that is, $S = \{e_1, e_2, e_3, e_4\}$ where $e_1 \leftrightarrow$ the card is the king of spades, $e_2 \leftrightarrow$ the card is the king of diamonds, $e_3 \leftrightarrow$ the card is the king of clubs, $e_4 \leftrightarrow$ the card is the king of hearts; and if we let $P(e_1) = P(e_2) = P(e_3) = P(e_4) = \frac{1}{4}$, then $P(B \mid A) = $___ .

$\frac{1}{4}$, since in S, $B = \{e_3\}$

528 So, in the last example, we had a situation in which $P(B) = P(B \mid A)$. Intuitively, in this case, the reason is obvious. The proportion of clubs in the whole deck $(\frac{13}{52} = \frac{1}{4})$ is the same as the proportion of clubs in the set of four kings $(\frac{1}{4})$, and since each card has the same chance of being drawn, $P(B) = P(B \mid A)$. Note also in this case that (1) $P(A) = $___ and (2) $P(A \mid B) = $___ .

(1) $\frac{1}{13}$ (2) $\frac{1}{13}$

529 Recall, if two events A and B are such that $P(B) = P(B \mid A)$, then A and B are called _____ events.

independent

530 If, for two events A and B, $P(B) \neq P(B \mid A)$, then A and B are called _____ events.

dependent

531 You might keep the words straight if you keep in mind that, roughly speaking, if the probability of the occurrence of B is independent of whether or not A has occurred, that is, if ___ = ___ , then A and B are independent events.

$P(B) = P(B \mid A)$

532 In the same vein, if the probability of the occurrence of B is affected by the occurrence of A, that is, if ___ $\neq$ ___ , then A and B are dependent events.

$P(B) \neq P(B \mid A)$

533 However, if you were asked for definitions, you would have to say: Two events A and B are independent if and only if (1) _____ , and they are dependent if and only if (2) _____ .

(1) $P(B) = P(B \mid A)$ or $P(A) = P(A \mid B)$
(2) $P(B) \neq P(B \mid A)$ or $P(A) \neq P(A \mid B)$

534 Similarly, if you were given an experiment and two events, say A and B, and you were asked to prove them (1) dependent, you would have to show that (1) _____ , or (2) independent, you would have to show that (2) _____ .

(1) $P(B) \neq P(B \mid A)$ or $P(A) \neq P(A \mid B)$
(2) $P(B) = P(B \mid A)$ or $P(A) = P(A \mid B)$

535 Casey Fungo, manager of the West Futility Canaries, a semiprofessional baseball team, kept a record of the team's wins W and losses L at home H and away A for the last season. The results are shown in the chart.

	H	A
W	10	4
L	30	36

If relative frequencies are used as probabilities, show that the events W (a game is won) and H (the game is played at home) are dependent.

$P(W) = \frac{14}{80} = \frac{7}{40}$ $P(W \mid H) = \frac{10}{40}$
$\therefore$ $P(W) \neq P(W \mid H)$ $\therefore$ W and H are dependent
or $P(H) = \frac{1}{2}$ $P(H \mid W) = \frac{10}{14} = \frac{5}{7}$
$\therefore$ $P(H) \neq P(H \mid W)$

536 You have seen earlier, on the basis of relative frequencies, a justification for the conclusion that if A and B are events, then $P(A \cap B) = P(A) \cdot P(B \mid A)$. Let us now look at a similar result from the viewpoint of a sample space. Copy the following and save it.

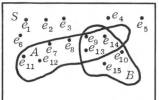

$S =$ _____

$\{e_1, e_2, \ldots, e_{15}\}$
Have a correct drawing of the sample space.

537 From your sketch, $S = \{e_1, e_2, \ldots, e_{15}\}$, $A =$ _____ .

$\{e_7, e_8, e_9, e_{11}, e_{12}, e_{13}, e_{14}\}$

538 From your sketch, $B =$ _____ .

$\{e_9, e_{10}, e_{13}, e_{14}, e_{15}\}$

539 From your sketch, $A \cap B =$ _____ .

$\{e_9, e_{13}, e_{14}\}$

540 Suppose, for this sample space, we let $P(e_1) = P(e_2) = \cdots = P(e_{15}) = \frac{1}{15}$. Add this information to your sketch. Now, since $A = \{e_7, e_8, e_9, e_{11}, e_{12}, e_{13}, e_{14}\}$, $P(A) =$ _____ .

$P(e_7) + P(e_8) + P(e_9) + P(e_{11}) + P(e_{12}) + P(e_{13}) + P(e_{14}) = \frac{7}{15}$

541 Similarly, since $B = \{e_9, e_{10}, e_{13}, e_{14}, e_{15}\}$, $P(B) =$ _____ .

$P(e_9) + P(e_{10}) + P(e_{13}) + P(e_{14}) + P(e_{15}) = \frac{5}{15} = \frac{1}{3}$

542 Since $A \cap B = \{e_9, e_{13}, e_{14}\}$, $P(A \cap B) =$ _____ .

$P(e_9) + P(e_{13}) + P(e_{14}) = \frac{3}{15} = \frac{1}{5}$

543 *Look carefully at the drawing.* To find $P(B \mid A)$ we mean to find the conditional probability of B given A; that is, we are given that the sample space to work in is A, not S. So we proceed as follows: Treating A as the sample space, we have $A = \{e_7, e_8, e_9, e_{11}, e_{12}, e_{13}, e_{14}\}$ In this sample space, following the pattern in S that each element has the same probability, we let $P(e_7) = P(e_8) = P(e_9) = P(e_{11}) = P(e_{12}) = P(e_{13}) = P(e_{14}) = \underline{\quad}$.

$\frac{1}{7}$

544 Now, the elements of B in A are e_9, e_{13}, e_{14}; so $P(B \mid A) = \underline{\quad}$.

$\frac{3}{7}$ Note also that $\dfrac{P(A \cap B)}{P(A)} = \dfrac{3/15}{7/15} = 3/7$

545 Recall, we found that $P(B) = \frac{1}{3}$ and $P(B \mid A) = \frac{3}{7}$. Therefore, $P(B) \neq P(B \mid A)$; so A and B are _____ events.

dependent

546 Copy the following:

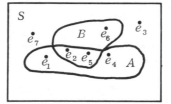

$P(e_1) = 0.1$, $P(e_2) = 0.2$, $P(e_3) = 0.1$, $P(e_4) = 0.3$, $P(e_5) = 0.1$, $P(e_6) = 0.1$, $P(e_7) = 0.1$
(1) $P(e_1) + P(e_2) + \cdots + P(e_7) = \underline{\quad}$
(2) $\underline{\quad} \leq P(e_i) \leq \underline{\quad}$ for $i = 1, 2, \ldots, 7$
[Copy $\leq P(e_i) \leq$ when you answer.]

(1) 1   (2) $0 \leq P(e_i) \leq 1$
Have a correct copy of the drawing and the probabilities.

547 From the sketch, (1) $A = \underline{\qquad\qquad}$, so (2) $P(A) = \underline{\qquad\qquad}$.

(1) $\{e_1, e_2, e_4, e_5\}$
(2) $P(e_1) + P(e_2) + P(e_4) + P(e_5)$
     $= 0.1 + 0.2 + 0.3 + 0.1 = 0.7$

548 From the sketch, (1) $B =$ _____ , so (2) $P(B) =$ _____ .

(1) $\{e_2, e_5, e_6\}$
(2) $P(e_2) + P(e_5) + P(e_6)$
$= 0.2 + 0.1 + 0.1 = 0.4$

549 From the sketch, (1) $A \cap B =$ _____ , so
(2) $P(A \cap B) =$ _____ .

(1) $\{e_2, e_5\}$
(2) $P(e_2) + P(e_5)$
$= 0.2 + 0.1 = 0.3$

550 To find $P(B \mid A)$ we assume that we are working with a restricted sample space containing only the elements of A. In other words, in the drawing, we are now working inside the set A; so our sample space contains only the elements _____ .

e_1, e_2, e_4, e_5

551 So, for the purpose of finding $P(B \mid A)$ we assume we have a sample space containing only the elements e_1, e_2, e_4, e_5, and we need to assign probabilities in this sample space such that (1) their sum is 1, (2) each lies between 0 and 1, and (3) they are consistent with their probabilities in S. Here, essentially, is the problem. Suppose $X_1 + X_2 + \cdots + X_n = L$, and we wish to find a constant K such that $KX_1 + KX_2 + \cdots + KX_n = 1$, then $K(X_1 + X_2 + \cdots + X_n) = 1$. $K \cdot L = 1$ $\therefore$ $K =$ ___ if $L \neq 0$.

$\dfrac{1}{L}$

552 In our problem, then, we have that $P(e_1) + P(e_2) + P(e_3) + P(e_4) = 0.7$, and we want to find a constant K such that $K \cdot P(e_1) + K \cdot P(e_2) + K \cdot P(e_3) + K \cdot P(e_4) = 1$. Then $K \cdot [P(e_1) + P(e_2) + P(e_3) + P(e_4)] = 1$. $\therefore$ $K \cdot (0.7) = 1$, $K =$ ___ .

$\dfrac{1}{0.7}$

553 So, in our problem, to assign probabilities to each element in the sample space A, we simply divide each probability in S by 0.7. Therefore, in A, $P(e_1) = 0.1/0.7 = 1/7$; in A, $P(e_2) = 0.2/0.7 = 2/7$; in A, $P(e_4) = $ (1) _____ ; in A, $P(e_5) = $ (2) _____ .

(1) $0.3/0.7 = 3/7$ (2) $0.1/0.7 = 1/7$
Note: In A, $P(e_1) + P(e_2) + P(e_4) + P(e_5) = 1$, and the probabilities are in the same proportion as they were in S.

554 Look at the sketch. We are now in a position to compute $P(B \mid A)$. In A, $P(e_1) = \frac{1}{7}$, $P(e_2) + \frac{2}{7}$, $P(e_4) = \frac{3}{7}$, $P(e_5) = \frac{1}{7}$. The elements of B in A are (1) _____; so (2) $P(B \mid A) =$ _____.

(1) e_2, e_5 (2) $\frac{2}{7} + \frac{1}{7} = \frac{3}{7}$

555 Of course, each time that you are given two events A and B in a sample space S, you would not care to go through this process of reassigning probabilities to every element of A and then finding $P(B \mid A)$ by working in A as we have just done. We need a more general process. First note, if, $X_1 + X_2 + \cdots + X_n = K$, then

$$\frac{1}{K} \cdot X_1 + \frac{1}{K} \cdot X_2 + \cdots + \frac{1}{K} \cdot X_n = (1) \underline{\quad}, \text{ if } K \neq 0. \text{ Therefore,}$$

since the sum of the probabilities of the elements of $A = P(A)$, then if each probability is divided by $P(A)$ if $P(A) \neq 0$, the sum of these new numbers is (2) ___ .

(1) 1   (2) 1

556 So, in reassigning probabilities to elements of A when considering A as the new sample space, we need only to divide each of the probabilities (given with respect to S) by (1) ___ if (2) ___ $\neq$ 0.

(1) $P(A)$ (2) $P(A)$

557 For example, suppose

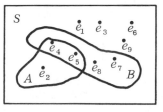

and suppose *with S as a sample space*, $P(e_2) = 0.2$, $P(e_4) = 0.1$, and $P(e_5) = 0.5$. Then with A as a sample space, we would assign, since $P(A) = 0.8$, in A:
$P(e_2) = 0.2/0.8 = 1/4$
$P(e_4) =$ _____
$P(e_5) =$ _____

$0.1/0.8 = 1/8$, $0.5/0.8 = 5/8$

558 (1) In frame 557, where A is a sample space,
$P(e_2) + P(e_4) + P(e_5) =$ ___ .
(2) Are $P(e_2)$, $P(e_4)$, and $P(e_5)$ in the same proportion with A as a sample space as they are in S?

---

(1) 1 (2) yes

---

559 Now, we know automatically how to reassign the probabilities in A as a sample space. Then, to find $P(B \mid A)$ we need only find the elements of B which are also in A. But in set language, what is the set of all elements of B which are also in A?

$A \cap B$

---

560 So really, $P(B \mid A)$ is the sum of the reassigned probabilities with respect to A of elements of $A \cap B$. Rather than reassigning each probability in A with A as a sample space, it is easier to find $P(A \cap B)$ with respect to the original probabilities and then convert to the reassigned probabilities by dividing by $P(A)$. Hence we get $P(B \mid A) = P(A \cap B) / P(A)$ if $P(A) \neq 0$; so $P(A \cap B) =$ _____ .

$P(A) \cdot P(B \mid A)$
Note we get the same result as earlier.

---

561 *Experiment:* Two cards are drawn in succession without replacement from a deck of cards.
Event A: Both cards are hearts.
Copy this experiment and event.
A sample space for A would contain quite a few elements; so we shall let B be the event that the first card is a heart and let C be the event that the second card is a heart.
Then $A = B \cap C$ *(B and C)*
$\therefore \ P(A) = P(B \cap C)$
$= P(B) \cdot$ _____

$P(C \mid B)$
Have a correct copy of the experiment and event A.

---

562 So we have that $P(A) = P(B) \cdot P(C \mid B)$, where B is the event that the first card is a heart and C is the event that the second card is a heart. $P(B) = \frac{13}{52}$ (since there are 52 cards, 13 of which are hearts). Now to find $P(C \mid B)$ we assume that B has occurred. Then there remain (1) ___ cards, (2) ___ of which are hearts. Therefore (3) $P(C \mid B) =$ ___ .

---

(1) 51 (2) 12 (3) $\frac{12}{51}$

563 We now have all the information that we need to find $P(A)$. We found in frame 562 that $P(B) = \frac{13}{52}$ and $P(C \mid B) = \frac{12}{51}$.   Find $P(A)$.

$$P(A) = P(B) \cdot P(C \mid B)$$
$$= \tfrac{13}{52} \cdot \tfrac{12}{51} = \tfrac{3}{51}$$

564 Given two events A and B, $P(A \cap B) =$ _____ .
[Copy $P(A \cap B) =$ when you answer.]

$$P(A \cap B) = P(A) \cdot P(B \mid A)$$
or
$$P(A \cap B) = P(B) \cdot P(A \mid B)$$

565 An experiment consists of drawing two cards in succession without replacement from a deck of cards. To find the probability that the first card is a king and the second is an ace, we let A be the event that the first card is a king and B be the event that the second card is an ace.
Then $P(A \cap B) = P(A) \cdot P(B \mid A)$
$$= \tfrac{4}{52} \cdot \text{\_\_\_\_} = \text{\_\_\_\_}$$

$$\tfrac{4}{51} = \tfrac{4}{663}$$

●566 An experiment consists of drawing from a deck of cards two cards in succession with replacement. (The first card drawn is replaced, the deck is shuffled before the second card is drawn.) Find the probability that both cards are kings.

$$P(A \cap B) = P(A) \cdot P(B \mid A)$$
$$= 4/52 \cdot 4/52 = 1/169$$
Note: $P(B \mid A)$ is the same as $P(B)$ since, even if A occurred (or did not occur), the card was replaced in the deck; so the deck still contains 52 cards, four of which are kings.

567 In the last problem, $P(B \mid A) = P(B)$; so A and B are _____ events.

independent

568 Precisely, events A and B are independent if and only if
$P(B) = P(B \mid A)$ [or $P(A) = P(A \mid B)$]. Roughly speaking, A and B are independent if the occurrence of A does not affect the probability of the occurrence of B. For example, if an experiment consists of tossing a coin twice and A is the event that the first toss is

▼

a head and B is the event that the second toss is a head, we know $P(B) = \frac{1}{2}$. Suppose you are given that A has occurred; then $P(B \mid A) = \underline{\quad}$.

$\frac{1}{2}$ It makes no difference that A has occurred.

---

569 So, if a coin is tossed twice and we want to know the probability of getting heads both times, we let A be the event that the first toss is a head and B be the event that the second toss is a head.   Then $P(A \cap B) = P(A) \cdot P(B \mid A)$. But since A and B are independent, $P(B \mid A) = P(B)$.

$\therefore\ P(A \cap B) = P(A) \cdot P(B)$

$= \underline{\quad} \cdot \underline{\quad}$

$= \underline{\quad}$

$\frac{1}{2} \cdot \frac{1}{2}$

$\frac{1}{4}$

---

570 So, if a coin is tossed three times and we wish to find the probability of getting three heads, it is apparent that the three events (heads on the first coin A, heads on the second coin B, heads on the third coin C) are independent,

$\therefore\ P(A \cap B \cap C) = P(A) \cdot P(B) \cdot P(C)$

$= \underline{\quad\quad}$

$= \underline{\quad}$

$\frac{1}{2} \cdot \frac{1}{2} \cdot \frac{1}{2}$

$\frac{1}{8}$

---

571 Recall that if A, B, C are events, then $P(A \cap B \cap C) = P(A) \cdot P(B \mid A) \cdot P(C \mid A \cap B)$. We will define three events A, B, C as independent if and only if $P(B) = P(B \mid A)$ and $P(C) = P(C \mid A \cap B)$. Then, for independent events A, B, and C, $P(A \cap B \cap C) = \underline{\quad\quad\quad}$.

$P(A) \cdot P(B) \cdot P(C)$

●**572** Find the probability of getting four heads when tossing a coin four times.

$P(A \cap B \cap C \cap D) = P(A) \cdot P(B) \cdot P(C) \cdot P(D)$

$= \frac{1}{2} \cdot \frac{1}{2} \cdot \frac{1}{2} \cdot \frac{1}{2} = \frac{1}{16}$

---

573 A pair of dice is rolled twice.   To find the probability of rolling a seven both times, we let A be the event that the first roll is a seven and B be the event that the second roll is a seven.   It is apparent that these events are independent; that is, the occurrence of A has no affect on the probability of the occurrence of B.

▼

$\therefore P(A \cap B) = P(A) \cdot P(B)$

$= \underline{\quad} \cdot \underline{\quad}$

[Use Panel 1 to find $\overline{P(A)}$ and $P(B)$.]

$1/6 \cdot 1/6 = 1/36$

---

574 Similarly, find the probability of rolling three sevens in a row when tossing a pair of dice three times.

$P(A \cap B \cap C) = P(A) \cdot P(B) \cdot P(C)$

$= \frac{1}{6} \cdot \frac{1}{6} \cdot \frac{1}{6} = \frac{1}{216}$

---

575 Three cards are drawn in succession, with replacement, from a deck of cards. Find the probability that the first two are not aces but the third one is. Let A be the event that the first card is not an ace, B be the event that the second card is not an ace, C be the event that the third card is an ace. Now, since after each drawing the card is replaced in the deck, it is obvious that A, B, and C are independent,

$\therefore P(A \cap B \cap C) = P(A) \cdot P(B) \cdot P(C) = \underline{\hspace{2cm}}$

$\frac{48}{52} \cdot \frac{48}{52} \cdot \frac{4}{52} = \frac{144}{2,197}$

---

576 From a hat containing four red balls, three white balls, and two blue balls, three balls are to be drawn in succession with replacement. To find the probability that the first ball is red (A), the second ball is white (B), and the third ball is blue (C), we note that, since we are sampling with replacement, the events are independent.

$\therefore P(A \cap B \cap C) = P(A) \cdot P(B) \cdot P(C)$

$= \underline{\quad} \cdot \underline{\quad} \cdot \underline{\quad}$

$\frac{4}{9} \cdot \frac{3}{9} \cdot \frac{2}{9} = \frac{8}{243}$

---

577 In the previous experiments, frames 566 to 576, tossing coins, dice, drawing from a deck of cards *with replacement*, it has been intuitively obvious that the events were independent. If you are ever questioned or in doubt, however, if two events A and B are independent, you can prove that A and B are independent by showing that $\underline{\hspace{2cm}}$.

$P(B) = P(B \mid A)$ or $P(A) = P(A \mid B)$

578 So, if two events A and B are independent, then
$P(A \cap B) = P(A) \cdot P(B)$, but if A and B are any events, dependent
or independent, $P(A \cap B) =$ _____ . [Copy $P(A \cap B) =$ when
you answer.]

$P(A \cap B) = P(A) \cdot P(B \mid A)$
or $P(A \cap B) = P(B) \cdot P(A \mid B)$

---

579 For example, from a deck of cards, two cards are to be drawn
without replacement. Find the probability that the first card is an
ace and the second card is not an ace. Let A be the event that the
first card is an ace and B be the event that the second card is not
an ace. Then $P(A \cap B) = P(A) \cdot P(B \mid A)$
= ___ · ___

$\frac{4}{52} \cdot \frac{48}{51} = \frac{48}{663} = \frac{16}{221}$

Note: To find $P(B \mid A)$ we assume that A has occurred, that is,
that an ace was drawn. Because the card was not replaced in the
deck, the deck now has only 51 cards, 48 of which are not aces.

●**580** Two defective pogo sticks have been mixed up with 10 good pogo
sticks. From the 12 pogo sticks, two are to be chosen at random
(without replacement). Find the probability that both sticks
chosen are good.

$\frac{10}{12} \cdot \frac{9}{11} = \frac{15}{22}$

---

581 If A, B, and C are events, then
$P(A \cap B \cap C) = P(A) \cdot P(B \mid A) \cdot P(C \mid A \cap B)$.
For example, an experiment consists of drawing three cards in
succession from a deck of cards without replacement. To find
the probability that the first card is an ace (A), the second card
is an ace (B), and the third card is a king (C),
$P(A \cap B \cap C) = P(A) \cdot P(B \mid A) \cdot P(C \mid A \cap B)$
$= \frac{4}{52} \cdot \frac{3}{51} \cdot$ ___
$=$ ___

$\frac{4}{50}$ or $\left(\frac{2}{25}\right)$, $\frac{2}{5,525}$

Note: To find $P(C \mid A \cap B)$ we assume A and B have occurred.
Then two aces have been drawn from the deck and not replaced.
Therefore, the deck contains 50 cards, four of which are kings.

---

582 A hat contains five red balls, four blue balls, and one white ball.
Three balls are to be drawn in succession without replacement.
Find the probability that the third ball drawn is the white ball.

▼

Hint: Let A be the event the first ball is not white, B be the event that the second ball is not white, and C be the event that the third ball is white.

$$P(A \cap B \cap C) = P(A) \cdot P(B \mid A) \cdot P(C \mid A \cap B)$$
$$= \tfrac{9}{10} \cdot \tfrac{8}{9} \cdot \tfrac{1}{8} = \tfrac{1}{10}$$

583 It has been found that, with exposure to disease X, the probability that a hamster will contract disease X is $\tfrac{9}{10}$. If three hamsters are to be exposed to disease X, find the probability that all three contract disease X. (Assume the three events are independent.)

$$\frac{9}{10} \cdot \frac{9}{10} \cdot \frac{9}{10} = \frac{729}{1,000}$$

Self-test V

1 (1) Given two events A and B, if $P(A) \neq P(A \mid B)$[or $P(B) \neq P(B \mid A)$], then A and B are _____ events.

 (2) Given two events A and B, if $P(A) = P(A \mid B)$[or $P(B) = P(B \mid A)$], then A and B are _____ events.

2 A hat contains three red balls and two white balls. One ball is to be drawn, its color is noted, and it is returned to the hat. Then a second ball is to be drawn and its color noted. Let A be the event that the first ball is red. Let B be the event that the second ball is white. Find **(1)** $P(B)$ and **(2)** $P(B \mid A)$. **(3)** Are A and B dependent or independent? How do you know?

3 A hat contains three red balls and two white balls. Two balls are to be drawn from the hat, one after the other, without replacement. Let A be the event that the first ball is red. Let B be the event that the second ball is white. Find **(1)** $P(B)$ and **(2)** $P(B \mid A)$. **(3)** Are A and B dependent or independent? How do you know?

4 A hat contains two red balls and two white balls. Suppose an experiment consists of drawing two balls at the same time and noting their color.

Let $S = \{e_1, e_2\}$ where $e_1 \leftrightarrow$ both balls are red
$e_2 \leftrightarrow$ both balls are white

(1) Is S an acceptable sample space? Why?

Consider the same experiment.

Let $S_1 = \{e_1, e_2, e_3, e_4\}$ where $e_1 \leftrightarrow$ both balls are red
$e_2 \leftrightarrow$ both balls are white
$e_3 \leftrightarrow$ one ball is red
$e_4 \leftrightarrow$ one ball is white

(2) Is S an acceptable sample space? Why?

5 We want to use a double deck of cards for an experiment. This means that we will have 104 cards: 26 hearts, 26 spades, etc. We will have eight aces: two aces of hearts, two aces of spades, etc. Suppose an experiment consists of drawing two cards in succession without replacement from the double deck of cards. Find the probability that both cards are aces of hearts.

6 Find the probability of getting three heads when tossing a coin three times.

7 Two defective light bulbs have been put into a box with 18 good light bulbs by mistake. From the 20 bulbs, two are chosen and tested (without replacement). Find the probability that both bulbs are defective.

4. Union of Events

584 Now, we have been concerned with finding the probability occurrence of *A and B* where *A* and *B* are events. There are many times when we are interested in the probability of the oc-currence of event *A or* event *B* (or both). For example: A die is tossed. If *A* is the event that the number is even and *B* is the event the number is ≤ 3, then event *A* or event *B* will occur if a —, —, —, —, or — turns up.

1, 2, 3, 4, 6

585 Recall, if *A* and *B* are sets, then $A \cup B$ is the set of all elements in *A* or in *B* or in both. For example, if $A = \{1, 3, a, 10\}$ and $B = \{X, 1, 3, b\}$, then $A \cup B = $ _____ .

$\{1, 3, a, 10, X, b\}$

586 Symbolically, given sets *A* and *B*, $A \cup B = \{X \mid X \epsilon A \text{ or } X \epsilon B\}$. This is read, $A \cup B$ is equal to the set of all *X* such that *X* is an ele-ment of *A* or *X* is an element of *B*. Note that the use of "or" will include the possibility that $X \epsilon A$ and $X \epsilon B$. So, if $A = \{e_1, e_3, e_5, e_6\}$ and $B = \{e_2, e_3, e_5, e_7\}$, then $A \cup B = $ _____ .

$\{e_1, e_2, e_3, e_5, e_6, e_7\}$

587 In *ordinary usage*, the word "or" is used in two ways and you often have to guess what a person means when he uses it. If Joe Zilch says, "I am going to take Carmela or Lenore to the dance next Saturday," you would probably be right in assuming that he means

▼

one or the other but not both. This use of or is called the "exclusive or." It excludes the possibility of both. Suppose a mathematics teacher were to say to a class, "I will give an A to anyone getting an average of better than 89 in the weekly quizzes *or* to anyone getting better than 94 on the final examination." Suppose John Lemma got both quiz average greater than 89 and a final examination grade greater than 94. Do you feel that the use of the exclusive or would be justified in this case?

You should not.

588 This second use of the word "or" is called the "inclusive or." It includes the possibility of both events. If you were told by one of your friends, "If it rains or snows, I will not meet you." If the weather then turns up mixed snow and rain, you would probably be right in assuming that he meant the "or" in the _____ (inclusive, exclusive) sense.

inclusive;   in other words, he will not show up.

589 There is no point in discussing the relative merits of the inclusive and the exclusive "or." The important thing in mathematics is that we have no confusion. We must decide on one use of or. The use of *or* unless specifically pointed out, will be in the *inclusive* sense. Thus, if an experiment consists of tossing a die, A is the event that an even number appears, and B is the event that a number less than 4 appears. By A *or* B we mean event A or event B or both. Thus, if a 2 appears, A or B has occurred. If a 1 appears, has A or B occurred?

Yes, B has occurred; so A or B has occurred.

590 Let S, A, and B be as shown:

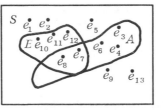

(1) $A =$ _____
(2) $B =$ _____
(3) $A \cup B =$ _____

(1) $\{e_3,\ e_4,\ e_6,\ e_7,\ e_8\}$
(2) $\{e_7,\ e_8,\ e_{10},\ e_{11},\ e_{12}\}$
(3) $\{e_3,\ e_4,\ e_6,\ e_7,\ e_8,\ e_{10},\ e_{11},\ e_{12}\}$

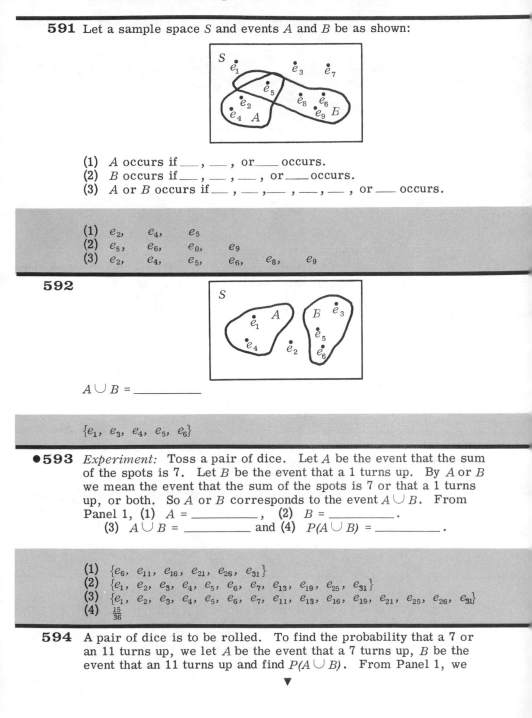

591 Let a sample space S and events A and B be as shown:

(1) A occurs if ___ , ___ , or ___ occurs.
(2) B occurs if ___ , ___ , ___ , or ___ occurs.
(3) A or B occurs if ___ , ___ , ___ , ___ , ___ , or ___ occurs.

(1) e_2, e_4, e_5
(2) e_5, e_6, e_0, e_9
(3) e_2, e_4, e_5, e_6, e_8, e_9

592

$A \cup B =$ _____

$\{e_1, \ e_3, \ e_4, \ e_5, \ e_6\}$

●**593** *Experiment:* Toss a pair of dice. Let A be the event that the sum of the spots is 7. Let B be the event that a 1 turns up. By A or B we mean the event that the sum of the spots is 7 or that a 1 turns up, or both. So A or B corresponds to the event $A \cup B$. From Panel 1, (1) $A =$ _____,   (2) $B =$ _____.
      (3) $A \cup B =$ _____ and (4) $P(A \cup B) =$ _____.

(1) $\{e_6, \ e_{11}, \ e_{16}, \ e_{21}, \ e_{26}, \ e_{31}\}$
(2) $\{e_1, \ e_2, \ e_3, \ e_4, \ e_5, \ e_6, \ e_7, \ e_{13}, \ e_{19}, \ e_{25}, \ e_{31}\}$
(3) $\{e_1, \ e_2, \ e_3, \ e_4, \ e_5, \ e_6, \ e_7, \ e_{11}, \ e_{13}, \ e_{16}, \ e_{19}, \ e_{21}, \ e_{25}, \ e_{26}, \ e_{31}\}$
(4) $\frac{15}{36}$

594 A pair of dice is to be rolled. To find the probability that a 7 or an 11 turns up, we let A be the event that a 7 turns up, B be the event that an 11 turns up and find $P(A \cup B)$. From Panel 1, we

▼

find (1) $A =$ _____ , (2) $B =$ _____ . ∴ (3) $A \cup B =$ _____
and (4) $P(A \cup B) =$ ___ .

(1) $\{e_6,\ e_{11},\ e_{16},\ e_{21},\ e_{26},\ e_{31}\}$
(2) $\{e_{30},\ e_{35}\}$
(3) $\{e_6,\ e_{11},\ e_{16},\ e_{21},\ e_{26},\ e_{30},\ e_{31},\ e_{35}\}$
(4) $\frac{8}{36}$

595 In the experiment in frame 594, does $P(A \cup B)$ equal $P(A) + P(B)$?
Show how you obtained your answer.

yes
$$P(A \cup B) \overset{?}{=} P(A) + P(B)$$
$$P(A) + P(B) = \frac{6}{36} + \frac{2}{36} = \frac{8}{36}$$
$$P(A \cup B) = \frac{8}{36}$$
∴ $P(A \cup B) = P(A) + P(B)$ *in this case.*

596 Consider this experiment: A pair of dice is rolled. Let A be the
event that both dice have the same number of spots. Let B be the
event that the sum of the spots is 4. Then to find $P(A \cup B)$, we find
from Panel 1, (1) $A =$ _____ , (2) $B =$ _____ ,
∴ (3) $A \cup B =$ _____ and (4) $P(A \cup B) =$ ___.

(1) $\{e_1,\ e_8,\ e_{15},\ e_{22},\ e_{29},\ e_{36}\}$
(2) $\{e_3,\ e_8,\ e_{13}\}$
(3) $\{e_1,\ e_3,\ e_8,\ e_{13},\ e_{15},\ e_{22},\ e_{29},\ e_{36}\}$
(4) $\frac{8}{36}$

597 In the experiment in frame 596, does $P(A \cup B)$ equal $P(A) + P(B)$?
Show how you obtained your answer.

no
$$P(A \cup B) \overset{?}{=} P(A) + P(B)$$
$$P(A) + P(B) = \frac{6}{36} + \frac{3}{36} = \frac{9}{36}$$
$$P(A \cup B) = \frac{8}{36}$$
∴ $P(A \cup B) \neq P(A) + P(B)$ *in this case.*

598 We are, of course, searching for a technique of finding $P(A \cup B)$
from probabilities of simpler events. If we look at a typical sample
space, and events A and B, we get a clue.
▼

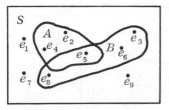

Note: $P(A) + P(B) = P(e_2) + P(e_4)$
$+ P(e_5) + P(e_3) + P(e_5) + P(e_6) + P(e_8)$
$P(A \cup B) = P(e_2)$ + _____

$P(e_3) + P(e_4) + P(e_5) + P(e_6) + P(e_8)$

●**599** Let S and events A and B be as given:

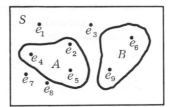

(1) $P(A) =$ _____
(2) $P(B) =$ _____
(3) $P(A) + P(B) =$ _____
(4) $P(A \cup B) =$ _____

(1) $P(e_2) + P(e_4) + P(e_5)$
(2) $P(e_6) + P(e_9)$
(3) $P(e_2) + P(e_4) + P(e_5) + P(e_6) + P(e_9)$
(4) $P(e_2) + P(e_4) + P(e_5) + P(e_6) + P(e_9)$

●**600** Let S and events A and B be as given:

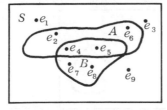

(1) $P(A) =$ _____
(2) $P(B) =$ _____
(3) $P(A) + P(B) =$ _____
(4) $P(A \cup B) =$ _____

(1) $P(e_2) + P(e_4) + P(e_5) + P(e_6)$
(2) $P(e_4) + P(e_5) + P(e_7) + P(e_8)$
(3) $P(e_2) + P(e_4) + P(e_5) + P(e_6) + P(e_4) + P(e_5) + P(e_7) + P(e_8)$
(4) $P(e_2) + P(e_4) + P(e_5) + P(e_6) + P(e_7) + P(e_8)$

601 Notice, then,

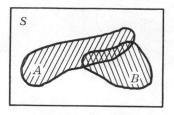

$P(A \cup B)$ will be the sum of the probabilities of the elements in the shaded area. $P(A)$ will be the sum of the probabilities of elements in the area shaded by ⁄⁄⁄⁄. $P(B)$ will be the sum of the probabilities of the elements in the area shaded by ⟍⟍⟍. Then $P(A) + P(B)$ will include probabilities of certain elements twice, namely, in the section shaded by _____ .

or double cross-hatching

602 Suppose $S = \{e_1, e_2, e_3, e_4, e_5, e_6\}$
$A = \{e_1, e_2, e_3, e_4\}$ $B = \{e_3, e_4, e_5\}$
$P(A) + P(B) = P(e_1) + P(e_2) + P(e_3) + P(e_4) + P(e_3) + P(e_4) + P(e_5)$
But **(1)** $A \cup B = $ _____
∴ **(2)** $P(A \cup B) = $ _____

(1) $\{e_1, e_2, e_3, e_4, e_5\}$
(2) $P(e_1) + P(e_2) + P(e_3) + P(e_4) + P(e_5)$

603 By now it should be obvious that in the general case, where $A \cap B \neq \emptyset$. $P(A) + P(B)$ differs from $P(A \cup B)$ in that the probabilities of elements in $A \cap B$ are added twice in $P(A) + P(B)$, once from $P(A)$ and once from $P(B)$. ∴ $P(A \cup B) = P(A) + P(B) - $ _____ .

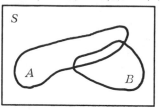

$P(A \cap B)$

604 Of course, if $A \cap B = \emptyset$, $P(A \cup B) = P(A) + P(B)$

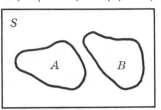

but the formula $P(A \cup B) = P(A) + P(B) - P(A \cap B)$ still works, since in this case, $P(A \cap B) = $ ___ .

0

605 In West Futility, a survey has shown that among male residents over twenty-one years of age, if A is the event that a person owns his own house and B is the event that a person owns a car, $P(A) = 0.4$ and $P(B) = 0.8$. Joe Zilch has reached the conclusion that, since $A \cup B$ is the event that a person owns a house or a car (or both), then $P(A \cup B) = 0.4 + 0.8 = 1.2$. This, on the face of it, is ridiculous since, if X is any event, $0 \le P(X) \le 1$. Where did Joe go wrong?

$P(A \cup B) = P(A) + P(B) - P(A \cap B)$.
The people who own both a house and a car have been counted twice, once in A and once in B.

606 A single card is to be drawn from a deck of cards. To find the probability that it is a king or a club, let A be the event that the card is a king and B be the event that the card is a club. Then
$$P(A \cup B) = P(A) + P(B) - P(A \cap B)$$
$$= P(A) + P(B) - [P(A) \cdot P(B \mid A)]$$
$$= \tfrac{1}{13} + \underline{\quad} - (\tfrac{1}{13}) \cdot (\quad)$$
$$= \underline{\qquad\qquad}$$

$\frac{1}{4}, \qquad \frac{1}{4}$
$\frac{1}{13} + \frac{1}{4} - \frac{1}{52}$
$\dfrac{4 + 13 - 1}{52} = \dfrac{16}{52} = \dfrac{4}{13}$

Remember this problem? It was more difficult to do earlier.

607 Hat 1 contains two red balls and one white ball. Hat 2 contains two red balls and two white balls. An experiment consists of drawing one ball from each hat. To find the probability that at least one red ball is drawn, we let A be the event that the ball from hat 1 is

▼

red, B be the event that the ball from hat 2 is red. Then
$$P(A \cup B) = P(A) + P(B) - P(A \cap B)$$
$$= P(A) + P(B) - P(A) \cdot P(B \mid A)$$
$$= \underline{\hspace{3cm}}$$

$$\tfrac{2}{3} + \tfrac{1}{2} - \tfrac{2}{3} \cdot \tfrac{1}{2}$$
$$= \frac{4 + 3 - 2}{6} = \tfrac{5}{6}$$

608 In frame 607 are A and B independent events? How do you know?

yes, $P(B \mid A) = \tfrac{1}{2}$ $P(B) = \tfrac{1}{2}$
$P(B \mid A) = P(B)$
$\therefore$ A and B are independent events.

609 The last problem was: Hat 1 contains two red balls and one white ball. Hat 2 contains two red balls and two white balls. An experiment consists of drawing one ball from each hat. Find the probability that at least one red ball is drawn. We let A be the event the ball from hat 1 is red and B be the event the ball from hat 2 is red. Then
$$P(A \cup B) = P(A) + P(B) - P(A \cap B)$$
$$= P(A) + P(B) - P(A) \cdot P(B \mid A)$$
$$= \tfrac{2}{3} + \tfrac{1}{2} - \tfrac{2}{3} \cdot \tfrac{1}{2} = \tfrac{5}{6}$$
Copy the experiment, events, and solution.
It might be profitable to do this problem using our old techniques.
To set up a sample space, consider the balls in hat 1 to be R_1, R_2, and W_1 and the balls in hat 2 to be R_3, R_4, W_2, and W_3. Then one outcome might be that we draw R_2 from hat 1 and W_2 from hat 2.
Let us indicate this outcome by R_2W_2, the first letter indicating the ball from hat 1 and W_2 that from hat 2. Note that the order of drawing is not important.
Then $S = \{e_1, e_2, \ldots, e_{12}\}$. Set up the correspondence for example,
$e_1 \leftrightarrow R_1R_3$ $e_2 \leftrightarrow R_1R_4$
Complete listing the outcomes through e_{12}.

$e_1 \leftrightarrow R_1R_3$ $e_2 \leftrightarrow R_1R_4$ $e_3 \leftrightarrow R_1W_2$ $e_4 \leftrightarrow R_1W_3$
$e_5 \leftrightarrow R_2R_3$ $e_6 \leftrightarrow R_2R_4$ $e_7 \leftrightarrow R_2W_2$ $e_8 \leftrightarrow R_2W_3$
$e_9 \leftrightarrow W_1R_3$ $e_{10} \leftrightarrow W_1R_4$ $e_{11} \leftrightarrow W_1W_2$ $e_{12} \leftrightarrow W_1W_3$

Of course, you may have them listed in a different order. However, change your answer to this one so that we can refer to it.

610 If, as it seems reasonable, we let $P(e_1) = P(e_2) = \cdots = P(e_{12}) = \tfrac{1}{12}$, note that if C is the event that at least one ball is red, then
(1) $C = \underline{\hspace{2cm}}$,   (2) $P(C) = \underline{\hspace{1.5cm}}$.

(1) $\{e_1, e_2, e_3, e_4, e_5, e_6, e_7, e_8, e_9, e_{10}\}$
(2) $\tfrac{10}{12} = \tfrac{5}{6}$
This is the same answer that we got in frame 607.

611 We found $P(C)$, using our new techniques, by letting A be the event that the ball from hat 1 is red and B be the event that the ball from hat 2 is red. Then
$A = \{e_1,\ e_2,\ e_3,\ e_4,\ e_5,\ e_6,\ e_7,\ e_8\}$
$B = $ _____

$\{e_1,\ e_2,\ e_5,\ e_6,\ e_9,\ e_{10}\}$

612 Here is a picture of S. Copy it and show A and B, from frame 611, on it.

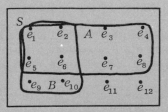

If you do not have a correct drawing, copy this and save it.

613 Now look at the sketch. We found, using our old method, that
$C = \{e_1,\ e_2,\ e_3,\ e_4,\ e_5,\ e_6,\ e_7,\ e_8,\ e_9,\ e_{10}\}$. We found C by our new techniques, that is, by noting that $C = A \cup B$, then
$P(C) = P(A \cup B)$
$\quad\quad = P(A) + P(B) - P(A \cap B)$
From the sketch, $(A \cap B) = \{$ _____ $\}$

$e_1,\ e_2,\ e_5,\ e_6$

614 The sketch shows quite clearly, then, that in adding $P(A)$ and $P(B)$, the probabilities of elements of $A \cap B$, that is, e_1, e_2, e_5, e_6, are used twice, so that to find $P(A \cup B)$ we take $P(A) + P(B) - $ _____ .

$P(A \cap B)$

615 Look at your copy of the original drawing. Joe Zilch, the point killer, says, "Let C be the event that at least one of the balls is red. Then C' is the event that both balls are white. So

▼

$P(C) = 1 - P(C')$." To find C', Joe says, "Let D be the event that the ball from hat 1 is white and E be the event that the ball from hat 2 is white. Then

$$C' = D \cap E$$
$$P(C') = P(D \cap E)$$
$$P(D \cap E) = P(D) \cdot P(E \mid D)$$
$$= \tfrac{1}{3} \cdot \underline{\quad} = \underline{\quad}"$$

$\tfrac{1}{2}$, $\tfrac{1}{6}$

---

616 Therefore, using the Zilch technique, $P(C') = \tfrac{1}{6}$. So $P(C) = \underline{\hspace{2cm}}$. The point is that a problem, even using these new methods, can usually be done in more than one way; and if you arrive at the same answer as listed here, you *may* have a method which is just as good as or better than the one pointed out.

$1 - P(C') = \tfrac{5}{6}$

●**617** Note that the problem in frames 607 to 616 was not too difficult to do by listing a sample space. Now consider this one: hat 1 contains 20 red balls and five white balls, and hat 2 contains 30 red balls and 10 white balls. Again, an experiment consists of drawing a ball from each hat, and C is the event that at least one ball is red. Let A be the event that the ball from hat 1 is red and B be the event that the ball from hat 2 is red. Then $C = A \cup B$.
$$P(C) = P(A \cup B)$$
$$= \underline{\hspace{3cm}}$$

(Do not attempt this problem by listing a sample space.)

$$P(A) + P(B) - P(A \cap B)$$
$$= P(A) + P(B) - P(A) \cdot P(B \mid A)$$
$$= \tfrac{20}{25} + \tfrac{30}{40} - \tfrac{20}{25} \cdot \tfrac{30}{40} = \tfrac{19}{20}$$

---

618 Hat 1 contains 15 red balls and five white balls. Hat 2 contains one red ball and four white balls.
Experiment: A coin is tossed. If a head appears, draw a ball from hat 1. If a tail appears, draw a ball from hat 2. Let A be the event of getting a red ball.
Copy this experiment and the event.
Look at the problem: Event A could happen by (1) tossing a head and getting a red ball from hat 1 *or* (2) $\underline{\hspace{3cm}}$.

---

tossing a tail and getting a red ball from hat 2.
Have a correct copy of the experiment and the event.

---

619 So, our first thought is that event $A = B \cup C$ where: B is the event of tossing a head and getting a red ball from hat 1, C is the event of tossing a tail and getting a red ball from hat 2. Note that a trial of

▼

the experiment consists of one toss of the coin and one ball
drawn; so B and C **(1)** _____ (can, cannot) both occur; that is,
$B \cap C =$ **(2)** ___ .

---

(1)   cannot   **(2)** $\emptyset$

---

620   Since $B \cap C = \emptyset$, B and C are mutually exclusive events.   Therefore, if we let $A = B \cup C$ then
$P(A) = P(B) + P(C) - P(B \cap C)$
      $= P(B) + P(C) - 0$
Now we need to find $P(B)$ and $P(C)$.
B is the event of tossing a head _and_ drawing a red ball from hat 1.
Therefore, we let $B = (D \cap E)$, where D is the event of tossing a
head and E is the event of drawing a red ball from hat 1.   We let
$C = (F \cap G)$, where _____ .

F is the event of getting a tail and G is the event of getting a red
ball from hat 2.

---

621   We have reached this point: A is the event of **(1)**   tossing a head
and getting a red ball from hat 1 or **(2)**   tossing a tail _and_ getting
a red ball from hat 2.   Symbolically:
      $A = B \cup C$
      $A = (D \cap E) \cup (F \cap G)$
$\therefore \ P(A) = P(D \cap E) + P(F \cap G) - 0$
      $P(A) = P(D) \cdot P(E \mid D) +$ _____ $- 0$
(Note the 0 since the probability of the intersection of the events
joined by $\cup$, as we saw, was 0.)

$P(F) \cdot P(G \mid F)$

---

622   Now, the probability of getting a head is $\frac{1}{2}$.   Then, given that a
head has been tossed, the probability of getting a red ball from hat
1 is $\frac{15}{20}$, or $\frac{3}{4}$.   So, the probability of getting a head _and_ drawing a
red ball from hat 1 $[P(B)] = \frac{1}{2} \cdot \frac{3}{4} = \frac{3}{8}$.   The probability of getting
a tail is **(1)** ___.   Then, given that a tail has been tossed, the
probability of getting a red ball from hat 2 is **(2)** ___.   So, the
probability of getting a tail _and_ drawing a red ball from hat 2
$[P(C)] =$ **(3)** _____ .

---

(1) $\frac{1}{2}$ **(2)** $\frac{1}{5}$ **(3)** $\frac{1}{2} \cdot \frac{1}{5} = \frac{1}{10}$

---

623   So, we have finally: If B is the event of tossing a head and getting
a red ball from hat 1, $P(B) = \frac{3}{8}$.   If C is the event of tossing a tail
and getting a red ball from hat 2, $P(C) = \frac{1}{10}$.

▼

$$A = B \cup C$$
$$P(A) = P(B) + P(C) - P(B \cap C)$$
$$= \underline{(1)} \underline{\quad} + \underline{\quad} - 0 = \underline{\qquad}$$

(2)　Why is $P(B \cap C) = 0$?

---

(1)　$\frac{3}{8} + \frac{1}{10} - 0 = \dfrac{15 + 4}{40} = \frac{19}{40}$

(2)　B and C are mutually exclusive or $B \cap C = \emptyset$
or B and C annnot both occur on the same trial of the
experiment.

5. Review

624 Recall the methods we have to work with.　If B and C are events,
the set of elements for which we say B *or* C has occurred is _____.

$B \cup C$

---

625 If A and B are events, the set of elements for which we say A *and*
B has occurred is _____.

$A \cap B$

---

626 If A and B are events, $P(A \cap B) = \underline{\qquad}$.
[Copy $P(A \cap B) =$ when you answer.]

$$P(A \cap B) = P(A) \cdot P(B \mid A)$$
or $P(A \cap B) = P(B) \cdot P(A \mid B)$

---

627 If A and B are events, then $P(A \cup B) = \underline{\qquad}$.
[Copy $P(A \cup B) =$ when you answer.]

$P(A \cup B) = P(A) + P(B) - P(A \cap B)$

---

628 If X and Y are mutually exclusive events, then (1)　$X \cap Y = \underline{\quad}$.
Therefore, for mutually exclusive events, (2)　$P(X \cup Y) = \underline{\qquad}$.
[Copy $X \cap Y =$ and $P(X \cup Y) =$ when you answer.]

---

(1)　$X \cap Y = \emptyset$
(2)　$P(X \cup Y) = P(X) + P(Y)$　[since $P(X \cap Y) = 0$]

629 Given events A and B, $P(B \mid A)$ means _____.

the conditional probability of B given A

630 If two events A and B are such that $P(B \mid A) = P(B)$, then A and B are called _____.

independent events

631 If A and B are independent events, then $P(A \cap B) = $ _____.
[Copy $P(A \cap B) =$ when you answer.]

$P(A \cap B) = P(A) \cdot P(B)$

632 Let us illustrate these methods by some simple problems. A hat contains five red balls and five white balls. Two balls in succession are to be drawn without replacement. Suppose A is the event that the first ball is red *and* the second ball is white. Then $A = B \cap C$ where B is the event that the first ball is red and C is the event that the second ball is white.
$\therefore P(A) = P(B \cap C)$
$\qquad = P(B) \cdot P(C \mid B)$
$\qquad = \underline{\ \ } \cdot \underline{\ \ } = \underline{\ \ }$

$\frac{5}{10} \cdot \frac{5}{9} = \frac{25}{90}$ or $\frac{5}{18}$
Note: To find $P(C \mid B)$, assume B has occurred; then the hat contains nine balls, five of which are white.

633 *Experiment:* Two cards are drawn in succession without replacement from a deck of cards. Find the probability that both are kings.

$\frac{1}{221}$ since, if A is the event the first card is a king and B is the event the second card is a king, then $P(A \cap B) = P(A) \cdot P(B \mid A)$
$\qquad = \dfrac{4}{52} \cdot \dfrac{3}{51} = \dfrac{12}{2,652} = \dfrac{1}{221}$

634 *Experiment:* One card is to be drawn from a deck of cards. To find the probability that it is an ace or a spade, let A be the event that the card is an ace, B be the event that the card is a spade. We want the probability of A or B.
$\therefore P(A \cup B) = P(A) + P(B) - P(A \cap B)$
$\qquad = P(A) + P(B) - P(A) \cdot P(B \mid A)$
$\qquad = $ _____

$\frac{4}{52} + \frac{13}{52} - \frac{4}{52} \cdot \frac{1}{4} = \frac{16}{52} = \frac{4}{13}$

635 *Experiment:* A pair of dice is thrown. To find the probability of getting a 7 or an 11, we let A be the event that a 7 appears, B be the event that an 11 appears. We want the probability of A or B.
$$P(A \cup B) = P(A) + P(B) - P(A \cap B)$$
$$= \underline{} + \underline{} - \underline{}$$
Use Panel 1 to find $P(A)$ and $P(B)$.

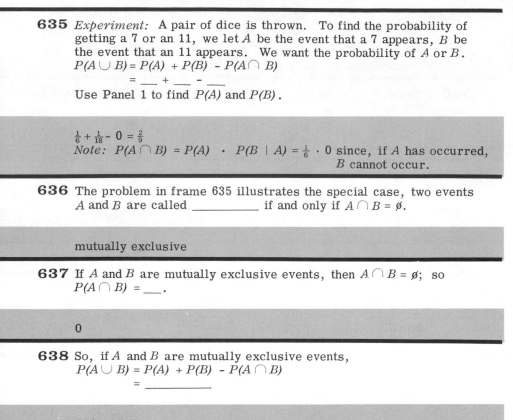

$\frac{1}{6} + \frac{1}{18} - 0 = \frac{2}{9}$
Note: $P(A \cap B) = P(A) \cdot P(B \mid A) = \frac{1}{6} \cdot 0$ since, if A has occurred,
                                                    B cannot occur.

636 The problem in frame 635 illustrates the special case, two events A and B are called _____ if and only if $A \cap B = \emptyset$.

mutually exclusive

637 If A and B are mutually exclusive events, then $A \cap B = \emptyset$; so $P(A \cap B) = \underline{}$.

0

638 So, if A and B are mutually exclusive events,
$$P(A \cup B) = P(A) + P(B) - P(A \cap B)$$
$$= \underline{}$$

$P(A) + P(B)$

639 This result in frame 638 can be extended: If A_1, A_2, . . ., A_n are mutually exclusive events, then $P(A_1 \cup A_2 \cup \cdots \cup A_n) = P(A_1) + P(A_2) + \cdots + P(A_n)$. For example, let an experiment consist of drawing a card from a deck of cards. Let B be the event that the card is a king. Let C be the event that the card is a 9. Let D be the event that the card is the ace of hearts. Then the probability that the card is a king, a 9, or the ace of hearts is $P(B \cup C \cup D)$, and obviously, B, C, and D are mutually exclusive events.
$\therefore \ P(B \cup C \cup D) = P(B) + P(C) + P(D)$
$$= \underline{} + \underline{} + \underline{} = \underline{}$$

$\frac{4}{52} + \frac{4}{52} + \frac{1}{52} = \frac{9}{52}$

640 A and B are independent events if and only if _____.

$P(A) = P(A \mid B)$
or $P(B) = P(B \mid A)$

641 If A and B are independent events, then $P(A \cap B) = $ _____ .
[Copy $P(A \cap B) = $ when you answer.]

$P(A \cap B) = P(A) \cdot P(B)$ [since $P(B) = P(B \mid A)$]

642 If A, B, C, and D are events, then $P(A \cap B \cap C \cap D) = $ _____ .
[Copy $P(A \cap B \cap C \cap D) = $ when you answer.]

$P(A \cap B \cap C \cap D) = P(A) \cdot P(B \mid A) \cdot P(C \mid A \cap B) \cdot P(D \mid A \cap B \cap C)$

643 If A, B, C, and D are independent events, then
$P(A \cap B \cap C \cap D) = $ _____ .
[Copy $P(A \cap B \cap C \cap D) = $ when you answer.]

$P(A \cap B \cap C \cap D) = P(A) \cdot P(B) \cdot P(C) \cdot P(D)$

644 If A and B are events, then $P(A \cup B) = $ _____ .
[Copy $P(A \cup B) = $ when you answer.]

$P(A \cup B) = P(A) + P(B) - P(A \cap B)$

645 Two events A and B are mutually exclusive if and only if
$A \cap B = $ _____ .   (Copy $A \cap B = $ when you answer.)

$A \cap B = \emptyset$

646 If A and B are mutually exclusive events, $P(A \cup B) = $ _____ .
[Copy $P(A \cup B) = $ when you answer.]

$P(A \cup B) = P(A) + P(B)$

647 If A, B, C, and D are mutually exclusive events, then
$P(A \cup B \cup C \cup D) = $ _____ .
[Copy $P(A \cup B \cup C \cup D) = $ when you answer.]

$P(A \cup B \cup C \cup D) = P(A) + P(B) + P(C) + P(D)$

648 Copy this information for the next series of items:
Hat 1 contains five red balls and one white ball.
Hat 2 contains one red ball and two white balls.
If an experiment consists of drawing a single ball from hat 1 and
if event A is the event that the ball is red, then $P(A) = $ ___ .

$\frac{5}{6}$

Have a correct copy of the information.

649 If a single *red* ball is drawn from hat 1 and placed in hat 2, then hat 2 now contains (1) ___ balls, (2) ___ of them red and (3) ___ of them white.

(1) 4   (2) 2   (3) 2

650 Now, if event A is that a *red* ball is drawn from hat 1 and placed into hat 2, and event B is that a single ball drawn from hat 2 is white, $P(B \mid A) =$ _____ .

$\frac{2}{4}$ since, if A has occurred, then hat 2 has four balls, two white and two red.

651 Similarly, if C is the event that a white ball is drawn from hat 1 and placed in hat 2, and B is the event that a single ball drawn from hat 2 is white, $P(B \mid C) =$ _____ .

$\frac{3}{4}$ since, if C has occurred, hat 2 now has four balls, three white and one red.

652 Look at your copy of the information about the hats. An experiment consists of drawing a single ball from hat 1, putting the ball into hat 2, and then drawing a single ball from hat 2. If A is the event that the ball drawn from hat 1 is red and B is the event that the ball from hat 2 is white, then $P(A \cap B) = P(A) \cdot P(B \mid A)$
= ___

$\frac{5}{6} \cdot \frac{1}{2} = \frac{5}{12}$

653 An experiment consists of drawing one ball from hat 1, placing it in hat 2, and then drawing a ball from hat 2. Find the probability that both balls are white.

If A is the event that the ball from hat 1 is white and B is the event that the ball from hat 2 is white, $P(A \cap B) = P(A) \cdot P(B \mid A)$
$= \frac{1}{6} \cdot \frac{3}{4} = \frac{3}{24} = \frac{1}{8}$

654 *Experiment:* Hat 1 contains four red balls and two white balls. Hat 2 contains one red ball and three white balls. A ball is to be drawn from hat 1 and put into hat 2, then a ball is to be drawn from hat 2. Let A be the event that the ball drawn from hat 2 is white. You will find the probability of A by completing frames 655 to 659; so make a copy of the experiment and event A.

Have a copy of the experiment and event A.

655 Suppose:
1. *B* is the event that a white ball is drawn from 1 *and* a white ball from 2.
2. *C* is the event that a red ball is drawn from 1 *and* a white ball from 2.
3. *D* is the event that a red ball is drawn from 1 *and* a red ball from 2.

(1) If you know that either *C* or *D* has occurred, can you be sure that *A* has occurred?
(2) (a) If you know that either *B* or *C* has occurred, can you be sure that *A* has occurred? (b) If *A* has occurred, then has either *B* or *C* occurred?
(3) Use any of *B*, *C*, or *D* to complete this:
$A = \underline{\quad} \cup \underline{\quad}$
(Copy *A* = when you answer.)
(4) (a) $B \cap C = \underline{\quad}$ (b) $\therefore P(B \cap C) = \underline{\quad}$
(5) Make a copy of the two events we will be concerned with in this problem.

(1) no   (If *D* occurs, *A* has not.)
(2) (a) yes   (b) yes
(3) $A = B \cup C$
(4) (a) ∅   (b) 0
(5) Have a copy of events *B* and *C*.

656 Which of the following is true for our experiment:
$P(A) = P(B \cap C) \qquad P(A) = P(B \cup C)$

$P(A) = P(B \cup C)$

657 Note that $P(A) = P(B) + P(C) - P(B \cap C)$
$= P(B) + P(C)$
Our next problem is to find $P(B)$ and $P(C)$. $P(B)$ is the probability that both balls drawn from the two hats in the experiment are white. Find $P(B)$.

$\frac{4}{15}$ (Save this answer.)

Solution: $P(B) = \frac{1}{3} \cdot \frac{4}{5}$
$P(B) = \frac{4}{15}$

658 $P(C)$ is the probability that the first ball drawn is red and the second ball is white. Find $P(C)$.

$\frac{2}{5}$ (Save this answer.)

Solution: $P(C) = \frac{2}{3} \cdot \frac{3}{5}$
$P(C) = \frac{2}{5}$

659 Use the information you have saved from frames 657 and 658, and find *P(A)*.

$\frac{2}{3}$ *Solution:* $P(A) = \frac{4}{15} + \frac{2}{5} = \frac{2}{3}$

●**660** *Experiment:* Hat 1 contains three red balls and two white balls. Hat 2 contains two red balls and four white balls. A ball is drawn from hat 1 and put into hat 2; then a ball is drawn from hat 2. What is the probability that the ball drawn from hat 2 is red?

$\frac{13}{35}$

Self-test VI

1 (1) If *A* and *B* are events, the set of elements for which we say *A or B* has occurred is ___.
   (2) If *A* and *B* are events, the set of elements for which we say *A and B* has occurred is ___.

2 (1) If *A* and *B* are events, $P(A \cap B) =$ _____.
   (2) If *A* and *B* are events, $P(A \cup B) =$ _____.
   [Copy $P(A \cap B) =$ and $P(A \cup B) =$ when you answer.]

3 If *A* and *B* are mutually exclusive events, then **(1)** $A \cap B =$ ___ , so **(2)** $P(A \cap B) =$ ___. So, if *A* and *B* are mutually exclusive events, **(3)** $P(A \cup B) = P(A) + P(B) - P(A \cap B) =$ _____
   [Copy $A \cap B =$ and $P(A \cap B) =$ when you answer.]

4 (1) If *A*, *B*, *C*, and *D* are independent events, then
   $P(A \cap B \cap C \cap D) =$ _____.
   (2) If *A*, *B*, *C*, and *D* are mutually exclusive events,
   $P(A \cup B \cup C \cup D) =$ _____.
   [Copy $P(A \cap B \cap C \cap D) =$ and $P(A \cup B \cup C \cup D) =$ when you answer.]

5 (1) What do we mean by the "exclusive or" as this pertains to events and probability?
   (2) What do we mean by the "inclusive or" as this pertains to events and probability?
   (3) We have agreed that unless specifically pointed out, we will use the _____ or in this program.

6 Let S, A, and B be as shown:

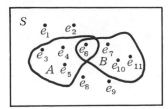

   (1) $P(A) =$ _____
   (2) $P(B) =$ _____
   (3) $P(A) + P(B) =$ _____
   (4) $P(A \cup B) =$ _____

7 Hat 1 contains 10 red balls and 20 white balls. Hat 2 contains 5 red balls and 10 white balls. An experiment consists of drawing a ball from each hat. What is the probability that at least one ball is red?

8 A coin is flipped. If it turns up heads, a ball is drawn from hat 1, which contains three red balls and two white balls. If the coin turns up tails, a ball is drawn from hat 2, which contains one red ball and one white ball. What is the probability of drawing a white ball if the above experiment is performed?

part V BINOMIAL DISTRIBUTION, PERMUTATIONS, AND COMBINATIONS

1. Introduction

---

661 Given an experiment having a sample space S, where $S = \{e_1, e_2, \ldots, e_{10}\}$, if $A = \{e_1, e_2, e_5\}$, A is a subset of S; so A is an _____ .

---

event

---

662 Given an experiment having a sample space S, and if A is any event, then A', called the complement of A, is the event: $A' = (x \mid X \in S \text{ and } X \notin A)$. Thus, if $S = \{e_1, e_2, \ldots, e_{10}\}$ and $A = \{e_1, e_3, e_4, e_5, e_6\}$, then $A' =$ _____ .

$\{e_2, e_7, e_8, e_9, e_{10}\}$

---

663 Roughly speaking, A', the complement of A, means "not A." A' is the set of all elements of S which are not elements of A. Graphically, if S and event A are as shown,

then $A' =$ _____ .

$\{e_1, e_2, e_4, e_8\}$

664 Given a sample space $S = \{e_1,\ e_2,\ \ldots,\ e_n\}$, suppose event $A = S$. Then $A' =$ ___.

ø

665 Given a sample space $S = \{e_1,\ e_2,\ \ldots,\ e_n\}$ and event $A = \emptyset$, then $A' =$ ___.

S or $\{e_1,\ e_2,\ \ldots,\ e_n\}$

666 If S is a sample space for a given experiment, and $S = \{e_1,\ e_2,\ \ldots,\ e_n\}$, we assign to each e_i, $i = 1, 2, \ldots, n$, of S, a number $P(e_i)$ called the probability of e_i. These numbers are assigned in such a way that:
(1) ___ $\leq P(e_i) \leq$ ___ for $i = 1, 2, \ldots, n$
(2) $P(e_1) + P(e_2) + \cdots + P(e_n) =$ _____.
[Copy $\leq P(e_i) \leq$ when you answer.]

(1) $0 \leq P(e_i) \leq 1$ (2) 1

667 Thus, if $e_k \in S$, a nonnegative number less than or equal to 1 is associated with the e_k. This number is called the _____ of e_k and is indicated by $P(e_k)$.

probability

668 So, whatever is the method of assigning probabilities to each element of S, each probability assigned must be less than or equal to ___ *and* greater than or equal to ___.

1,   0

669 Moreover, when probabilities have been assigned to each $e_i \in S$, where $S = \{e_1,\ e_2,\ \ldots,\ e_n\}$, it must also hold that $P(e_1) + P(e_2) + \cdots + P(e_n) =$ ___.

1

670 Here is an example of a sample space with probabilities assigned to each element $S = \{e_1,\ e_2,\ e_3,\ e_4\}$ where $P(e_1) = 0.3$, $P(e_2) = 0$, $P(e_3) = 0.5$, $P(e_4) = 0.2$. Note that the two conditions are satisfied:
(1) ___ $\leq P(e_i) \leq$ ___ for $i = 1, 2, 3, 4$
(2) $P(e_1) + P(e_2) + P(e_3) + P(e_4) =$ ___
[Copy $\leq P(e_i) \leq$ when you answer (1).]

(1) $0 \leq P(e_i) \leq 1$ (2) 1

671 Given a sample space S having probabilities assigned to each $e_i \in S$, if A is any subset of S, we define $P(A)$ as the sum of the probabilities of the elements of A. For example, suppose $S = \{e_1,\ e_2,\ e_3,\ e_4,\ e_5\}$ and $P(e_1) = 0.1$, $P(e_2) = 0.2$, $P(e_3) = 0$, $P(e_4) = 0.4$, $P(e_5) = 0.3$. [*Note:* $0 \le P(e_i) \le 1$ and $P(e_1) + P(e_2) + P(e_3) + P(e_4) = 1$.] If $A = \{e_2,\ e_3,\ e_5\}$, $P(A) = $ _____.

$P(e_2) + P(e_3) + P(e_5)$
$= 0.2 + 0 + 0.3 = 0.5$

672 Any subset of S is called an event. If $S = \{e_1,\ e_2,\ e_3\}$, there would be eight subsets (events) of S:

$\emptyset$
S or $\{e_1,\ e_2,\ e_3\}$
$\{e_1,\ e_2\}\ \ \{e_1,\ e_3\}\ \ \{e_2,\ e_3\}$
List the other three subsets of S.

$\{e_1\}\quad \{e_2\}\quad \{e_3\}$

673 Do not forget, if S is any set, $S \subset S$ and $\emptyset \subset S$. Therefore, if S is a sample space, S itself is an event and $\emptyset$ is an event. If $S = \{e_1,\ e_2,\ \ldots,\ e_n\}$, $P(S) = P(e_1) + P(e_2) + \cdots + P(e_n) = $ ___

1   (This was one of the conditions imposed upon the probabilities assigned to the elements of S.)

674 We also define $P(\emptyset) = $ ___.

0

675 Let S be a sample space of an experiment. Suppose $S = \{e_1,\ e_2,\ e_3\}$ where $P(e_1) = 0.2$, $P(e_2) = 0.3$, $P(e_3) = 0.5$. List all the events of S (there are eight), and find their probabilities.

$A_1 = \emptyset$ $\qquad\qquad P(A_1) = 0$
$A_2 = \{e_1\}$ $\qquad\qquad P(A_2) = P(e_1) = 0.2$
$A_3 = \{e_2\}$ $\qquad\qquad P(A_3) = P(e_2) = 0.3$
$A_4 = \{e_3\}$ $\qquad\qquad P(A_4) = P(e_3) = 0.5$
$A_5 = \{e_1,\ e_2\}$ $\qquad P(A_5) = P(e_1) + P(e_2) = 0.5$
$A_6 = \{e_1,\ e_3\}$ $\qquad P(A_6) = P(e_1) + P(e_3) = 0.7$
$A_7 = \{e_2,\ e_3\}$ $\qquad P(A_7) = P(e_2) + P(e_3) = 0.8$
$A_8 = \{e_1,\ e_2,\ e_3\}$ $\quad P(A_8) = P(e_1) + P(e_2) + P(e_3) = 1$

676 Recall, if A and B are events in a sample space S and $A \cap B = \emptyset$ (A and B are disjoint sets), A and B are called _____ events.

mutually exclusive

677 Two events A and B are mutually exclusive if and only if they have no elements in common, that is, if and only if $A \cap B = \emptyset$. Thus, in terms of outcomes of an experiment, if one of two mutually exclusive events occurs on a trial, the other cannot. They cannot both occur on a single trial of the experiment. Now consider event A and its complement A'. (1) $A \cap A' =$ ___. Therefore, A and A' are (2) _____ events.

(1) $\emptyset$ (2) mutually exclusive

678 Moreover, recall, *if A and B are mutually exclusive events*, the probability of A or B is given by $P(A \cup B) = P(A) + P(B)$. For example, let $S = \{e_1, e_2, e_3, e_4, e_5\}$ where $P(e_1) = 0.1$, $P(e_2) = 0.1$, $P(e_3) = 0.3$, $P(e_4) = 0.2$, $P(e_5) = 0.3$. If $A = \{e_1, e_2\}$ and $B = \{e_4\}$, $A \cap B = \emptyset$. Therefore, A and B are mutually exclusive. *Note:* $A \cup B = \{e_1, e_2, e_4\}$. $\therefore$ (1) $P(A \cup B) =$ ___, (2) $P(A) =$ ___, (3) $P(B) =$ ___, (4) $P(A) + P(B) =$ ___.

(1) 0.4   (2) 0.2   (3) 0.2   (4) 0.4

679 So, if A and B are mutually exclusive events, the probability of A or B is given by $P(A \cup B) = P(A) + P(B)$. Consider any event C and its complement C'. C and C' are mutually exclusive; so $P(C \cup C') =$ _____.

$P(C) + P(C')$ or 1

680 Moreover, if C is any event in a sample space S, $C \cup C' =$ ___.

S

681 For any event C, $P(C \cup C') = P(C) + P(C')$, but $C \cup C' = S$ and (1) $P(S) =$ ___; therefore (2) ___ $= P(C) + P(C')$.

(1) 1   (2) 1

682 So we remember the important theorem, if A is any event in a sample space S, $P(A) + P(A') =$ ___.

1

683 We have that if A is any event, $P(A) = 1 - P(A')$. Roughly speaking then, the probability that A occurs equals 1 minus the probability that A does not occur. If the probability that Joe Zilch passes Algebra I is 0.9, what is the probability that Joe Zilch does not pass Algebra I?

0.1

684 As a result of experimenting, it has been determined that if a hamster has disease X, the probability that he will recover is 0.8. Therefore, the probability that he will not recover is___.

0.2

685 The probability that a hamster will recover from disease X is 0.8. The probability that a hamster will not recover from disease X is 0.2.
An experiment consists of observing two hamsters having disease X. To find the probability that both hamsters will recover, we let:
A be the event that the first hamster recovers
B be the event that the second hamster recovers
We want the probability of A and B; so
$$P(A \cap B) = P(A) \cdot P(B)$$
$$= (0.8)\,(0.8)$$
$$= 0.64$$
Note that we are considering the events to be independent. Find the probability that *both* hamsters fail to recover. Also copy the probabilities of recovery and nonrecovery.

$$P(A' \cap B') = P(A') \cdot P(B')$$
$$= (0.2)\,(0.2)$$
$$= 0.04$$
Have a correct copy of the probabilities for recovery and for non-recovery.

686 In the same experiment as in frame 685, to find the probability that one hamster will recover and the other will not recover, we note that A is the event that the first hamster will recover and B is the event that the second hamster will recover. The event that we are interested in is $A \cap B'$ or $A' \cap B$. The two events joined by "or" are mutually exclusive.
$$\therefore \quad P\left[(A \cap B') \cup (A' \cap B)\right] = P(A \cap B') + P(A' \cap B)$$
$$= P(A) \cdot P(B') + P(A') \cdot P(B)$$
$$= \underline{\qquad\qquad}$$

$(0.8)\,(0.2) + (0.2)\,(0.8) = 0.32$

687 So, in the experiment of observing two hamsters having disease X, the probability they both recover is 0.64, the probability that exactly one recovers is 0.32, the probability that neither recovers is 0.04. Suppose an experiment consists of observing three hamsters having disease X. Find the probability that all three recover.

(0.8) (0.8) (0.8) = 0.512
(*Note:* We let A be the event that the first hamster recovers, we let B be the event that the second hamster recovers, we let C be the event that the third hamster recovers. Then, for all three hamsters to recover, we need the event $A \cap B \cap C$, and we consider these to be independent events; that is, the probability of recovery of any hamster does not depend on the recovery of any of the others.)

688 In order to simplify the notation, let us indicate recovery by R and failure to recover by F. Then, we shall use subscripts to indicate the individual hamsters. Thus R_1 will be the event that the first hamster recovers. F_2 will be the event that the second hamster fails to recover. Thus, the event that all three hamsters recover is $R_1 \cap R_2 \cap R_3$ and
$$P(R_1 \cap R_2 \cap R_3) = P(R_1) \cdot P(R_2) \cdot P(R_3)$$
$$= (0.8)\ (0.8)\ (0.8) \quad [\textit{Note:}\ \text{This could be written}$$
$$= 0.512 \qquad\qquad (0.8)^3]$$
The event that all three hamsters fail to recover is $F_1 \cap F_2 \cap F_3$. Find $P(F_1 \cap F_2 \cap F_3)$.

$$P(F_1 \cap F_2 \cap F_3) = P(F_1) \cdot P(F_2) \cdot P(F_3)$$
$$= (0.2)\ (0.2)\ (0.2) \quad [\textit{Note:}\ \text{This could be written}$$
$$= 0.008 \qquad\qquad (0.2)^3]$$

689 In the experiment of observing three hamsters having disease X, exactly one hamster would fail to recover if $F_1 \cap R_2 \cap R_3$ occurred. What other two events would result in exactly one hamster failing to recover?

$R_1 \cap F_2 \cap R_3$ or $R_1 \cap R_2 \cap F_3$

690 If $R_1 \cap F_2 \cap R_3$ occurs, then neither $R_1 \cap R_2 \cap F_3$ nor $F_1 \cap R_2 \cap R_3$ can occur. Therefore these events are _____.

mutually exclusive

691 In the experiment of observing three hamsters having disease X, the probability that the second and third hamsters recover, but that *the first hamster fails to recover*, is designated by $P(F_1 \cap R_2 \cap R_3)$.

▼

Then, $P(F_1 \cap R_2 \cap R_3) = P(F_1) \cdot P(R_2) \cdot P(R_3)$
$= \underline{\hspace{2cm}}$

$(0.2) (0.8) (0.8) = 0.128$

692 In the same experiment, the probability that the first and the third hamsters recover, but *the second hamster fails to recover*, is designated by $P(R_1 \cap F_2 \cap R_3)$. Find $P(R_1 \cap F_2 \cap R_3)$.

$P(R_1 \cap F_2 \cap R_3) = P(R_1) \cdot P(F_2) \cdot P(R_3)$
$= (0.8) (0.2) (0.8) = 0.128$

693 In the same experiment, the probability that the first and second hamsters recover, but *the third hamster fails to recover*, is designated by $P(R_1 \cap R_2 \cap F_3)$. Find $P(R_1 \cap R_2 \cap F_3)$.

$P(R_1 \cap R_2 \cap F_3) = P(R_1) \cdot P(R_2) \cdot P(F_3)$
$= (0.8) (0.8) (0.2) = 0.128$

694 In the experiment of observing three hamsters having disease X, we might want the probability that exactly one hamster fails to recover. This event is the event that $F_1 \cap R_2 \cap R_3$ *or* $R_1 \cap F_2 \cap R_3$ *or* $R_1 \cap R_2 \cap F_3$. These three events joined by "or" are mutually exclusive.
$\therefore\ P\ (F_1 \cap R_2 \cap R_3) \cup (R_1 \cap F_2 \cap R_3) \cup (R_1 \cap R_2 \cap F_3)$
$= P(F_1 \cap R_2 \cap R_3) + P(R_1 \cap F_2 \cap R_3) + P(R_1 \cap R_2 \cap F_3)$
$= \underline{\hspace{2cm}}$

$(0.2) (0.8) (0.8) + (0.8) (0.2) (0.8) + (0.8) (0.8) (0.2)$
$= 3\ [(0.8) (0.8) (0.2)]$ [*Note:* This could be written $3(0.8)^2 (0.2)$]
$= 0.384$

695 In the experiment of observing three hamsters having disease X, one event in which exactly one hamster will recover is $R_1 \cap F_2 \cap F_3$. The two other events such that exactly one hamster will recover are $\underline{\hspace{1.5cm}}$ and $\underline{\hspace{1.5cm}}$.

$F_1 \cap R_2 \cap F_3,$ $F_1 \cap F_2 \cap R_3$

696 So, in this experiment, exactly one hamster will recover if
$R_1 \cap F_2 \cap F_3$ *or* $F_1 \cap R_2 \cap F_3$ *or* $F_1 \cap F_2 \cap R_3$ occurs, and these are
mutually exclusive events.
$\therefore\ P\ (R_1 \cap F_2 \cap F_3) \cup (F_1 \cap R_2 \cap F_3) \cup (F_1 \cap F_2 \cap R_3)\ =$ _____

> $P(R_1 \cap F_2 \cap F_3) + P(F_1 \cap R_2 \cap F_3) + P(F_1 \cap F_2 \cap R_3)$
> $= P(R_1)\ \cdot\ P(F_1)\ \cdot\ P(F_3) + P(F_1)\ \cdot\ P(R_2)\ \cdot\ P(F_3)$
> $\ \ + P(F_1)\ \cdot\ P(F_2)\ \cdot\ P(R_3)$
> $= (0.8)\ (0.2)\ (0.2) + (0.2)\ (0.8)\ (0.2) + (0.2)\ (0.2)\ (0.8)$
> $= 3(0.8)\ (0.2)\ (0.2)$ [*Note:* This could be written $3(0.8)\ (0.2)^2$]
> $= 0.096$

697 Let us collect the information that we have computed: If the probability that a hamster with disease X will recover is 0.8, then the
probability that it will not recover is 1-0.8 or 0.2.
An experiment consists of observing three hamsters having disease
X, then:
1. The probability of getting exactly three recoveries out of three
    hamsters is 0.512 or $(0.8)^3$.
2. The probability of getting exactly two recoveries out of three
    hamsters is 0.384 or $3(0.8)^2(0.2)$.
3. The probability of getting exactly one recovery out of three
    hamsters is 0.096 or $3(0.8)\ (0.2)^2$.
4. The probability of getting zero recoveries out of three hamsters
    is _____ .

> 0.008 or $(0.2)^3$

698 A manufacturer of widgets claims that 1 per cent of his production
is defective; that is, if an experiment consists of selecting a widget
at random, the probability that it is defective D is 0.01 and the
probability that it is not defective G is ___.
Copy this information and save it.

> 0.99
> Have a correct copy of the information.

699 *Experiment:* Two widgets are chosen at random and inspected. Let
us again indicate the events by letter and subscript. Thus, the
event that the first widget is good *and* the second widget is defective
will be $G_1 \cap D_2$. The event that the first widget is good *and* the second widget is good is _____.

> $G_1 \cap G_2$ or $G_2 \cap G_1$

700 Thus, if two widgets are chosen, there are four events we are interested in: that both widgets are good $\longrightarrow G_1 \cap G_2$, that exactly one widget is good $\longrightarrow G_1 \cap D_2$ or (1) _____ , that neither widget is good $\longrightarrow$ (2) _____ .

(1) $D_1 \cap G_2$　　(2) $D_1 \cap D_2$

701 We also assume that the quality of one widget has no effect upon the probability of the defectiveness or goodness of the second widget; for example, $P(G_2) = P(G_2 \mid D_1)$, etc. In other words, G_2 and D_1 are independent events.
∴ $P(D_1 \cap G_2) = P(D_1) \cdot P(G_2)$
= _____

(0.01) (0.99) = 0.0099

702 For this problem, the probability that both widgets are good is $P(G_1 \cap G_2) =$ _____ .

$P(G_1) \cdot P(G_2)$
$= (0.99)(0.99) = (0.99)^2$

703 To find the probability that exactly one widget is defective, we note that exactly one defective is the event $D_1 \cap G_2$ or $G_1 \cap D_2$ and that the two events joined by "or" are mutually exclusive.
∴ $P\ (D_1 \cap G_2) \cup (G_1 \cap D_2)\ =$ _____ .

$P(D_1 \cap G_2) + P(G_1 \cap D_2)$
$= P(D_1) \cdot P(G_2) + P(G_1) \cdot P(D_2)$
$= 2(0.99)(0.01)$

704 For this problem, find the probability that neither widget is good (both are defective).

$P(D_1 \cap D_2) = P(D_1) \cdot P(D_2)$
$= (0.01)^2$

705 Let us gather the information about this experiment. (You may use frames 691 to 697.)
If the probability that a single widget drawn at random is good is 0.99, then the probability that it is defective is 0.01. If two widgets are selected at random, then the probability that exactly two widgets of the two chosen are good is $(0.99)^2$.
(1) The probability that exactly one widget of the two chosen is good is _____.

▼

(2)   The probability that zero widgets of the two chosen are good is
_____ .

Write your answers in the simplest possible exponential form without multiplying, as $(0.99)^2$.

---

(1) $2(0.99)(0.01)$ (2) $(0.01)^2$

---

comment

Beginning with frame 706, write your answers in the simplest possible exponential form without multiplying; continue until told to do otherwise.

---

706 Suppose three widgets are to be chosen from the same manufacturer. Find the probability that all three are good.

$P(G_1 \cap G_2 \cap G_3) = (0.99)(0.99)(0.99) = (0.99)^3$

707 If three widgets are chosen at random, find the probability that exactly two are good.
Remember: $P[(G_1 \cap G_2 \cap D_3) \cup (G_1 \cap D_2 \cap G_3) \cup (D_1 \cap G_2 \cap G_3)]$
$= P(G_1 \cap G_2 \cap D_3) + P(G_1 \cap D_2 \cap G_3) + P(D_1 \cap G_2 \cap G_3)$
$= P(G_1) \cdot P(G_2) \cdot P(D_3) + P(G_1) \cdot P(D_2) \cdot P(G_3) +$
$P(D_1) \cdot P(G_2) \cdot P(G_3)$

$= (0.99)(0.99)(0.01) + (0.99)(0.01)(0.99) + (0.01)(0.99)(0.99)$
$= 3(0.99)^2(0.01)$

708 If three widgets are chosen at random, find the probability that exactly one is good.
$P[(G_1 \cap D_2 \cap D_3) \cup (D_1 \cap G_2 \cap D_3) \cup (D_1 \cap D_2 \cap G_3)]$

$= P(G_1 \cap D_2 \cap D_3) + P(D_1 \cap G_2 \cap D_3) + P(D_1 \cap D_2 \cap G_3)$
$= P(G_1) \cdot P(D_2) \cdot P(D_3) + P(D_1) \cdot P(G_2) \cdot P(D_3) +$
$P(D_1) \cdot P(D_2) \cdot P(G_3)$
$= (0.99)(0.01)(0.01) + (0.01)(0.99)(0.01) + (0.01)(0.01)(0.99)$
$= 3(0.99)(0.01)^2$

709 If three widgets are chosen at random, find the probability that none of them is good.

$P(D_1 \cap D_2 \cap D_3) = P(D_1) \cdot P(D_2) \cdot P(D_3)$
$= (0.01)^3$

710 Again let us gather information. (You may use frames 699 to 702.)
If the probability that a widget chosen at random is good is 0.99,
then the probability that it is defective is 0.01. If three widgets
are chosen at random then,
  (1) The probability that exactly three of the three widgets chosen
      are good is _____.
  (2) The probability that exactly two of the three widgets chosen
      are good is _____.
  (3) The probability that exactly one of the three widgets chosen
      is good is _____.
  (4) The probability that zero widgets of the three chosen is good
      is _____.

(1) $(0.99)^3$ (2) $3(0.99)^2(0.01)$
(3) $3(0.99)(0.01)^2$ (4) $(0.01)^3$

711 In taking a mathematics test, Joe Zilch recognizes only two
outcomes:
S (success) $\leftrightarrow$ he passes
F (failure) $\leftrightarrow$ he fails
From past experience, Joe has found that $P(S) = 0.9$.
Then $P(F) = \underline{\hspace{1em}}$.

0.1   [Since $F = S'$ and $P(S) + P(S') = 1$]

712 This month, three mathematics tests are scheduled for Joe's
class. If Joe takes all three tests, let us list the possible outcomes. We simplify our notation by listing success S or failure
F for each one of the three tests in order. Thus, the outcome
that Joe passes the first test, fails the second test, and passes
the third test will be indicated by SFS. List all eight of the possible outcomes and save the list.

SSS SSF SFS FSS SFF FSF FFS FFF

713 Look at the list of possible outcomes. Obviously each of the outcomes does not have the same probability. For example, if
$P(S) = 0.9$ for any single test, then
$P(SSF) = P(S) \cdot P(S) \cdot P(F)$
           $= (0.9)(0.9)(0.1)$
           $= (0.9)^2(0.1)$
We consider S and F to be independent; that is, we assume that
success or failure in one test does not affect the probability of

▼

success or failure in another test.
Find the probability of each outcome in the list.

$P(SSS) = (0.9)^3$ $P(SSF) = (0.9)^2(0.1)$
$P(SFS) = (0.9)^2(0.1)$ $P(FSS) = (0.9)^2(0.1)$
$P(SFF) = (0.9)(0.1)^2$ $P(FSF) = (0.9)(0.1)^2$
$P(FFS) = (0.9)(0.1)^2$ $P(FFF) = (0.1)^3$

714 From the list, we see that there is only one element corresponding to the outcome of passing all three tests, namely, SSS and P(SSS) = $(0.9)^3$. Similarly, the probability that Joe fails all three tests is _____ .

$P(FFF) = P(F) \cdot P(F) \cdot P(F) = (0.1)^3$

715 Look at the list of outcomes again. We see that the event that Joe passes exactly two of the tests is made up of three events; SSF, SFS, FSS, and they are mutually exclusive; so the probability that one of these events occurs is the sum of the probabilities of the events. [Recall, $P(A \cup B \cup C) = P(A) + P(B) + P(C)$ if A, B, and C are mutually exclusive.] Therefore, the probability that SSF or SFS or FSS occurs is $P(SSF) + P(SFS) + P(FSS)$ = _____ .

$3(0.9)^2(0.1)$

716 Find the probability that Joe passes exactly one of the three tests.

$3(0.9)(0.1)^2$

717 Let us gather the information just computed: An experiment consists of Joe Zilch taking a mathematics test. In any trial of the experiment, $P(S) = 0.9$ and $P(F) = 0.1$. If the experiment is performed three times, then, assuming the trials are independent,
(1) The probability of getting exactly three successes in the three trials is ___.
(2) The probability of getting exactly two successes in the three trials is ___.
(3) The probability of getting exactly one success in the three trials is ___.
(4) The probability of getting exactly zero successes in the three trials is ___.

(1) $(0.9)^3$ (2) $3(0.9)^2(0.1)$ (3) $3(0.9)(0.1)^2$ (4) $(0.1)^3$

●**718** Another similar problem: In a single toss of a foul shot in a basketball game, the probability that Joe Zilch will make a basket is 0.8. So if S (success) is the event that he makes the shot, $P(S) = 0.8$.

▼

Therefore, if F (failure) is the event that he does not make the shot, $P(F) = $ ___.

0.2

●**719** An experiment consists of having Joe Zilch toss three foul shots. List the possible outcomes by indicating an S (success) or F (failure) for the first, second, and third shot, in that order. Keep a copy of the list.

SSS   SSF   SFS   FSS   SFF   FSF   FFS   FFF

●**720** Now, since $P(S) = (0.8)$ and $P(F) = (0.2)$, we can write the probability of $P(SFS) = P(S) \cdot P(F) \cdot P(S)$
$$= (0.8)(0.2)(0.8)$$
$$= (0.8)^2(0.2)$$
Write the probability of each of the outcomes on your list.

$P(SSS) = (0.8)^3$ $P(SSF) = (0.8)^2(0.2)$
$P(SFS) = (0.8)^2(0.2)$ $P(FSS) = (0.8)^2(0.2)$
$P(SFF) = (0.8)(0.2)^2$ $P(FSF) = (0.8)(0.2)^2$
$P(FFS) = (0.8)(0.2)^2$ $P(FFF) = (0.2)^3$

●**721** From your list, what is the probability that Joe makes all three of the foul shots?

$(0.8)^3$ (all three S's)

●**722** From your list, what is the probability that Joe makes exactly two of the three shots (two successes out of three)?

$3(0.8)^2(0.2)$
$[P(SSF) + P(SFS) + P(FSS)]$

●**723** Use your list to write the probability that Joe makes exactly one of the three shots.

$3(0.8)(0.2)^2$

●**724** Use your list to write the probability that Joe makes none of the three foul shots.

$(0.2)^3$

---

725 Note carefully in the problem in frames 718 to 724: *SFS* indicates success on the first shot *and* failure on the second shot *and* success on the third shot. If we indicate these three events by A, B, and C, respectively, then we were interested in $P(A \cap B \cap C)$, and since we assumed the trials were independent, $P(A \cap B \cap C) =$ _____ .

$P(A) \cdot P(B) \cdot P(C)$

726 In each of the problems of this type which we have seen, the word "independent" was important. Suppose Joe is a person who becomes careless after a success, and he is to shoot twice. Then, if A is the event of success on the first shot and B is the event of success on the second shot, the probability of success on both shots would be $P(A \cap B) =$ _____ . (Just indicate the probabilities needed.)

$P(A) \cdot P(B \mid A)$
Note: The conditional probability of B given A would be less than $P(A)$ since in this case we assume that Joe becomes careless after a success. In other words, the events are not independent.

727 But, if A and B are independent events, that is, if the occurrence of one of the events has no effect upon the probability of occurrence of the other, then the probability that event A and event B will occur is given by $P(A \cap B) =$ _____ . (Just indicate the probabilities needed.)

$P(A) \cdot P(B)$

728 So, for the problem of shooting a foul shot, we found:
$P(SSF) = (0.8)\ (0.8)\ (0.2) = (0.8)^2(0.2)$
$P(SFS) = (0.8)\ (0.2)\ (0.8) = (0.8)^2(0.2)$
$P(FSS) = (0.2)\ (0.8)\ (0.8) = (0.8)^2(0.2)$
In order to determine the probability of exactly two successes, we noted that:
1. Exactly two successes occur if *SSF or SFS or FSS* occurs; so we want $P(SSF \cup SFS \cup FSS)$.
2. These events are *mutually exclusive*; that is, $P(SSF \cup SFS \cup FSS) = 3(0.8)^2(0.2)$ or in terms of $P(SSF)$, $P(SFS)$, and $P(FSS)$, $P(SSF \cup SFS \cup FSS) =$ _____ .

$P(SSF) + P(SFS) + P(FSS)$

729 *Note carefully:* If A and B are events which are *not* mutually exclusive, then the probability of A *or* B occurring is given by $P(A \cup B) =$ _____ .

$P(A) + P(B) - P(A \cap B)$

comment

In all the recent problems, if the trials had not been independent or if the events listed had not been mutually exclusive, the results would have been more difficult to obtain.

---

730 Copy the following: Given an experiment, each trial of which will have an outcome of either S (success) or F (failure).
If $P(S) = p$, $P(F) =$ ___ .

$1-p$

---

731 We now consider an experiment consisting of three trials of the experiment just described. Each of the three trials will result in either S or F. A sample space S of possible outcomes of the three trials consists of eight elements; list such a sample space and save it. *(Note:* Use the notation $e_1 \leftrightarrow SSS$, $e_2 \leftrightarrow SSF$, etc.)

$e_1 \leftrightarrow SSS$ $e_2 \leftrightarrow SSF$ $e_3 \leftrightarrow SFS$ $e_4 \leftrightarrow FSS$
$e_5 \leftrightarrow SFF$ $e_6 \leftrightarrow FSF$ $e_7 \leftrightarrow FFS$ $e_8 \leftrightarrow FFF$

---

732 It is understood that each trial of the experiment is performed under essentially the same conditions and that the trials are independent. Thus, $P(S) = p$ is the same for every trial, and success or failure on one trial has no effect upon the probability of success (or failure) of another trial. Therefore, the probability of any element of S can be found by multiplying the three probabilities involved. For example,
$P(e_1) = P(S) \cdot P(S) \cdot P(S) = p^3$
$P(e_2) = P(S) \cdot P(S) \cdot P(F) = p^2(1-p)$
$P(e_3) = P(S) \cdot P(F) \cdot P(S) = p^2 (1-p)$
Complete for the remaining elements of S and add these to your data.

$P(e_4) = p^2(1-p)$
$P(e_5) = p(1-p)^2$
$P(e_6) = p(1-p)^2$
$P(e_7) = p(1-p)^2$
$P(e_8) = (1-p)^3$

---

733 Remember, since probability of success $= p$, the probability of failure = ___ .

$1-p$

734 Before going any further, we might verify a property of S; that is, if we have made no mistakes, $P(e_1) + P(e_2) + \cdots + P(e_8)$ should equal ___.

1

735 Let us try to prove that $P(e_1) + P(e_2) + \cdots + P(e_8) = 1$.
$P(e_1) = p^3$
$P(e_2) = p^2(1-p) = p^2 - p^3$
$P(e_3) = p^2(1-p) = p^2 - p^3$
$P(e_4) = p^2(1-p) = p^2 - p^3$
$P(e_5) = p(1-p)^2 = p(1 - 2p + p^2) = p - 2p^2 + p^3$
$P(e_6) = (1)$ _____
$P(e_7) = (2)$ _____
$P(e_8) = (3)$ _____
$\therefore\ P(e_1) + P(e_2) + \cdots + P(e_8) = (4)$ ___

(1) $p(1-p)^2 = p(1-2p + p^2) = p - 2p^2 + p^3$
(2) $p(1-p)^2 = p(1-2p + p^2) = p - 2p^2 + p^3$
(3) $(1-p)^3 = 1 - 3p + 3p^2 - p^3$
(4) 1

736 It is instructive to note:
1. $P(e_1) + P(e_2) + \cdots + P(e_8) = p^3 + 3p^2(1-p) + 3p(1-p)^2 + (1-p)^3$
Now, recall from algebra (or verify by multiplication):
2. $(X + Y)^3 = X^3 + 3X^2Y + 3XY^2 + Y^3$
If we let $X \leftrightarrow p$ and $Y \leftrightarrow (1-p)$, the expression on the right in equation 1 could be written in the form $[\underline{\hspace{2cm}}]^3$.
(Copy $[\underline{\hspace{2cm}}]^3$ when you answer.)

$[p + (1-p)]^3$
Note: $[p + (1-p)]^3 = (\not{p} + 1 - \not{p})^3 = (1)^3 = 1$

737 Look at the sample space from frame 731 that you have copied. Which elements correspond to outcomes in which exactly three successes occurred?

e_1

738 Look at the sample space. Which elements correspond to outcomes in which exactly two successes occurred?

$e_2,\ e_3,\ e_4$

739 Look at the sample space. Which elements correspond to outcomes in which exactly one success occurred?

e_5, e_6, e_7

740 Look at the sample space. Which elements correspond to outcomes in which no successes occurred?

e_8

741 Consider the information that you have copied from frames 731 and 732. We are interested in finding the probability of a certain number of successes (zero, one, two, or three) out of three trials. For example, if A_3 is the event that three successes occur on the three trials, $A_3 = \{e_1\}$ and $P(A_3) = P(e_1) = p^3$. If A_2 is the event that exactly two successes occur out of three trials,
$$A_2 = \{e_2,\ e_3,\ e_4\} \text{ and } P(A_2) = P(e_2) + P(e_3) + P(e_4)$$
$$= p^2(1-p) + p^2(1-p) + p^2(1-p)$$
$$= 3p^2(1-p)$$
If A_1 is the event that exactly one success occurs out of three trials, (1) $A_1 =$ _____ and (2) $P(A_1) =$ _____
(Write a final answer in terms of p.)

(1) $\{e_5,\ e_6,\ e_7\}$
(2) $P(e_5) + P(e_6) + P(e_7)$
    $= p(1-p)^2 + p(1-p)^2 + p(1-p)^2$
    $= 3p(1-p)^2$

742 If A_0 is the event that exactly zero successes occurred in the three trials, find $P(A_0)$.

$A_0 = \{e_8\}$ $P(A_0) = P(e_8) = (1-p)^3$

743 Now note: A_0 was the event of getting exactly zero successes in three trials of an experiment where the probability of success on any given trial is p. The notation we will use for the probability of A_0 is $P(0;\ 3,\ p)$ and is read, "the probability of getting zero successes in three trials of an experiment where the probability of success on any given trial is p." We found $P(0;\ 3,\ p) = (1-p)^3$. Similarly, $P(1;\ 3,\ p)$ would be read _____.

the probability of getting exactly one success out of three trials of an experiment where the probability of success on any given trial is p
Note: We found that $P(1;\ 3,\ p) = 3p(1-p)^2$.

•744 The probability of getting exactly two successes in three trials of an experiment where the probability of success on any given trial is p would be indicated by _____.

$P(2; 3, p)$
Note: We found that $P(2; 3, p) = 3p^2(1-p)$.

•745 $P(3; 3, p)$ would read, _____ .

the probability of getting (exactly) three successes in three trials of an experiment where the probability of success on any given trial is p.
Note: We found $P(3; 3, p) = p^3$.

746 So we have that if a single trial of an experiment can result only in either a success or a failure and if the probability of success on any trial is p and if three trials of the experiment are performed, then
1. $P(3; 3, p) = p^3$
2. $P(2; 3, p) = 3p^2(1-p)$
3. $P(1; 3, p) = 3p(1-p)^2$
4. $P(0; 3, p) = (1-p)^3$
Copy the information given in formulas 1 to 4 and use it when needed for frames 747 to 774.

Have a correct copy of the information.

747 Let us try some examples. Copy the following information: The mortality rate of disease X is 0.3; that is, if a person contracts the disease, the probability that he will die is 0.3. Therefore, the probability that he will live is ___.

0.7

748 We have an experiment: Observe a person having disease X and see if he recovers or fails to recover. Thus the experiment can result in exactly one of two outcomes. We will consider recovery from the disease to be a success. Therefore, from the information you copied, the probability of success on any trial of the experiment is ___.

0.7

749 So we have an experiment which can result only in either a success or a failure and $p = 0.7$ (recall we used p as representing the probability of success). . Now suppose we have three persons having disease X and we wish to find the probability that all three will

▼

recover. We want the probability of (1)_____ successes in
(2) _____ trials of an experiment where the probability of success on any given trial is numerically (3) __.

---

(1) three   (2) three   (3) 0.7

---

750 Look at the formulas you copied in frame 746. The probability of
exactly three successes in three trials of an experiment where the
probability of success on any given trial is 0.7 is given by formula
1.   In this case p = 0.7; so $P(3; 3, p)$ = __.

$(0.7)^3$ or approximately 0.34

---

751 So, the probability that all three persons will recover is about
0.34.   Now to find the probability that exactly two of the three
persons will recover, we use formula 2, and since in this case
p = 0.7; $P(2; 3, 0.7)$ = _____ .
(Compute the answer to two decimal places.)

$3(0.7)^2(1-0.7)$ = $3(0.7)^2(0.3)$ or about 0.44

---

752 Use the information you copied from frame 746 to find the probability that exactly one of the three persons having disease X
recovers.
(Compute the answer to two decimal places.)

$P(1; 3, 0.7)$ = $3(0.7)$ $(0.3)^2$ or about 0.19

---

753 Use the formulas you copied from frame 746 to find the probability that none of the three recovers.
(Compute the answer to two decimal places.)

$P(0; 3, 0.7)$ = $(0.3)^3$ or about 0.03

---

754 So we have that if the probability that a person having disease X
will recover is 0.7, then out of three people suffering from disease X:
1.   The probability that exactly three will recover:
$P(3; 3, 0.7)$ = $(0.7)^3 \approx 0.34$
2.   The probability that exactly two will recover:
$P(2; 3, 0.7)$ = $3(0.7)^2(0.3) \approx 0.44$
3.   The probability that exactly one will recover:
$P(1; 3, 0.7)$ = $3(0.7)$ $(0.3)^2 \approx 0.19$

▼

4. The probability that exactly zero will recover:
    $P(0; 3, 0.7) = (0.3)^3 \approx 0.03$
    Note: The sum of the probabilities is ___.

1, although it might have been slightly more or less than 1 using approximations

---

755 Another example. If three coins are tossed, find the probability that exactly two are heads. We shall consider heads to be a success; we know that $p = 0.5$ on a single toss; therefore, we want the probability of exactly two successes on three trials of an experiment where the probability of success on a single trial is 0.5.
(1) To work this problem, which formula from frame 746 would you use, 1, 2, 3, or 4?
(2) Work the example above.
(Compute your answer to three decimal places.)

---

(1) 2   (2) $P(2; 3, 0.5) = 3(0.5)^2(1-0.5) = 0.375$

---

756 $P(2; 3, 0.5)$ is read _____ .

---

the probability of getting exactly two successes in three trials of an experiment where the probability of success on any given trial is 0.5

---

757 An experiment consists of tossing three coins.
(1) If you are to find the probability that all three coins are heads, which of the formulas from frame 746 would you use, 1, 2, 3, or 4?
(2) Show how you use the formula asked for in (1) to find the probability that all three coins are heads. Write a common fraction for an answer, using $p = \frac{1}{2}$ rather than 0.5.

---

(1) 1   (2) $P(3; 3, \frac{1}{2}) = (\frac{1}{2})^3 = \frac{1}{8}$

---

758 $P(1; 3, \frac{1}{2})$ is read, _____ and is equal to $3(\frac{1}{2})(1-\frac{1}{2})^2$.

---

the probability of getting exactly one success in three trials of an experiment where the probability of success on any given trial is $\frac{1}{2}$

---

759 If three coins are tossed, find the probability that exactly one is a head.
(Write a common fraction for an answer.)

$P(1; 3, \frac{1}{2}) = 3(\frac{1}{2})(1-\frac{1}{2})^2 = \frac{3}{8}$

760 If three coins are tossed, find the probability that exactly none turns up heads.
(Write a common fraction for an answer.)

$P(0; 3, \frac{1}{2}) = (1 - \frac{1}{2})^3 = \frac{1}{8}$

761 Another example: On a certain bombing mission, the probability that a plane will not return is 0.2. If three planes are sent on the mission, find the probability that all three will return. Here again, let us for a single trial of the experiment consider the planes' return a success. Then we want the probability of three successes in three trials of an experiment where p, the probability of success on a single trial, is 0.8.
(Compute your answer to two decimal places.)

$P(3; 3, p) = (p)^3$. So, since $p = 0.8$ then
$P(3; 3, 0.8) = (0.8)^3$ or about 0.51

762 If the probability that a plane will return from a bombing mission is 0.8 and three planes are sent on the mission, find the probability that exactly two will return.
(Compute your answer to two decimal places.)

$P(2; 3, 0.8) = 3(0.8)^2(0.2)$ or about 0.38

763 Find the probability that exactly one of three planes sent on a mission will return if the probability that a single plane will return from the mission is 0.8.
(Compute your answer to two decimal places.)

$P(1; 3, 0.8) = 3(0.8)(0.2)^2$ or about 0.10

764 Find the probability that none of the three planes sent on the mission will return. (Remember $p = 0.8$, where p is the probability that a single plane will return.)
(Compute your answer to two decimal places.)

$P(0; 3, 0.8) = (1-0.8)^3 = (0.2)^3$ or about 0.01

765 Even if an experiment has more than two simple outcomes, this procedure can be used if a certain set of the outcomes is considered a success (and the set of the remaining outcomes is considered a failure) and the probability of success p is known. For example, if a single die is tossed, there are six possible outcomes. (The die tosses up one, two, three, four, five, or six.) In a certain problem, however, it might be appropriate that a

▼

result of a one or a two is considered a success and the others a failure. In this case $p =$ ___.
(Write a common fraction for an answer.)

$\frac{2}{6}$ or $\frac{1}{3}$

766 So, suppose we consider a problem in which a single roll of a die is considered a success if a one or a two turns up. Then we have $p = \frac{1}{3}$. Now, if three dice are rolled (or a single die is rolled three times), find the probability of getting exactly two successes.
(Write a common fraction for an answer.)

$$P(2; 3, \tfrac{1}{3}) = 3(\tfrac{1}{3})^2 (1 - \tfrac{1}{3}) = 3(\tfrac{1}{9})(\tfrac{2}{3}) = \tfrac{2}{9}$$

●**767** A roll of a die is considered a success if a one or a two turns up. So we have an experiment with $p = \frac{1}{3}$. If three dice are rolled, find the probability of getting (1) three successes, (2) exactly two successes, (3) exactly one success, (4) zero successes.
(Write common fractions for answers.)

(1) $P(3; 3, \tfrac{1}{3}) = (\tfrac{1}{3})^3 = \tfrac{1}{27}$
(2) $P(2; 3, \tfrac{1}{3}) = 3(\tfrac{1}{3})^2 (\tfrac{2}{3}) = \tfrac{2}{9}$
(3) $P(1; 3, \tfrac{1}{3}) = 3(\tfrac{1}{3})(\tfrac{2}{3})^2 = \tfrac{4}{9}$
(4) $P(0; 3, \tfrac{1}{3}) = (\tfrac{2}{3})^3 = \tfrac{8}{27}$
Note the sum of the probabilities.

768 The probability that a certain type of seed will germinate is 0.9. If three such seeds are planted, find the probability that (1) all three will germinate, (2) exactly two will germinate, (3) exactly one will germinate, (4) exactly zero will germinate.
(You may leave your answers in exponential form.)

(1) $P(3; 3, 0.9) = (0.9)^3$
(2) $P(2; 3, 0.9) = 3(0.9)^2(0.1)$
(3) $P(1; 3, 0.9) = 3(0.9)(0.1)^2$
(4) $P(0; 3, 0.9) = (0.1)^3$

769 Notice that the trials of the experiment must be independent and the experiment performed under essentially the same conditions on each trial. Thus p has the same value for every trial. This technique would not work on the following problem. Why? A hat contains five red balls and three white balls. If three balls are drawn from the hat without replacement, find the probability that all three are white.

▼

(Do not try to do the problem, just tell why our present procedure will not work.)

The trials are not independent, that is, the results of one trial have an effect upon the results of the next trial because the ball drawn is not replaced.

770 However, a hat contains five red balls and three white balls. A ball is drawn from the hat and its color noted. *The ball is then replaced.* If this experiment is performed three times, find the probability that (1) all three are white, (2) exactly two are white, (3) exactly one is white, (4) exactly zero are white. Consider a white ball drawn to be a success. Then $p = \frac{3}{8}$.
(You may leave your answer in exponential form.)

(1) $P(3; 3, \frac{3}{8}) = \left(\frac{3}{8}\right)^3$
(2) $P(2; 3, \frac{3}{8}) = 3\left(\frac{3}{8}\right)^2\left(\frac{5}{8}\right)$
(3) $P(1; 3, \frac{3}{8}) = 3\left(\frac{3}{8}\right)\left(\frac{5}{8}\right)^2$
(4) $P(0; 3, \frac{3}{8}) = \left(\frac{5}{8}\right)^3$

771 Joe Zilch is a pitcher on the local baseball team. The probability that one of Joe's pitches is a strike (regardless what the batter does to it) is 0.6. If Joe throws three pitches in succession, what is the probability that *at least* two of them are strikes? (We want the probability that exactly two of the three pitches *or* exactly three of the three pitches are strikes. These are mutually exclusive events; so the probability of one or the other occurring is the sum of the two probabilities.)
(Compute your answer to two decimal places.)

$P(2; 3, 0.6) = 3(0.6)^2(0.4) \approx 0.43$
$P(3; 3, 0.6) = (0.6)^3 \approx 0.22$
Therefore, the probability that at least two are strikes is approximately $0.43 + 0.22 = 0.65$.

772 In rolling three dice, we want to find the probability that *at least one six* will turn up. Here we have $p = \frac{1}{6}$. We need to find the sum of the probabilities of exactly one, exactly two, and exactly three successes in three trials.
∴ $P(1; 3, \frac{1}{6}) + P(2; 3, \frac{1}{6}) + P(3; 3, \frac{1}{6}) = \_\_ + \_\_ + \_\_ = \_\_$

$3\left(\frac{1}{6}\right)\left(\frac{5}{6}\right)^2 + 3\left(\frac{1}{6}\right)^2\left(\frac{5}{6}\right) + \left(\frac{1}{6}\right)^3$
$= \frac{75}{216} + \frac{15}{216} + \frac{1}{216} = \frac{91}{216}$

773 Would we get the same answer if we found the probability that exactly zero successes occur in the three trials and then subtracted
that answer from 1? Work it out to show that your answer is correct. You should get $\frac{91}{216}$ for your answer.

yes, $1-P(0; 3, \frac{1}{6}) = 1 -(\frac{5}{6})^3 = 1 - \frac{125}{216} = \frac{91}{216}$

774 If a widget is chosen from the assembly line of the Nadir Manufacturing Company, the probability that it is defective is 0.01. If
three widgets are drawn at random (and we assume that the trials
are independent, that is, the condition of one widget has no effect
upon the probability of another being defective), find the probability
that:
(1) All three are good
(2) Exactly two are good
(3) Exactly one is good
(4) Exactly zero are good
(You may leave your answers in exponential form.)

If we consider a good widget a success, we have $p = 0.99$. Then
(1) $P(3; 3, 0.99) = (0.99)^3$
(2) $P(2; 3, 0.99) = 3(0.99)^2(0.01)$
(3) $P(1; 3, 0.99) = 3(0.99) (0.01)^2$
(4) $P(0; 3, 0.99) = (0.01)^3$

775 Suppose we have an experiment which results in either success or
failure on any single trial, and the probability of success is p. Suppose we now perform four independent trials of the experiment under essentially the same conditions. We are again interested in the
probability of getting a certain number of successes out of the four
trials. Note, if the probability of success $= p$, then the probability
of failure $=$ ___.

$1-p$

776 Now, indicating the results S or F in order of the first, second,
third, and fourth trial of the experiment, there is only one way in
which we can get exactly four successes in four trials, namely,
$SSSS$; and since the trials are independent, the probability of
getting $SSSS$ is the product of the probabilities involved. Therefore, since the probability of getting a success $S = p$, the probability of getting $SSSS$ is _____.

$p \cdot p \cdot p \cdot p = p^4$

777 Using the same notation as before: $P(4; 4, p) = p^4$ is read, the probability of getting **(1)** _____ successes in **(2)** _____ trials of an experiment where the probability of a success on a given trial is **(3)** ___ equals p^4.

> **(1)** four **(2)** four **(3)** p

778 Now consider the ways in which exactly three successes out of four trials could occur. There are four ways, namely, $SSSF$, _____, _____, _____ .

> $SSFS,$ $SFSS,$ $FSSS$

779 So, the elements $SSSF$, $SSFS$, $SFSS$, and $FSSS$ of our sample space represent all the outcomes in which exactly three successes occur. Consider $SSSF$. Since the trials are independent, the probability of $SSSF$ is the product of the probabilities involved. Therefore, $P(SSSF) = p \cdot p \cdot p(1-p) = p^3(1-p)$. Similarly, **(1)** $P(SSFS)$ = _____, **(2)** $P(SFSS)$ = _____, **(3)** $P(FSSS)$ = _____.

> **(1)** $p^3(1-p)$ **(2)** $p^3(1-p)$ **(3)** $p^3(1-p)$

780 So, there are four elements of our sample space corresponding to exactly three successes out of the four trials. Each has a probability of $p^3(1-p)$. Thus the probability of the event of exactly three successes out of the four trials is the sum of the probabilities of the four elements. Therefore, $P(3; 4, p) =$ _____ .

> $4p^3(1-p)$

781 If we wish to find $P(2; 4, p)$, that is, the probability of exactly two successes in four trials of an experiment where the probability of success on a given trial is p, we must find those elements of the sample space containing exactly two S's and two F's. These would be $SFSF$, $SFFS$, etc. But note, each of these elements has the same probability, namely, _____.

> $p^2(1-p)^2$
> For example, since the probability of $S = p$ and the probability of $F = (1-p)$ and the trials are independent,
> $P(SFFS) = p(1-p)(1-p)p = p^2(1-p)^2$

782 Thus, all we need do is find how many of the elements of the sample space contain two S's (and two F's). List them. There are six.

> $SSFF$ $SFSF$ $SFFS$ $FSSF$ $FSFS$ $FFSS$

783 So we have six elements of our sample space corresponding to outcomes in which exactly two successes occurred, each of which has a probability of $p^2(1-p)^2$. $\therefore$ $P(2; 4, p) =$ _____.

$6p^2(1-p)^2$

784 Similarly, to find $P(1; 4, p)$, list the elements of the sample space having exactly one S.

SFFF   FSFF   FFSF   FFFS

785 You found four such points, and since each has exactly one S and three F's, each has a probability of
$p(1-p)(1-p)(1-p) = p(1-p)^3$. $\therefore$ $P(1; 4, p) =$ _____.

$4p(1-p)^3$

786 Finally, list the elements having exactly zero successes.

FFFF

787 $P(FFFF) = (1-p)(1-p)(1-p)(1-p)$
$= (1-p)^4$
Since this is the only element containing exactly zero S's,
$P(0; 4, p) =$ _____.

$(1-p)^4$

788 Copy this information and save it: If a single trial of an experiment can result only in either success or failure and if the probability of success on any given trial is p, then if four independent trials of the experiment are performed under essentially the same conditions,
$P(4; 4, p) = p^4$ $P(3; 4, p) = 4p^3(1-p)$
$P(2; 4, p) = 6p^2(1-p)^2$ $P(1; 4, p) = 4p(1-p)^3$
$P(0; 4, p) = (1-p)^4$
If four coins are tossed, find the probability that all four are heads. Here we have $p = \frac{1}{2}$.
(Write a common fraction for the answer.)

$P(4; 4, \frac{1}{2}) = (\frac{1}{2})^4 = \frac{1}{16}$
Have a copy of the information.

789 If four coins are tossed, find the probability that exactly three are heads.
(Write a common fraction for the answer.)

$P(3; 4, \frac{1}{2}) = 4(\frac{1}{2})^3 (1 - \frac{1}{2}) = \frac{1}{4}$

790 If four coins are tossed, find the probability that exactly two are heads.
(Write a common fraction for the answer.)

$P(2; 4, \frac{1}{2}) = 6(\frac{1}{2})^2 (1 - \frac{1}{2})^2 = \frac{3}{8}$

791 If four coins are tossed, find the probability that exactly one is a head.
(Write a common fraction for the answer.)

$P(1; 4, \frac{1}{2}) = 4(\frac{1}{2})(1 - \frac{1}{2})^3 = \frac{1}{4}$

792 If four coins are tossed, find the probability that no heads occur.
(Write a common fraction for the answer.)

$P(0; 4, \frac{1}{2}) = (1 - \frac{1}{2})^4 = \frac{1}{16}$

793 To collect the information; Four coins are tossed and a head is considered a success. You may use your answers from frames 788 to 792 to answer the following:
(1) $P(4; 4, \frac{1}{2}) = (\frac{1}{2})^4 =$ ___
(2) $P(3; 4, \frac{1}{2}) = 4(\frac{1}{2})^3(1 - \frac{1}{2}) =$ ___
(3) $P(2; 4, \frac{1}{2}) = 6(\frac{1}{2})^2(1 - \frac{1}{2}) =$ ___
(4) $P(1; 4, \frac{1}{2}) = 4(\frac{1}{2})(1 - \frac{1}{2})^3 =$ ___
(5) $P(0; 4, \frac{1}{2}) = (1 - \frac{1}{2})^4 =$ ___
(6) The sum of the probabilities is ___.

(1) $\frac{1}{16}$ (2) $\frac{1}{4}$ (3) $\frac{3}{8}$ (4) $\frac{1}{4}$ (5) $\frac{1}{16}$ (6) 1

794 The probability that the West Futility Tigers will win a baseball game is 0.1. Out of the next four games, find the probability that they will win (1) exactly four games, (2) exactly three games, (3) exactly two games, (4) exactly one game, (5) exactly zero games.
(You may leave your answers in exponential form.)

(1) $P(4; 4, 0.1) = (0.1)^4$
(2) $P(3; 4, 0.1) = 4(0.1)^3(0.9)$
(3) $P(2; 4, 0.1) = 6(0.1)^2(0.9)^2$
(4) $P(1; 4, 0.1) = 4(0.1)(0.9)^3$
(5) $P(0; 4, 0.1) = (0.9)^4$

●**795** The probability that a certain type of seed will germinate is 0.95. Of four such seeds, find the probability that *at least* three will germinate.
(You may leave your answer in exponential form.)

$P(3; 4, 0.95) + P(4; 4, 0.95) = 4(0.95)^3(0.05) + (0.95)^4$
(Note: At least three will occur if exactly three or exactly four occur.)

796 The mortality rate of a certain disease is 0.14. Of four persons having this disease, find the probability that *at least* two survive.
[If we consider survival success, we want to find
$P(2; 4, 0.86) + P(3; 4, 0.86) + P(4; 4, 0.86)$.]
(You may leave your answer in exponential form.)

$6(0.86)^2 (0.14)^2 + 4(0.86)^3 (0.14) + (0.86)^4$

797 If Joe Zilch fires five shots with a rifle at a target 100 yards away, the probability that all five will hit in the bull's eye is 0.9. If Joe fires five shots each at four different targets 100 yards away, find the probability that *at least* three of the targets will have all five shots in the bull's eye.

Note: Each target represents a single trial of the experiment, and $p = 0.9$ is the probability of a success where success is all bull's eyes. We want the probability of *at least* three successes in four trials with $p = 0.9$; so
$P(3; 4, 0.9) + P(4; 4, 0.9) = 4(0.9)^3(0.1) + (0.9)^4$

798 In rolling a single die, the probability that a 6 turns up is $\frac{1}{6}$. If four dice are rolled, find the probability that no more than one 6 occurs.
[No more than one success (a 6) means exactly zero successes or exactly one success.]
(You may leave your answer in exponential form.)

$P(0; 4, \frac{1}{6}) + P(1; 4, \frac{1}{6}) = (1 - \frac{1}{6})^4 + 4(\frac{1}{6})(1 - \frac{1}{6})^3$
$$= (\frac{5}{6})^4 + 4(\frac{1}{6})(\frac{5}{6})^3$$
If you consider "not a 6" to be a success, then $p = \frac{5}{6}$ and you want the probability of exactly three successes or exactly four successes.
$P(3; 4, \frac{5}{6}) + P(4; 4, \frac{5}{6}) = 4(\frac{5}{6})^3(\frac{1}{6}) + (\frac{5}{6})^4$.   *Note:* The answers are equal.

799 Recall: If three coins are tossed, the probability that two heads appear is $3(\frac{1}{2})^3 = \frac{3}{8}$.
Now, suppose we perform the above experiment four times (that is, we toss three coins and record the number of heads, do it again,

▼

again, and again). Find the probability that exactly two heads
occur on *at least* one of the trials. That is, find:
$P(1; 4, \frac{3}{8}) + P(2; 4, \frac{3}{8}) + P(3; 4, \frac{3}{8}) + P(4; 4, \frac{3}{8})$.
(You may leave your answer in exponential form.)

$4(\frac{3}{8})(\frac{5}{8})^3 + 6(\frac{3}{8})^2(\frac{5}{8})^2 + 4(\frac{3}{8})^3(\frac{5}{8}) + (\frac{3}{8})^4$

800 Consider again the experiment in frame 799. It would probably
be easier to find the probability of 0 successes and subtract that
from 1, that is, 1 - probability of the complementary event. Find
$1 - P(0; 4, \frac{3}{8})$.
(You may leave your answer in exponential form.)

$1 - (\frac{5}{8})^4$

801 If four coins are tossed, find the probability that *at least* one head
occurs. That is, find
$P(1; 4, \frac{1}{2}) + P(2; 4, \frac{1}{2}) + P(3; 4, \frac{1}{2}) + P(4; 4, \frac{1}{2})$
(Write a common fraction for the final answer.)

$4(\frac{1}{2})(\frac{1}{2})^3 + 6(\frac{1}{2})^2(\frac{1}{2})^2 + 4(\frac{1}{2})^3(\frac{1}{2}) + (\frac{1}{2})^4 = \frac{4}{16} + \frac{6}{16} + \frac{4}{16} + \frac{1}{16} = \frac{15}{16}$

●802 Consider again the experiment in frame 801. Use the simpler
method of subtracting the probability of the complementary event
(no heads occur) from 1.
(Write a common fraction for the answer.)

$1 - P(0; 4, \frac{1}{2}) = 1 - (\frac{1}{2})^4 = \frac{16}{16} - \frac{1}{16} = \frac{15}{16}$

803 Consider an experiment which can result only in either a success
S or a failure F and $P(S) = p$. If five independent trials of the
experiment are performed, find the probability that exactly two
successes will occur:
(1) List the elements of the sample space in which exactly two
     $S's$ occur.
(2) Find the probability of each of these elements.
(3) Add the probabilities in (2) to find $P(2; 5, p)$.

(1) 1. *SSFFF*   (2) 1. $p^2(1-p)^3$
     2. *SFSFF*   2. $p^2(1-p)^3$
     3. *SFFSF*   3. $p^2(1-p)^3$
     4. *SFFFS*   4. $p^2(1-p)^3$
     5. *FFFSS*   5. $p^2(1-p)^3$
     6. *FFSSF*   6. $p^2(1-p)^3$
     7. *FSSFF*   7. $p^2(1-p)^3$
     8. *FFSFS*   8. $p^2(1-p)^3$
     9. *FSFFS*   9. $p^2(1-p)^3$
    10. *FSFSF*   10. $p^2(1-p)^3$
(3) $P(2; 5, p) = 10p^2(1-p)^3$

804 $P(1; 8, p)$ is read, _____ .

the probability of getting exactly one success in eight trials of an
experiment where the probability of success on any given trial is p

805 Find $P(1; 8, p)$.

$P(1; 8, p) = 8p(1-p)^7$
There are eight elements representing exactly one success out of
eight trials, namely: $SFFFFFFF$, $FSFFFFFF$, $FFSFFFFF$, etc..
Each has a probability of $p(1-p)^7$. $\therefore$ $P(1; 8, p) = 8p(1-p)^7$

806 Find $P(3; 5, p)$.

$P(3; 5, p) = 10p^3(1-p)^2$
The elements representing outcomes in which exactly three
successes occurred are:
$SSSFF$, $SSFSF$, $SFSSF$, $FSSSF$, $SSFFS$, $SFSFS$,
$FSSFS$, $SFFSS$, $FSFSS$, $FFSSS$. Therefore, there are 10 such
elements in S, and each has a probability of $p^3(1-p)^2$.
$\therefore$ $P(3; 5, p) = 10p^3(1-p)^2$

807 Note once again, if six *independent* trials of an experiment which
can result only in S or F are performed and $P(S) = p$, then the
symbol $SFSFFF$ means success on the first trial *and* failure on
the second trial *and* success on the third trial *and* etc. Therefore,
since the trials are independent, we are justified in using an extended form of the theorem:
$P(A \cap B) = P(A) \cdot P(B)$. The probability of $SFSFFF$ = _____ .

$p(1-p)p(1-p)(1-p)(1-p) = p^2(1-p)^4$

808 Find $P(2; 8, p)$

$P(2; 8, p) = 28p^2(1-p)^6$
There are 28 elements of the sample space in which exactly two
successes occur: $SSFFFFFF$, $SFSFFFFF$, etc. . Each has a probability of $p^2(1-p)^6$. $\therefore$ $P(2; 8, p) = 28p^2(1-p)^6$.

809 Find $P(3; 7, p)$.

$P(3; 7, p) = 35p^3(1-p)^4$
You should find 35 elements such as $SSSFFFF$, $SSFSFFF$, $SSFFSFF$,
etc. Each has a probability of $p^3(1-p)^4$. $\therefore$ $P(3; 7, p) = 35p^3(1-p)^4$.

810 At the moment, to find $P(6; 10, p)$, you would first list all the elements of the sample space containing exactly six S's and four F's (such elements as $FSSFSSSSFF$, etc.). This is quite a job; so suppose we tell you there are 210 such elements.
∴ $P(6; 10, p)$ = _____ .

$210p^6(1-p)^4$, since each one of these elements has a probability of $p^6(1-p)^4$ and there are 210 such elements

Self-test VII

1 In a single shot of a gun, the probability that Joe Zilch will break a skeet is 0.7. Let S (success) be the event that he breaks the skeet, $P(S) = 0.7$. Therefore, if F (failure) is the event that he does not break the skeet, $P(F)$ = _____ .

2 An experiment consists of having Joe Zilch shoot at three skeets. List the possible outcomes by indicating an S (success) or F (failure) for the first, second, and third shot; in that order. (Keep a copy of your list for Probs. 3 and 4.)

3 Since we know that $P(S) = 0.7$ and $P(F) = 0.3$, we can find the probability of each of the outcomes listed in Prob. 2. Find them and save them for Prob. 4. (Write your answers in exponential form.)

4 From your list find:
(1) The probability that Joe breaks all three skeets.
(2) The probability that Joe breaks exactly two of the three skeets.
(3) The probability that Joe breaks exactly one of the three skeets.
(4) The probability that Joe breaks none of the three skeets.
(Write your answers to three decimal places.)

5 The probability of getting exactly one success in three trials of an experiment where the probability of success on any given trial is 0.8 would be indicated by _____ .

6 $P(0; 3, p)$ would be read, _____ .

7 A roll of a die is considered a success if a six turns up, a failure if a one, two, three, four, or five turns up. If three dice are rolled, find the probability of getting
(1) three successes
(2) exactly two successes
(3) exactly one success
(4) zero successes

8 If three coins are tossed, find the probability that at least one head occurs.

9 If four coins are tossed, find the probability that at least one head occurs. Use the method of subtracting the probability of the complementary event from 1.

2. Binomial Distribution and Permutations

By now, the general problem we are attacking should be obvious. Suppose we consider five independent trials of an experiment, each trial of which can result only in either a success or a failure, and the probability of success on a given trial is p. We would then want formulas for exactly zero successes in five trials, one success in five trials, two successes in five trials, three successes in five trials, four successes in five trials, and five successes in five trials. But, soon after that, we would consider six trials, etc. The process would be tedious, and we would never be finished using this technique of considering successive integral values of trials. What we would like to find is a formula for the probability of exactly x successes in n independent trials of an experiment where the probability of success on any single trial is p. Using our previous notation, this would be indicated by $P(x; n, p)$.

811 First let us consider 10 independent trials of an experiment which can result only in either a success *(S)* or a failure *(F)*. Indicating elements of our sample space in the usual manner, we would have elements such as *SSFSSSSFFSF*, where we have indicated the results of 10 trials in the order in which they occurred. Note that *SSFSSSSFFSF* represents an outcome in which exactly _____ success(es) occurred out of the 10 trials.

six

812 It would be discouraging to list the elements of the sample space for 10 such trials because there are 2^{10} = ___ elements.

1,024

813 Let us take a different approach. Suppose we are interested in the probability of exactly two successes in the 10 trials of the experiment. We would be interested in elements such as *SFFFFSFFFF*, *FFFSFFFFFS*, *FFSFFSFFFF*, etc. Now look at any one of the elements. Since the trials are independent, the probability of any

▼

one element is found by multiplying the 10 probabilities involved. $P(S) = p$ and $P(F) = (1-p)$; so whatever the order of the two S's and eight F's, the product which is the probability of any *one* element is _____.

$p^2(1-p)^8$

---

814 Now, we know that to find $P(2; 10, p)$:
1. We are interested in those elements of the sample space which have exactly two S's and eight F's.
2. Each element has a probability of $p^2(1-p)^8$.
If we are told that there are 45 elements containing exactly two S's and eight F's, we know that $P(2; 10, p) = $ _____.

$45p^2(1-p)^8$ (the sum of the probabilities of the elements containing exactly two S's and eight F's)

---

815 Suppose we wish to find $P(38; 100, p)$, we are interested in those elements of the sample space in which there are exactly **(1)** ___ successes *(S)* and **(2)** ___ failures *(F)*.

---

(1) 38   **(2)** 62

---

816 Continuing from frame 815. Now, each of the elements in which there are exactly 38 successes and 62 failures has a probability of **(1)** _____. We know this because the probability of any of the elements is the product of the **(2)** _____ of the S's and the F's occurring in the element.

---

(1) $p^{38}(1-p)^{62}$ **(2)** probabilities

---

817 Now, we know that to find $P(38; 100, p)$:
1. We are interested in those elements of the sample space which have exactly 38 S's and 62 F's.
2. Each element has a probability of $p^{38}(1-p)^{62}$.
If we are told that there are K elements containing exactly 38 S's and 62 F's, we know that $P(38; 100, p) = $ _____.

$Kp^{38}(1-p)^{62}$

---

818 Look at another example. Suppose we want to find $P(2; 6, p)$. Then we are interested only in the elements of the sample space containing exactly two S's. For example, *SSFFFF, SFSFFF, SFFSFF, SFFFSF, SFFFFS, FSSFFF*, etc., where again, we

▼

are indicating the results of the six trials in the order in which they occurred. List the remaining elements containing exactly two S's.

FSFSFF, FSFFSF, FSFFFS, FFSSFF, FFSFSF, FFSFFS, FFFSSF, FFFSFS, FFFFSS
Note: There are 15 such elements.

819 Now look at any such element listed, for example, *FSFFSF*. This element corresponds to the outcome of getting failure on the first trial *and* success on the second trial *and* failure on the third trial, etc. Since these trials are independent, the probability of the occurrence of all the events is the product of the probabilities involved. Therefore, since the probability of getting an S on a single trial is p and the probability of getting an F is $(1-p)$, we have
$P(FSFFSF) = (1-p)p(1-p)(1-p)p(1-p)$
$\qquad\qquad = p^2(1-p)^4$
Similarly, $P(SFFFSF) = $ _____ .

$p(1-p)(1-p)(1-p)p(1-p)$
$= p^2(1-p)^4$

820 Now, we know that to find $P(2; 6, p)$:
1. We are interested in those elements of the sample space which have exactly (1) _____ S's and (2) _____ F's.
2. Each element has a probability of (3) _____ .
We found in frame 818 that there are 15 elements such as described in 1. $\therefore$ **(4)** $P(2; 6, p) = $ _____ .

(1) two   (2) four   (3) $p^2(1-p)^4$ (4) $15p^2(1-p)^4$

821 So now, in order to find, say, $P(5; 38, p)$, we need decide only how many elements of the sample space contain $5\,S$'s (and 33 F's). We have already determined that for each element containing 5 S's and 33 F's, no matter how the S's and F's are arranged, the probability is **(1)** _____ . Then if there are K such elements,
(2) $P(5; 38, p) = $ _____ .

(1) $p^5(1-p)^{33}$ (2) $Kp^5(1-p)^{33}$

822 Similarly, $P(15; 100, p)$ will be $K \cdot$ _____ if there are K elements of the the sample space containing 15 S's and 85 F's. (Copy $K \cdot$ when you answer.)

$K \cdot (p)^{15}(1-p)^{85}$

823 So, in general, $P(x; n, p)$ will equal some constant times $p^x(1-p)^{n-x}$ where the constant is the number of elements of the sample space containing x S's and n-x F's. Once again, note that an element representing the results of n trials looks like this:

$$\underbrace{SSFFSSF \ldots}_{n \text{ trials}}$$

where S appears x times and F occurs (n-x) times; then, no matter what order the S's and F's appear, the probability of such an element is

$$p^x(1-p)^{n-x}$$

comment

Now our only problem is one of counting, that is, of deciding in how many ways we can arrange a certain number of S's and F's. This counting problem is one which hampered us in our earlier work. We often needed to list an entire sample space in order to compute probabilities, when if we had known a technique of determining the number of elements, our problem would have been simpler. Therefore, it would be valuable to find such techniques.

824 A specific example of a certain type of counting problem is as follows: Given the set $\{a, b, c\}$, the problem is to find the total number of arrangements which can be formed by choosing two distinct elements from the set at a time. Notice that each arrangement must contain two different elements from S, and two arrangements are the same if and only if they are identical. (Order, then, is important.) Then we list the possible arrangements: ab, ac, ba, bc, ca, cb. Thus, there are six such arrangements. List the 12 possible such arrangements of two distinct elements chosen from the set $\{1, 2, 3, 4\}$.

12	13	14
21	23	24
31	32	34
41	42	43

825 Find the number of such arrangements of three distinct objects which can be formed from the set $\{a, b, c, d\}$ by listing them. (Note again: Each arrangement must contain three distinct objects, and two arrangements are the same if and only if they

▼

are identical; thus, *abd, adb, bad,* etc., are different arrangements.)

There are 24.

abc	*abd*	*acb*	*acd*	*adb*	*adc*
bac	*bad*	*bca*	*bcd*	*bda*	*bdc*
cab	*cad*	*cba*	*cbd*	*cda*	*cdb*
dab	*dac*	*dba*	*dbc*	*dca*	*dcb*

826 Notice the problem is similar to that of listing the sample space for the following experiment: A hat contains three red balls $R_1R_2R_3$ and two white balls $W_1 W_2$. Two balls are chosen in succession *without replacement.* Then the sample space consists of the arrangements of the sort we have been discussing, by choosing two distinct elements from the set $\{R_1, R_2, R_3, W_1, W_2\}$. List them.

R_1R_2	R_1R_3	R_1W_1	R_1W_2
R_2R_1	R_2R_3	R_2W_1	R_2W_2
R_3R_1	R_3R_2	R_3W_1	R_3W_2
W_1R_1	W_1R_2	W_1R_3	W_1W_2
W_2R_1	W_2R_2	W_2R_3	W_2W_1

827 The name given to an arrangement of *K* distinct elements listed in a specific order in a straight line is a *permutation of K elements.* Thus *abd* is a permutation of the three elements *a, b,* and *d.* Two permutations are the same (equal) if and only if they are identical. Thus *adb* is a different permutation of the three elements *a, b,* and *d.* List the other permutations of *a, b,* and *d.*

We had *abd* and *adb*; the others are *bad, bda, dab, dba.*

●**828** Two permutations are the same (equal) if and only if they are _____.

identical

829 Given the set $\{a, b, c, d\}$. List the 12 possible permutations of two elements that can be formed from the set.

ab	*ac*	*ad*
ba	*bc*	*bd*
ca	*cb*	*cd*
da	*db*	*dc*

830 Now, suppose we consider the set $\{a, b, c, d, e, f, \}$. Suppose we wish to form permutations of two elements chosen from the six elements of the set. This means that we wish to fill two blanks such

▼

as these ___ ___ with two distinct elements of S in as many different ways as possible. Now, obviously, the first blank can be
filled with any one of the six elements.   For example, suppose
the first blank is filled with c. We now have <u>c</u> ___ . Now,
since the elements in a permutation are to be different, in how
many ways can the second blank be filled?

Five ways. Use either a, b, d, e, or f (c has been used).

831 Consider the set $S = \{a, b, c, d, e, f, g, h\}$.
The set of permutations of two elements from this set of eight
elements can be considered in the following manner: We wish to
fill the two blanks ___ ___ with two distinct elements of S. There
are (1) _____ distinct elements which could be placed in the first
blank. Suppose we fill the first blank with a. Now, there are
(2) _____ choices for the second blank, each giving a different
permutation.

(1) eight   (2) seven

832 We have found that from the set $S = \{a, b, c, d, e, f, g, h\}$, there
are eight distinct elements which could be placed in the first blank,
and with each one of these there are seven different permutations
which can be put in the second blank.   Therefore the total number
of permutations which can be formed is ___ · ___ = ___.

8 · 7 = 56

833 In order to form permutations of two elements from the set
$S = \{1, 2, a, *, \text{John}\}$, note that if the first blank of ___ ___ is
filled,

1 _____	1 _____	1 _____	1 _____
2 _____	2 _____	2 _____	2 _____
a _____	a _____	a _____	a _____
* _____	* _____	* _____	* _____
John _____	John _____	John _____	John _____

Then with each one of the five choices of the first element, there
are four choices for the second element for a total of 5·4 = 20
permutations. Fill in the blanks.

1 2	1 a	1 *	1 John
2 1	2 a	2 *	2 John
a 1	a 2	a *	a John
* 1	* 2	* a	* John
John 1	John 2	John a	John *

You may have a different arrangement.

834 If we wish to form permutations of two elements from the set of six elements $\{a,\ b,\ c,\ d,\ e,\ f\}$, we see that the first blank in ___ ___ can be filled in any one of **(1)** _____ ways. With each one of these six ways, there are **(2)** _____ ways in which the second blank can be filled. This gives us a total of **(3)** ___ ___ = ___ permutations.

835 If from $S = \{a, b, c, d, e, f\}$, we fill the first blank with $\underline{a}$ like this: $\underline{a}$ ___, there are five permutations beginning with a, namely, ab, ac, ad, ae, af. Similarly, if b is in the first position, we have

___ ___ , ___ ___ , ___ ___ , ___ ___ , ___ ___ .

●**836** Similarly, if we are to find the number of permutations of three elements from the set $\{a,\ b,\ c,\ d,\ e,\ f\}$, we see that we are trying to fill three blanks ___ ___ ___ with different elements from the set. The first blank can be filled with any one of **(1)** _____ elements. With each of these, the second blank can be filled with any one of the **(2)** _____ elements. The third blank can be filled with any one of **(3)** _____ elements. Thus there are **(4)** ___ · ___ · ___ = ___ permutations.

837 The number of possible permutations of k elements that can be formed from a set of n elements is denoted by $_nP_k$ where $k \leq n$.

Thus, the number of permutations of three elements formed from the set containing five distinct elements would be indicated by _____ .

838 Notice that in $_nP_k$ the first subscript n denotes the total number of elements with which we shall work. The second subscript k denotes how many distinct elements are to be in each permutation. Therefore, the symbol $_nP_k$ represents _____ .

839 In $_nP_k$ the first subscript n denotes (1) _____ . The second subscript k denotes (2) _____ .

> (1) the total number of elements with which we shall work
> (2) the number of distinct elements in each permutation

840 Now consider $_nP_2$, where $n \geq 2$. We have to fill two blanks __ __ in as many ways as possible. The first blank can be filled with any one of (1) __ elements, and with each of these the second can then be filled with any one of (2) __ remaining elements. Thus (3) $_nP_2$ = _____ .

> (1) n (2) n-1   (3) n $(n$-1)

841 Similarly, $_nP_3$ where $n \geq 3 = n(n$-1$)$ $(n$-2$)$. Therefore, $_nP_4$ where $n \geq 4$ = _____ .

> $n(n$-1$)$ $(n$-2$)$ $(n$-3$)$

842 Given a set of 10 elements, the number of permutations of three elements which can be formed is indicated by _____ and is equal to $10 \cdot 9 \cdot 8 = 720$.

> $_{10}P_3$

843 To find $_{30}P_5$, we note that we wish to fill the (1) _____ blanks, using distinct elements from the set of (2) __ elements.

> (1) five   (2) 30

844 Consider again $_{30}P_5$. We wish to fill five blanks __ __ __ __ __ using distinct elements from the set of 30 elements. The first blank can be filled in any one of (1) __ways. With each of these, the second blank can be filled in (2) __ ways. With each of these, the third blank can be filled in (3) __ ways. With each of these, the fourth blank can be filled in (4) __ways. And finally, with each of these, the fifth blank can be filled in (5) __ ways. Therefore, (6) $_{30}P_5$ = __ · __ · __ · __ · __ .

> (1) 30   (2) 29   (3) 28   (4) 27   (5) 26
> (6) $30 \cdot 29 \cdot 28 \cdot 27 \cdot 26$

●**845** $_8P_4$ = __ · __ · __ · __ = _____

> $8 \cdot 7 \cdot 6 \cdot 5 = 1,680$

846 In general, ${}_nP_k = n(n-1)(n-2) \cdots (n-k+1)$
For example, ${}_{100}P_5 = 100 \cdot 99 \cdot 98 \cdot 97 \cdot 96$
(Note: $n-k+1 = 100-5+1 = 96$)
${}_6P_4 =$ ___ • ___ • ___ • ___ = _________

$6 \cdot 5 \cdot 4 \cdot 3 = 360$ *(Note:* $n-k-+1 = 6-4+1 = 3$)

847 In the formula ${}_nP_k$, you need not memorize the factor $(n-k+1)$. You need remember only the product on the right contains one blank to be filled for each element in the permutation. For example, in ${}_{10}P_5$, we know that there will be (1) ______ blanks to be filled because each permutation contains (2) ______ elements.

(1) five (2) five

848 Consider but do not work the following:
${}_{10}P_5 =$ ___ • ___ • ___ • ___ • ___ .
(1) Note that if you were to find ${}_{10}P_5$ by using the above mentioned, you would have ______ blanks to fill.
(2) If you use $n-k+1$ to find the number in the last blank, this number would be ______.
(3) Find ${}_{10}P_5$.

(1) five (2) six
(3) ${}_{10}P_5 = 10 \cdot 9 \cdot 8 \cdot 7 \cdot 6 = 30{,}240$

●**849** Find ${}_8P_3$.

${}_8P_3 = 8 \cdot 7 \cdot 6 = 336$

comment

Since these counting techniques are probably familiar to many of you, and since we do not wish to go too far afield from our original study of probability, the formula ${}_nP_k$ (and subsequent counting formulas) will not be proved rigorously. We have been (and will be) appealing to your intuition that if a permutation of k elements is to be formed, then there are k blanks to fill ___ ___ ___ . . . ___ . The first can be filled in n ways, the second in $n-1$ ways, etc.

850 (1) Find $_4P_3$.
(2) Let the four elements be a, b, c, d and verify your answer to (1) by listing the permutations.

(1) $_4P_3 = 4 \cdot 3 \cdot 2 = 24$
(2)

abc	bac	cab	dab
abd	bad	cad	dac
acb	bca	cba	dba
acd	bcd	cbd	dbc
adb	bda	cda	dca
adc	bdc	cdb	dcb

851 $_4P_4 =$ _____ .

$4 \cdot 3 \cdot 2 \cdot 1 = 24$

852 · $_{10}P_3 =$ _____ .

$10 \cdot 9 \cdot 8 = 720$

853 $_{100}P_{27} =$ _____ .
(You need not multiply.)

$100 \cdot 99 \cdot 98 \cdot 97 \ldots 76 \cdot 75 \cdot 74$

854 $_{50}P_{47} =$ _____ .
(You need not multiply.)

$50 \cdot 49 \cdot 48 \ldots 6 \cdot 5 \cdot 4$

855 Note that the expression of such products is awkward. A symbol which is convenient in counting problems is $n!$, where n is a positive integer and is read "n factorial." For example, $4! = 4 \cdot 3 \cdot 2 \cdot 1$; so $4! = 24$. Similarly, $5! =$ _____ .

$5 \cdot 4 \cdot 3 \cdot 2 \cdot 1 = 120$

856 $_5P_5 = 5 \cdot 4 \cdot 3 \cdot 2 \cdot 1 = 5!$
Similarly, $_7P_7 =$ _____ .

$7 \cdot 6 \cdot 5 \cdot 4 \cdot 3 \cdot 2 \cdot 1 = 7!$

●857 $_{100}P_{100}$ = ___

100!, or for those who like to do things the hard way,
100 · 99 · 98 · 97... 4 · 3 · 2 · 1

858 $_nP_n$ = _____

$n(n-1) \cdot (n-2) \ldots 3 \cdot 2 \cdot 1$
= $n!$

●859 6! is read (1) _____ and stands for (2) _____ .

(1) six factorial　　(2) 6 · 5 · 4 · 3 · 2 · 1

860 The product of the integers from 1 to 100 would be
1 · 2 · 3 · 4 ... 97 · 98 · 99 · 100. This expression could be
written in a simpler manner as ___.

100!

861 Notice that $_7P_3$ = 7 · 6 · 5 may be written $_7P_3$ = (7 · 6 · 5)/1. Now,
the numerator would be a factorial expression if it contained the
factors 4 · 3 · 2 ·1, because 7! = _____ .

7 · 6 · 5 · 4 · 3 · 2 · 1

862 Consider again $_7P_3$ = (7 · 6 · 5)/1. In order to have the numerator
7!, we must multiply the numerator and the denominator of the
fraction by 4 · 3 · 2 · 1.
$$\therefore \quad _7P_3 = \frac{(7 \cdot 6 \cdot 5)(4 \cdot 3 \cdot 2 \cdot 1)}{4 \cdot 3 \cdot 2 \cdot 1} = \frac{7!}{4!}$$
Similarly, $_9P_4$ = (9 · 8 · 7 · 6)/1. Express this answer in factorial
notation.

$$_9P_4 = \frac{9!}{5!}$$
Solution:　$_9P_4 = \frac{(9 \cdot 8 \cdot 7 \cdot 6)(5 \cdot 4 \cdot 3 \cdot 2 \cdot 1)}{5 \cdot 4 \cdot 3 \cdot 2 \cdot 1} = \frac{9!}{5!}$

863 If we wish to find 6!, we can do it in this manner:
6! = 6 · 5 · 4 · 3 · 2 · 1 = 720
Or we may use a shorter and simpler way. Here again 6! =
6 · (5 · 4 · 3 · 2 · 1) = 720

▼

The part in parentheses is 5!, which in frame 855 you found to be 120; so 6! = 6 · 5! = 6 · 120 = 720. Use 6! = 720 to find 7!

$7! = 7 \cdot 6! = 7 \cdot 720 = 5,040$

---

comment

The formula for $_nP_k$ is sometimes written in factorial notation.

Since $_nP_k = \dfrac{n \cdot (n-1)(n-2) \ldots (n-k+1)}{1}$

multiply numerator and denominator by
$(n-k)(n-k-1)(n-k-2) \ldots 3 \cdot 2 \cdot 1$ and we get

$_nP_k = \dfrac{n \cdot (n-1)(n-2) \ldots (n-k+1)(n-k) \ldots 3 \cdot 2 \cdot 1}{(n-k)(n-k-1) \ldots 3 \cdot 2 \cdot 1}$

$\therefore \quad _nP_k = \dfrac{n!}{(n-k)!}$

---

864 Using the formula $_nP_k = n!/(n-k)!$, we find $_{10}P_4 = 10!/(10-4)!$
$= 10!/6!$
Similarly, $_{50}P_{36} =$ _____

$\dfrac{50!}{(50-36)!} = \dfrac{50!}{14!}$

●**865** (1) $_{100}P_{38} =$ ___
      (2) $_{30}P_{20} =$ ___
      (Write your answers in factorial form.)

---

(1) $\dfrac{100!}{62!}$ (2) $\dfrac{30!}{10!}$

---

866 Note, we have defined $n!$ only for positive integers n. If n is a positive integer, $n! =$ _____. For convenience, we make the following definition: 0! = 1.

$n(n-1)(n-2) \ldots 3 \cdot 2 \cdot 1$

---

867 (1) 0! = ___
      (2) 1! = ___
      (3) 2! = _____
      (4) 3! = _____

▼

204 Introduction to Probability

(5) $4! = \underline{\hspace{2cm}}$
(6) $5! = \underline{\hspace{2cm}}$

(1) 1 (by definition)
(2) 1
(3) $2 \cdot 1 = 2$
(4) $3 \cdot 2 \cdot 1 = 6$
(5) $4 \cdot 3 \cdot 2 \cdot 1 = 24$
(6) $5 \cdot 4 \cdot 3 \cdot 2 \cdot 1 = 120$

868 $_7P_7 = 7 \cdot 6 \cdot 5 \cdot 4 \cdot 3 \cdot 2 \cdot 1 = 7!$ Suppose we use the formula
$_nP_k = \dfrac{n!}{(n-k)!}$, $\qquad _7P_7 = \underline{\hspace{2cm}}$. Remember, by definition,
$0! = 1$.

$$\frac{7!}{(7-7)!} = \frac{7!}{0!} = \frac{7!}{1} = 7!$$

869 $_5P_5 = 5 \cdot 4 \cdot 3 \cdot 2 \cdot 1 = 5!$ Use $_nP_k = \dfrac{n!}{(n-k)!}$ to find $_5P_5$.

$$_5P_5 = \frac{5!}{(5-5)!} = \frac{5!}{0!} = \frac{5!}{1} = 5!$$

870 Using the formula $_nP_k = \dfrac{n!}{(n-k)!}$, find $_nP_0$.

$$_nP_0 = \frac{n!}{(n-0)!} = \frac{n!}{n!} = 1$$

871 How many permutations of two elements can be formed by taking
elements from the set $\{a, b, c, d\}$?

12   *Solution:* $_4P_2 = 4 \cdot 3$ or $\dfrac{4!}{(4-2)!} = \dfrac{4!}{2!} = \dfrac{4 \cdot 3 \cdot 2 \cdot 1}{2 \cdot 1} = 4 \cdot 3 = 12$

●872 How many permutations of five elements can be formed from the
set $\{a, b, c, d, e, f, g\}$?
(Write your answer in factorial form.)

$$_7P_5 = \frac{7!}{2!}$$

873 In how many different ways can 10 people be arranged in a row?
(Write your answer in factorial form.)

$$_{10}P_{10} = 10 \cdot 9 \cdot 8 \cdot 7 \cdot 6 \cdot 5 \cdot 4 \cdot 3 \cdot 2 \cdot 1 = 10!$$
$$\text{or} \quad _{10}P_{10} = \frac{10!}{(10-10)!} = \frac{10!}{0!} = \frac{10!}{1} = 10!$$

874 (1) How many permutations of three elements can be formed from the set $\{a,\ b,\ c\}$?

(2) Verify your answer by listing them.

(1) $_3P_3 = 3 \cdot 2 \cdot 1 = 6$ or 3!

(2) abc bac cab
acb bca cba

875 From a set of six people, two people are to be chosen at random to form a committee, the first person chosen to be chairman and the second person to be an ordinary member. Note then, if a and b are two of the six, the committee ab and the committee ba are different. In the first case a is the chairman, and in the second case b is the chairman. How many different committees can be formed?

(Write your answer in factorial form.)

$$_6P_2 = 6 \cdot 5 = 30 \quad \text{or} \quad _6P_2 = \frac{6!}{(6-2)!} = \frac{6!}{4!}$$

3. Combinations

876 The permutations $abc,\ acb,\ bac,\ bca,\ cab,$ and cba are different since for a permutation order is important. There are times, however, when the order in which K elements is presented is not important. For example, if from six people, two are to be chosen at random to form a committee and the two chosen have equal status, the committee ab and the committee ba are the same. List all such different committees which can be chosen if $a,\ b,\ c,\ d,\ e,\ f$ are the six people.

ab ac ad ae af
bc bd be bf
cd ce cf
de df
ef

Note that, for example, ac and ca are the same and should not be listed twice. You may, of course, have any of these listed in the reverse order rather than as they are listed here.

877 A set of K elements listed in a straight line *without regard to order* is called a *combination of K elements*. Two combinations are same if they contain the same elements. Thus,

▼

abd   bad   dba
adb   bda   dab
are just six different ways of indicating a *single combination* of the
three elements *a*, *b*, and *d*. Note that the six sets represent _____
(how many) permutations.

six

●878 (1)   A set of *K* elements listed in a straight line in a specific order
       is a _____ of *K* elements.
   (2)   A set of *K* elements listed in a straight line without regard to
       order is a _____ of *K* elements.

(1) permutation   (2) combination

●879 (1)   List the different *combinations* of three elements which can be
formed from the set {*a*, *b*, *c*, *d*}. (2) List the different
permutations of three elements which can be formed from the set
{*a*, *b*, *c*, *d*}.

(1) *abc, abd, acd, bcd*   (Note: You could have any of these
     listed in a different order, but only four combinations.)
(2) *abc   abd   acd   bcd*
     acb   adb   adc   bdc
     bac   bad   cad   cbd
     bca   bda   cda   cdb
     cab   dab   dac   dbc
     cba   dba   dca   dcb
(Note that each one of the combinations turns into six permutations.)

880 List the different *combinations* of three elements which can be
formed from the set {*a*, *b*, *c*, *d*, *e*}.

abc   abd   abe
acd   ace   ade
bcd   bce   bde
cde   Notice that there are 10 combinations.

881 The symbol $\binom{n}{k}$ with $n \geq k$ represents the number of combinations of
k elements which can be formed from a set of *n* elements. (We use
the more widely accepted $\binom{n}{k}$ in place of $_nC_k$ with which you may be
familiar.) The symbol $\binom{6}{3}$ represents the number of combinations
of (1) _____ elements which can be formed from a set of
(2) _____ elements.

(1) three   (2) six

882 The symbol ___ represents the number of combinations of three elements which can be formed from a set of six elements.

$\binom{6}{3}$

883 The number of combinations of three elements which can be formed from the set $\{a, b, c, d, e, f\}$ would be indicated by $\binom{6}{3}$. Find $\binom{6}{3}$ by listing them.

abc	*abd*	*abe*	*abf*	*acd*
ace	*acf*	*ade*	*adf*	*aef*
bcd	*bce*	*bcf*	*bde*	*bdf*
bef	*cde*	*cdf*	*cef*	*def*

$\therefore \binom{6}{3}=20$

884 We would like to find a formula for $\binom{n}{k}$ where $n \geq k$. A clue to finding such a formula is in the following: Look at the combinations of two elements which can be formed from the four elements $\{a, b, c, d\}$: *ab, ac, ad, bc, bd, cd.* Each one of these six combinations becomes two permutations when the order is rearranged. This gives us the 12 permutations *ab, ba, ac, ca,* ___, ___, ___, ___, ___, ___, ___, ___.

ad, da, bc, cb, bd, db, cd, dc

885 Similarly, consider the combinations of three elements which can be formed from the elements $\{a, b, c, d\}$: *abc, abd, acd, bcd.* If we are now to form permutations of three elements from $\{a, b, c, d\}$, we need only take each combination and write all permutations of those three elements. Thus, from the one combination *abc*, we get the six permutations *abc, acb, bac, bca, cab, cba.* Thus, each one of the four combinations becomes the basis for six permutations. $4 \cdot 6 = 24$ and $_4P_3 =$ _____.

$4 \cdot 3 \cdot 2 = 24$

•886 For example, suppose we were to form combinations of three elements from the set $\{1, 2, 3, 4, 5\}$. One of the combinations would be made up of 1, 3, and 4 in some order. From this combination of three elements, how many permutations of three elements can be formed?

3! or 6

887 So, given any combination of k elements, say $a_1 a_2 \ldots a_k$, we can form $_k P_k$ permutations from this one combination. But $_k P_k = $ _____ .

$k!$ or $k(k-1) \ldots 3 \cdot 2 \cdot 1$

888 Again, the number of permutations $_4 P_3$ which can be formed from $\{a, b, c, d\}$ could be computed by considering the following:
1. The number of combinations you can form is four:
    $abc, \ abd, \ acd, \ bcd.$
2. With *each* of the four combinations you can form 3! permutations.
3. The total permutations $_4 P_3$ you can form, then can be expressed
    $_4 P_3 = 4 \cdot 3!$

Suppose instead of four combinations in the above problem, you have $\binom{n}{k}$ combinations. Instead of three elements to a combination, you have k elements. Then $_n P_k = $ _____ $\cdot$ _____ .
(Copy $_n P_k = $ when you answer.)

$_n P_k = \binom{n}{k} \cdot \ k!$ or $_n P_k = k! \cdot \binom{n}{k}$

889 $k! \cdot \binom{n}{k} = $ ___

$_n P_k$

890 We have $(k!)\binom{n}{k} = \ _n P_k$. For example, given the set
$\{a, b, c, d, e, f\}$, consider one combination of three elements, say the combination made up of b, c, and f in some order.
$_3 P_3 = 3! = 6$; so b, c, and f will produce 3! permutations. If we do this for each of the combinations, we will get all the permutations. Therefore, $3! \binom{6}{3} = \ _6 P_3$. We solve for $\binom{6}{3}$ in this way: $3! \binom{6}{3} = \frac{6!}{3!}$
$\binom{6}{3} = \frac{6!}{3! \cdot 3!} = \frac{6 \cdot 5 \cdot 4 \cdot 3 \cdot 2 \cdot 1}{3 \cdot 2 \cdot 1 \cdot 3 \cdot 2 \cdot 1} = 20 \quad \therefore \binom{6}{3} = 20$
So, if $k! \binom{n}{k} = \ _n P_k$, find $\binom{n}{k}$.

$\binom{n}{k} = \frac{_n P_k}{k!}$ or $\binom{n}{k} = \ _n P_k \cdot \frac{1}{k!}$

891 If $k! \binom{n}{k} = \ _n P_k$, then $\binom{n}{k} = \frac{_n P_k}{k!}$. For example,
$\binom{5}{2} = \frac{_5 P_2}{2!} = \frac{5 \cdot 4}{1 \cdot 2} = 10.$ Find $\binom{8}{3}$.

$\binom{8}{3} = \frac{_8 P_3}{3!} = \frac{8 \cdot 7 \cdot 6}{1 \cdot 2 \cdot 3} = 56$

●**892** How many different ways can 13 cards be dealt at random from a deck of cards? *Note:* The order in which the 13 cards appear is not important; so we are dealing with combinations. (Do not do the arithmetic.)

$$\binom{52}{13} = \frac{52 \cdot 51 \cdot 50 \cdot 49 \cdot 48 \cdot 47 \cdot 46 \cdot 45 \cdot 44 \cdot 43 \cdot 42 \cdot 41 \cdot 40}{13!}$$

893 If you are going to do the arithmetic without any aids to computations, formula I: $\binom{n}{k} = \frac{nP_k}{k!}$ is probably the simpler to use. But, if you have tables of factorials, or techniques of approximating factorials, or if you are doing theoretical work in which the factorials present a more compact solution, then formula II: $\binom{n}{k} = \frac{n!}{k!\,(n-k)!}$ is better.
Use formula II to find $\binom{100}{70}$. (Do not do the arithmetic.)

$$\binom{100}{70} = \frac{100!}{70!\,(100-70)!} = \frac{100!}{70!\,30!}$$

894 You should be familiar with both expressions $\binom{n}{k} = \frac{nP_k}{k!}$ and $\binom{n}{k} = \frac{n!}{k!\,(n-k)!}$ and realize that they are equivalent, since $_nP_k = \frac{n!}{(n-k)!}$
Note: $\binom{8}{2} = \frac{8 \cdot 7}{1 \cdot 2} = 28$ or $\binom{8}{2} = \frac{8!}{2!\,6!} = 28$. Find $\binom{10}{5}$ both ways.

$$\binom{10}{5} = \frac{10 \cdot 9 \cdot 8 \cdot 7 \cdot 6}{1 \cdot 2 \cdot 3 \cdot 4 \cdot 5} = 252 \qquad \binom{10}{5} = \frac{10!}{5!\,5!} = 252$$

895 $\binom{5}{0} = \frac{5!}{0!\,5!}$, but, by definition $0! = 1$. $\therefore$ $\binom{5}{0} = $ ___

1

896 $\binom{n}{0} = \frac{n!}{0!\,n!} = $ ___

1

897 Now, let us reap the rewards of our diversion into some of the counting procedures. Recall that we were concerned with a problem such as the following example. (Copy the following.)
We have an experiment which can result only in success S or fail-

▼

failure F. The probability of S on any given trial of the experiment is p. Then the probability of F on any single trial is ___ .

$1-p$
Have a copy of the description.

---

898 Now, suppose 10 independent trials of this experiment are performed and we wish to find the probability that exactly three successes (S's) occur. We found that we were interested only in those elements of the sample space which contain three S's and seven F's, for example, such points as $SFFFSFFFSF$. The notation indicates the result, in order, of the 10 trials. For this particular element, since the trials are independent, the probability is the product of the probabilities involved; so
$P(SFFFSFFFSF) = p(1-p)(1-p)(1-p)p(1-p)(1-p)(1-p)p(1-p)$
$\qquad\qquad\qquad = p^3(1-p)^7$
In fact, every one of the elements containing three S's and seven F's has a probability of _____ .

$p^3(1-p)^7$

---

899 So, if there are k such elements, then $P(3;\ 10,\ p) = k\,(p)^3(1-p)^7$ where $P(3;\ 10,\ p)$ means _____ .

---

the probability of exactly three successes in 10 independent trials of an experiment for which the probability of success on any given trial is p

---

900 Now, our question is, how many elements of the sample space can we find that contain exactly three S's and seven F's. We could start listing $SSSFFFFFFF$, $SSFSFFFFFF$, etc. , but the reason we decided to find some techniques was that listing was too difficult. We now have the technique necessary. *Note:* We have 10 positions
$\underline{1}\quad \underline{2}\quad \underline{3}\quad \underline{4}\quad \underline{5}\quad \underline{6}\quad \underline{7}\quad \underline{8}\quad \underline{9}\quad \underline{10}$ to fill with three S's
and seven F's. Once the S's have been placed, the F's are fixed. Thus, if we decide to fill blanks number 3, 4, and 7 with S's, there is only one result, namely, _____ .

FFSSFFSFFF

---

901 The 10 positions $\underline{1}\quad \underline{2}\quad \underline{3}\quad \underline{4}\quad \underline{5}\quad \underline{6}\quad \underline{7}\quad \underline{8}\quad \underline{9}\quad \underline{10}$ will be filled in as many ways possible by three S's and seven F's, if we simply decide on the positions in which to place the three S's. So, our problem is one of finding the number of combinations of three elements (positions) which can be formed from a set of 10 elements (positions), that is, $\binom{10}{3}$. *(Note:* We use *combinations,*

▼

not permutations, because once the three positions are filled with three S's, rearranging the three positions will produce no new elements.) Now $\binom{10}{3}$ = _____ .

$$\frac{10 \cdot 9 \cdot 8}{1 \cdot 2 \cdot 3} = 120$$

902 Now, there are 120 elements, such as *SFSFFFFSFF*, *FFFSSSFFFF*, etc., containing exactly three S's. Each element has a probability of $p^3(1-p)^7$. Therefore, $P(3; 10, p)$ = _____ .

$120p^3(1-p)^7$

903 $P(x; n, p)$ can be found in the following way: In n trials of the experiment, we want exactly x S's and $(n-x)$ F's. Thus, each element of the sample space containing exactly x S's and $(n-x)$ F's will have a probability of $p^x(1-p)^{n-x}$ *and* there are $\binom{n}{x}$ of these elements.

Thus, $P(x; n, p) = \binom{n}{x}(p)^x(1-p)^{(n-x)}$

For example,

$P\left(4; 10, \frac{1}{3}\right) = \binom{10}{4}\left(\frac{1}{3}\right)^4\left(1 - \frac{1}{3}\right)^6 = \frac{10 \cdot 9 \cdot 8 \cdot 7}{1 \cdot 2 \cdot 3 \cdot 4}\left(\frac{1}{3}\right)^4\left(\frac{2}{3}\right)^6 = 210\left(\frac{1}{3}\right)^4\left(\frac{2}{3}\right)^6$

(Ordinarily, we will not do all the arithmetic.)

Find $P(2; 12, 0.8)$.

$$P(2; 12, 0.8) = \binom{12}{2}(0.8)^2(0.2)^{10}$$

$$= \frac{12 \cdot 11}{1 \cdot 2}(0.8)^2(0.2)^{10}$$

$$= 66(0.8)^2(0.2)^{10}$$

904 Although you will find that you save time and effort if you know the various formulas, the more important thing is to know how and when to use them. Some important formulas are listed on Panel 2, in case you forget them. You may use Panel 2 whenever you wish.

Find $P\left(8; 10, \frac{1}{2}\right)$ (Do not do the arithmetic.)

$$P\left(8; 10, \frac{1}{2}\right) = \binom{10}{8}\left(\frac{1}{2}\right)^8\left(\frac{1}{2}\right)^2$$

$$= \frac{10!}{8!(10-8)!}\left(\frac{1}{2}\right)^{10} \text{ or } = \frac{10 \cdot 9}{2 \cdot 1}\left(\frac{1}{2}\right)^{10}$$

$$= \frac{10!}{8!2!}\left(\frac{1}{2}\right)^{10} \qquad = 45\left(\frac{1}{2}\right)^{10}$$

905 It is important to know when to use the formula $P(x; n, p)$. We use it when we want to find the (1) _____ of exactly (2) ___ successes in (3) ___ independent trials of an experiment which, on any given trial, can result in only either S or F and for which the probability of success on any single trial is (4)_____.

(1) probability   (2) x (3) n (4) p

906 For example, suppose a multiple-choice question has four possible answers, only one of which is correct. Then, if a person were to guess, the probability of getting the correct one is obviously $\frac{1}{4}$. So we have an experiment where p is $\frac{1}{4}$ (if we consider a correct answer as a success). Now, if 10 such questions are answered by guessing, we have 10 independent trials of the experiment. The probability that exactly three of these answers are correct is given by $P($_____$)$.
[Copy $P($ $)$ when you answer.]

$$P\left(3;\, 10,\, \frac{1}{4}\right)$$

907 Continuing from frame 906, find $P\left(3;\, 10,\, \frac{1}{4}\right)$.

Using $P(x; n, p) = \binom{n}{x}(p)^{x}(1-p)^{n-x}$, we have:

$$P\left(3;\, 10,\, \frac{1}{4}\right) = \binom{10}{3}\left(\frac{1}{4}\right)^{3}\left(\frac{3}{4}\right)^{7} \quad \text{or} \quad \frac{10!}{3!\,7!}\left(\frac{1}{4}\right)^{3}\left(\frac{3}{4}\right)^{7}$$

$$= \frac{10 \cdot 9 \cdot 8}{1 \cdot 2 \cdot 3}\left(\frac{1}{4}\right)^{3}\left(\frac{3}{4}\right)^{7}$$

$$= \frac{120(3)^{7}}{4^{10}}$$

908 If 100 coins are tossed, find the probability that exactly 50 are heads. Here we have 100 trials of the experiment (tossing a single coin); so (1) $n =$ ___. We want the probability of exactly 50 successes (a head) so (2) $x =$ ___ . The probability of success on a single toss of a coin is $\frac{1}{2}$; so (3) $p =$ ___ . Therefore, we want to find (4) $P($_____$)$.
[Copy $P($_____$)$ when you answer.]

(1) 100   (2) 50   (3) $\frac{1}{2}$ (4) $P\left(50;\, 100,\, \frac{1}{2}\right)$

909 Find $P\left(50;\ 100,\ \frac{1}{2}\right)$. (Do not do the arithmetic.)

$$P(x;\ n,\ p) = \binom{n}{x}(p)^x(1-p)^{n-x}$$
$$P\left(50;\ 100,\ \frac{1}{2}\right) = \binom{100}{50}\left(\frac{1}{2}\right)^{50}\left(\frac{1}{2}\right)^{50}$$
$$= \frac{100!}{50!\,50!}\left(\frac{1}{2}\right)^{100}$$

●**910** The mortality rate of disease x is 0.3. If we observe 20 persons having disease x, we want to find the probability that exactly 15 recover. (We shall consider recovery a success.)
(1) $n =$ ___
(2) $x =$ ___
(3) $p =$ ___
(4) $P($ _____)   [Copy $P($ _____) when you answer.]

(1) 20   (2) 15   (3) 0.7   (4) $P(15;\ 20,\ 0.7)$

●**911** Continuing the experiment from frame 910, find $P(15;\ 20,\ 0.7)$.

$$P(15;\ 20,\ 0.7) = \binom{20}{15}(0.7)^{15}(0.3)^5 = \frac{20!}{15!\,5!}(0.7)^{15}(0.3)^5$$

912 The probability that a single seed of a certain type will germinate is 0.9. Of 10 such seeds, what is the probability that all 10 will germinate? *Hint:* $x^0 = 1$ for $x \neq 0$.

$$P(10;\ 10,\ 0.9) = \binom{10}{10}(0.9)^{10}(0.1)^0 = \frac{10!}{10!\,0!}(0.9)^{10}(1) = (0.9)^{10}$$

913 The Nadir Manufacturing Company, which makes widgets, claims that only 1 per cent of their products are defective. That is, if a single widget is chosen, the probability that it is defective is 0.01. If three widgets are chosen at random (assuming the results are independent), find the probability that (1) all are good, (2) exactly two are good, (3) exactly one is good, (4) exactly zero are good.

If we consider a good widget to be a success, we have $p = 0.99$.
Then:
(1) $P(3;\ 3,\ 0.99) = \binom{3}{3}(0.99)^3 = (0.99)^3$
(2) $P(2;\ 3,\ 0.99) = \binom{3}{2}(0.99)^2(0.01) = 3(0.99)^2(0.01)$
(3) $P(1;\ 3,\ 0.99) = \binom{3}{1}(0.99)(0.01)^2 = 3(0.99)(0.01)^2$
(4) $P(0;\ 3,\ 0.99) = \binom{3}{0}(0.01)^3 = (0.01)^3$

914 If five coins are tossed, find the probability that at least three are heads. (At least three means exactly three *or* exactly four *or* exactly five heads out of the five trials and, since these are mutually exclusive events, the probability of one of them occurring is the sum of their probabilities.)

$\dfrac{1}{2}$

Solution: $P\left(3;\ 5,\ \dfrac{1}{2}\right) + P\left(4;\ 5,\ \dfrac{1}{2}\right) + P\left(5;\ 5,\ \dfrac{1}{2}\right)$

$= \dbinom{5}{3}\left(\dfrac{1}{2}\right)^{3}\left(\dfrac{1}{2}\right)^{2} + \dbinom{5}{4}\left(\dfrac{1}{2}\right)^{4}\left(\dfrac{1}{2}\right) + \dbinom{5}{5}\left(\dfrac{1}{2}\right)^{5}$

$= \dfrac{5}{1}\dfrac{4}{2}\dfrac{3}{3}\left(\dfrac{1}{2}\right)^{5} + \dfrac{5}{1}\dfrac{4}{2}\dfrac{3}{3}\dfrac{2}{4}\left(\dfrac{1}{2}\right)^{5} + \left(\dfrac{1}{2}\right)^{5}$

$= 10\left(\dfrac{1}{2}\right)^{5} + 5\left(\dfrac{1}{2}\right)^{5} + \left(\dfrac{1}{2}\right)^{5}$

$= 16\left(\dfrac{1}{2}\right)^{5} = \dfrac{1}{2}$

●915 The probability that type X rocket will function properly is 0.6. If 10 such rockets are fired, find the probability that *at least* seven of them will function properly. (Do not do the arithmetic.)

$P(7;\ 10,\ 0.6) + P(8;\ 10,\ 0.6) + P(9;\ 10,\ 0.6) + P(10;\ 10,\ 0.6)$

$= \dbinom{10}{7}(0.6)^{7}(0.4)^{3} + \dbinom{10}{8}(0.6)^{8}(0.4)^{2} + \dbinom{10}{9}(0.6)^{9}(0.4) + \dbinom{10}{10}(0.6)^{10}$

$= 120(0.6)^{7}(0.4)^{3} + 45(0.6)^{8}(0.4)^{2} + 10(0.6)^{9}(0.4) + (0.6)^{10}$

916 Given an experiment having probability of success of $\dfrac{1}{3}$, if three independent trials of the experiment are performed, find

(1) $P\left(0;\ 3,\ \dfrac{1}{3}\right)$, (2) $P\left(1;\ 3,\ \dfrac{1}{3}\right)$, (3) $P\left(2;\ 3,\ \dfrac{1}{3}\right)$, (4) $P\left(3;\ 3,\ \dfrac{1}{3}\right)$.

(1) $P\left(0;\ 3,\ \dfrac{1}{3}\right) = \dbinom{3}{0}\left(\dfrac{1}{3}\right)^{0}\left(\dfrac{2}{3}\right)^{3} = \left(\dfrac{2}{3}\right)^{3} = \dfrac{8}{27}$

(2) $P\left(1;\ 3,\ \dfrac{1}{3}\right) = \dbinom{3}{1}\left(\dfrac{1}{3}\right)^{1}\left(\dfrac{2}{3}\right)^{2} = 3\left(\dfrac{1}{3}\right)\left(\dfrac{2}{3}\right)^{2} = \dfrac{4}{9}$

(3) $P\left(2;\ 3,\ \dfrac{1}{3}\right) = \dbinom{3}{2}\left(\dfrac{1}{3}\right)^{2}\left(\dfrac{2}{3}\right) + 3\left(\dfrac{1}{3}\right)^{2}\left(\dfrac{2}{3}\right) = \dfrac{2}{9}$

(4) $P\left(3;\ 3,\ \dfrac{1}{3}\right) = \dbinom{3}{3}\left(\dfrac{1}{3}\right)^{3}\left(\dfrac{2}{3}\right)^{0} = 1\left(\dfrac{1}{3}\right)^{3} = \dfrac{1}{27}$

comment

Given an experiment having the probability of success of p, if independent trials of the experiment are performed, we have found a technique for finding $P(x;\ n,\ p)$. For example, in the problem

you just completed in frame 916, $n = 3$ and $p = \frac{1}{3}$ and x assumes
the values of 0, 1, 2, and 3, with the following results:

$$P\left(0; 3, \frac{1}{3}\right) = \binom{3}{0}\left(\frac{1}{3}\right)^0 \left(\frac{2}{3}\right)^3$$

$$P\left(1; 3, \frac{1}{3}\right) = \binom{3}{1}\left(\frac{1}{3}\right)^1 \left(\frac{2}{3}\right)^2$$

$$P\left(2; 3, \frac{1}{3}\right) = \binom{3}{2}\left(\frac{1}{3}\right)^2 \left(\frac{2}{3}\right)^1$$

$$P\left(3; 3, \frac{1}{3}\right) = \binom{3}{3}\left(\frac{1}{3}\right)^3 \left(\frac{2}{3}\right)^0$$

These probabilities form what is called a binomial distribution.
In fact, any set of probabilities which result from $P(x; n, p)$, when
n and p are fixed and x varies from zero to n, is called a binomial
distribution. The binomial distribution, as it is related to probability, is considered next.

---

917 You know from your study of algebra, or by actually multiplying,
that the binomial $(a + b)^4$ is expanded this way:
$(a + b)^4 = a^4 + 4a^3b + 6a^2b^2 + 4ab^3 + b^4$

(1) The coefficient of a^4, above, is 1. Find $\binom{4}{0}$.

(2) The coefficient of a^3b, above, is 4. Find $\binom{4}{1}$.

(3) The coefficient of a^2b^2, above, is _____ . Find $\binom{4}{2}$.

(4) Which of the following combinations is equal to the coefficient
of ab^3:
$$\binom{4}{3}; \binom{4}{4}; \binom{4}{2}$$
Show why you made your choice for this question.

(1) $\binom{4}{0} = 1$ (2) $\binom{4}{1} = 4$ (3) 6; $\binom{4}{2} = 6$

(4) $\binom{4}{3}$, because $\binom{4}{3} = \frac{4 \cdot 3 \cdot 2}{3 \cdot 2 \cdot 1} = 4$

918 $(a + b)^4 = a^4 + 4a^3b + 6a^2b^2 + 4ab^3 + b^4$

$$\binom{4}{0}a^4 + \binom{4}{1}a^3b + \binom{4}{2}a^2b^2 + \underline{\ \ } ab^3 + \underline{\ \ } b^4$$

Write the missing coefficients as combinations by following the
pattern already started.

$\binom{4}{3}$, $\binom{4}{4}$

919 The point being made here is this:
$$(a + b)^4 = a^4 + 4a^3b + 6a^2b^2 + 4ab^3 + b^4$$
can be written with the coefficients as combinations which form a pattern:
$$(a + b)^4 = a^4 + 4a^3b + 6a^2b^2 + 4ab^3 \quad b^4$$
$$(a + b)^4 = \binom{4}{0}a^4 + \binom{4}{1}a^3b + \binom{4}{2}a^2b^2 + \binom{4}{3}ab^3 + \binom{4}{4}b^4$$
[It can be proved that these results can be extended for all positive integral values of n in the binomial $(a + b)^n$.]

Likewise the binomial $(a + b)^5$ could be written with combinations for coefficients of each term:
$$(a + b)^5 = \binom{5}{0}a^5 + \binom{5}{1}a^4b + \binom{5}{2}a^3b^2 + \_\_\_\_\_ + \_\_\_\_\_ + \_\_\_\_\_$$
Complete the pattern by writing the last three terms of the binomial expansion so that the coefficients are combinations.

$$\binom{5}{3}a^2b^3 + \binom{5}{4}ab^4 + \binom{5}{5}b^5$$

920 You saw in frame 919 that
$$(a + b)^5 = \binom{5}{0}a^5 + \binom{5}{1}a^4b + \binom{5}{2}a^3b^2 + \binom{5}{3}a^2b^3 + \binom{5}{4}ab^4 + \binom{5}{5}b^5$$
Expand the binomial $(a + b)^3$ by using the same pattern suggested by the above expansion of $(a + b)^5$; that is, expand $(a + b)^3$ by writing the coefficients of each term as combinations.

$$(a + b)^3 = \binom{3}{0}a^3 + \binom{3}{1}a^2b + \binom{3}{2}ab^2 + \binom{3}{3}b^3$$

●921 Expand $(a + b)^6$ by writing the coefficient of each term as a combination in the same pattern as was used in frames 916 to 920.

$$(a + b)^6 = \binom{6}{0}a^6 + \binom{6}{1}a^5b + \binom{6}{2}a^4b^2 + \binom{6}{3}a^3b^3 + \binom{6}{4}a^2b^4 + \binom{6}{5}ab^5 + \binom{6}{6}b^6$$

922 You know that $(a + b)^3$ can be expanded thus:
$$(a + b)^3 = \binom{3}{0}a^3 + \binom{3}{1}a^2b + \binom{3}{2}ab^2 + \binom{3}{3}b^3$$
Find the coefficient of each term in the binomial expansion by computing each combination.

$$\binom{3}{0} = 1; \; \binom{3}{1} = 3; \; \binom{3}{2} = 3; \; \binom{3}{3} = 1$$

923 You can expand $(a + b)^3$ by following three steps:
1. Write the expression with each coefficient as a combination:
$$(a + b)^3 = \binom{3}{0}a^3 + \binom{3}{1}a^2b + \binom{3}{2}ab^2 + \binom{3}{3}b^3$$

▼

2. Find the value of each combination:
$$\binom{3}{0} = 1; \quad \binom{3}{1} = 3; \quad \binom{3}{2} = 3; \quad \binom{3}{3} = 1$$

3. Rewrite the expansion by substituting the value of each combination:
$$(a + b)^3 = a^3 + 3a^2b + 3ab^2 + b^3$$
Expand $(a + b)^5$ by writing three steps similar to those above.

1. $(a + b)^5 = \binom{5}{0}a^5 + \binom{5}{1}a^4b + \binom{5}{2}a^3b^2 + \binom{5}{3}a^2b^3 + \binom{5}{4}ab^4 + \binom{5}{5}b^5$

2. $\binom{5}{0} = 1; \quad \binom{5}{1} = 5; \quad \binom{5}{2} = 10; \quad \binom{5}{3} = 10; \quad \binom{5}{4} = 5; \quad \binom{5}{5} = 1$

3. $(a + b)^5 = a^5 + 5a^4b + 10a^3b^2 + 10a^2b^3 + 5ab^4 + b^5$

●**924** Expand $(a + b)^4$. (Show how you can find the value of the coefficients of each term by using combinations.)

$(a + b)^4 = \binom{4}{0}a^4 + \binom{4}{1}a^3b + \binom{4}{2}a^2b^2 + \binom{4}{3}ab^3 + \binom{4}{4}b^4$

$\binom{4}{0} = 1; \quad \binom{4}{1} = 4; \quad \binom{4}{2} = 6; \quad \binom{4}{3} = 4; \quad \binom{4}{4} = 1$

$(a + b)^4 = a^4 + 4a^3b + 6a^2b^2 + 4ab^3 + b^4$

925 You know:
$$(a + b)^3 = \binom{3}{0}a^3 + \binom{3}{1}a^2b + \binom{3}{2}ab^2 + \binom{3}{3}b^3$$
Consider the expansion:
$$\binom{5}{0}a^5 + \binom{5}{1}a^4b + \binom{5}{2}a^3b^2 + \binom{5}{3}a^2b^3 + \binom{5}{4}ab^4 + \binom{5}{5}b^5$$
Of which of the following binomials is the above an expansion:
$(a + b)^2; \ (a + b)^3; \ (a + b)^4; \ (a + b)^5; \ (a + b)^6$

$(a + b)^5$

●**926** Of what binomial is the following an expansion:
$$\binom{7}{0}a^7 + \binom{7}{1}a^6b + \binom{7}{2}a^5b^2 + \binom{7}{3}a^4b^3 + \binom{7}{4}a^3b^4 + \binom{7}{5}a^2b^5 + \binom{7}{6}ab^6 \ \binom{7}{7}b^7$$

$(a + b)^7$

927 Consider the expansion:
$$(a + b)^4 = \binom{4}{0}a^4 + \binom{4}{1}a^3b + \binom{4}{2}a^2b^2 + \binom{4}{3}ab^3 + \binom{4}{4}b^4$$
Let $a = 1 - p$ and $b = p$. The expansion could then be written:

▼

$$[(1-p) + p]^4 = \binom{4}{0}(1-p)^4 + \binom{4}{1}(1-p)^3p + \binom{4}{2}(1-p)^2p^2 + \underline{\hspace{1cm}} + \underline{\hspace{1cm}}$$

(Complete the expansion by continuing the pattern.)

$$\binom{4}{3}(1-p)\,p^3, \qquad \binom{4}{4}p^4$$

928 Expand $[(1-p) + p]^3$ as in frame 927 by writing each coefficient as a combination.

$$[(1-p) + p]^3 = \binom{3}{0}(1-p)^3 + \binom{3}{1}(1-p)^2p + \binom{3}{2}(1-p)p^2 + \binom{3}{3}p^3$$

929 Consider this expansion:

$$[(1-p) + p]^4 = \binom{4}{0}(1-p)^4 + \binom{4}{1}(1-p)^3p + \binom{4}{2}(1-p)^2p^2 + \binom{4}{3}(1-p)p^3 + \binom{4}{4}p^4$$

Note the following:

$$P(0; 4, p) = \binom{4}{0}(1-p)^4$$

$$P(1; 4, p) = \binom{4}{1}(1-p)^3p$$

$$P(2; 4, p) = \binom{4}{2}(1-p)^2p^2$$

$$P(3; 4, p) = \underline{\hspace{1.5cm}}$$

$$P(4; 4, p) = \underline{\hspace{1.5cm}}$$

$$\binom{4}{3}(1-p)p^3, \qquad \binom{4}{4}p^4$$

930 In the expansion:

$$[(1-p) + p]^3 = \underbrace{\binom{3}{0}(1-p)^3}_{\substack{\text{first} \\ \text{term}}} + \underbrace{\binom{3}{1}(1-p)^2p}_{\substack{\text{second} \\ \text{term}}} + \underbrace{\binom{3}{2}(1-p)p^2}_{\substack{\text{third} \\ \text{term}}} + \underbrace{\binom{3}{3}p^3}_{\substack{\text{fourth} \\ \text{term}}}$$

The first term = $P(0; 3, p)$
The second term = $P(1; 3, p)$
The third term = $\underline{\hspace{1.5cm}}$
The fourth term = $\underline{\hspace{1.5cm}}$

$$P(2; 3, p), \qquad P(3; 3, p)$$

931 You know:

$$[(1-p) + p]^3 = \binom{3}{0}(1-p)^3 + \binom{3}{1}(1-p)^2p + \binom{3}{2}(1-p)p^2 + \binom{3}{3}p^3$$

Write the power that $[(1-p) + p]$ should be raised to in the following

▼

expansion:

$$[(1-p) + p]^{—} = \binom{2}{0}(1-p)^2 + \binom{2}{1}(1-p)p + \binom{2}{2}p^2$$

2

---

932 Consider again:

$$[(1-p) + p]^3 = \binom{3}{0}(1-p)^3 + \binom{3}{1}(1-p)^2 p + \binom{3}{2}(1-p)p^2 + \binom{3}{3}p^3$$

first term   second term   third term   fourth term

The third term is the probability of two successes and one failure in three independent trials, each of which has a probability of success equal to p. The second term is the probability of **(1)** _____ success(es) and **(2)** _____ failure(s) in **(3)** _____ independent trials, each of which has a probability of success equal to **(4)** ___ and a probability of failure equal to **(5)** _____ .

---

(1) one   **(2)** two   **(3)** three   **(4)** p **(5)** $1-p$

---

933 If the expression $[(1-p) + p]^4$ were expanded, each term would give the probability of x successes in four independent trials of an experiment in which either success or failure will occur with each trial, but if the expression $[(1-p) + p]^{10}$ were expanded, each term would give the probability of x successes in ___ independent trials of an experiment in which either success or failure will occur with each trial.

10

---

934 Consider the expansion:

$$[(1-p) + p]^5 = \binom{5}{0}(1-p)^5 + \binom{5}{1}(1-p)^4 p + \binom{5}{2}(1-p)^3 p^2 + \binom{5}{3}(1-p)^2 p^3$$
$$+ \binom{5}{4}(1-p)p^4 + \binom{5}{5}p^5$$

The terms of this expansion give the probabilities for any number of successes (or failures) which can occur in five independent trials of an experiment in which either success or failure will occur with each trial. If in such an experiment,

$p = \frac{1}{4}$, then $1-p = \frac{3}{4}$ and

$$[(1-p) + p]^5 = \left(\frac{3}{4} + \frac{1}{4}\right)^5 = \binom{5}{0}\left(\frac{3}{4}\right)^5 + \binom{5}{1}\left(\frac{3}{4}\right)^4\left(\frac{1}{4}\right) + \binom{5}{2}\left(\frac{3}{4}\right)^3\left(\frac{1}{4}\right)^2$$

$$+ \underline{\qquad} + \underline{\qquad} + \underline{\qquad}$$

(Answer by completing the pattern.)

$$\binom{5}{3}\left(\frac{3}{4}\right)^2\left(\frac{1}{4}\right)^3 + \binom{5}{4}\left(\frac{3}{4}\right)\left(\frac{1}{4}\right)^4 + \binom{5}{5}\left(\frac{1}{4}\right)^5$$

935 We will continue to work with the experiment in frame 934.

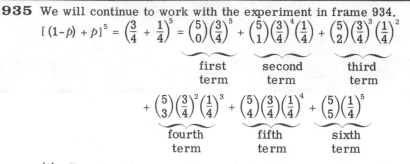

$$[(1-p) + p]^5 = \left(\frac{3}{4} + \frac{1}{4}\right)^5 = \binom{5}{0}\left(\frac{3}{4}\right)^5 + \binom{5}{1}\left(\frac{3}{4}\right)^4\left(\frac{1}{4}\right) + \binom{5}{2}\left(\frac{3}{4}\right)^3\left(\frac{1}{4}\right)^2$$

         first   second   third
         term   term   term

$$+ \binom{5}{3}\left(\frac{3}{4}\right)^2\left(\frac{1}{4}\right)^3 + \binom{5}{4}\left(\frac{3}{4}\right)\left(\frac{1}{4}\right)^4 + \binom{5}{5}\left(\frac{1}{4}\right)^5$$

    fourth   fifth   sixth
    term   term   term

(1) Consider the second term of the above expansion. The exponent of the $\frac{3}{4}$ is 4; of the $\frac{1}{4}$ it is 1. This second term is the probability of four failures and ___ success(es) in five independent trials.

(2) The exponent of the $\frac{3}{4}$ in the fifth term is ___; of the $\frac{1}{4}$ it is ___. This fifth term is the probability of exactly ___ failure(s) and ___ success(es) in five independent trials.

(3) Which term of the above expansion is the probability of exactly two failures and three successes in five independent trials?

(1) one (2) 1, 4, one, four (3) fourth

936 We will continue the experiment from frames 934 and 935.

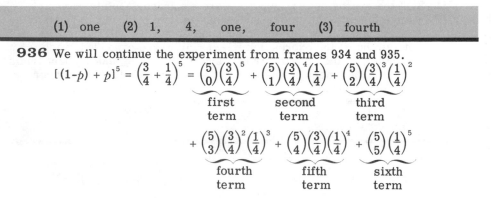

$$[(1-p) + p]^5 = \left(\frac{3}{4} + \frac{1}{4}\right)^5 = \binom{5}{0}\left(\frac{3}{4}\right)^5 + \binom{5}{1}\left(\frac{3}{4}\right)^4\left(\frac{1}{4}\right) + \binom{5}{2}\left(\frac{3}{4}\right)^3\left(\frac{1}{4}\right)^2$$

         first   second   third
         term   term   term

$$+ \binom{5}{3}\left(\frac{3}{4}\right)^2\left(\frac{1}{4}\right)^3 + \binom{5}{4}\left(\frac{3}{4}\right)\left(\frac{1}{4}\right)^4 + \binom{5}{5}\left(\frac{1}{4}\right)^5$$

    fourth   fifth   sixth
    term   term   term

The sum of the first, second, and third terms is the probability that *at least* three failures will occur. Which terms would you add to find the probability of *at least* three successes?

fourth, fifth, and sixth

937 Suppose you are given a multiple-choice quiz of five questions; each question has four possible choices for answers, only one of which is correct. We would consider the answer you write for each question as either a success or a failure, depending upon whether you write the correct answer or not. This quiz is similar to ___ independent

▼

trials of an experiment in which each trial will result in either success or failure.

five

938 If a quiz consists of five multiple-choice questions, each with four possible choices only one of which if chosen will result in success (the correct answer), (1) what is the probability for success in a given trial? (2) What is the probability of failure in a given trial?

(1) $\frac{1}{4}$ (2) $\frac{3}{4}$ (*Note:* In frames 938 to 946 and 1013, it is assumed that the probabilities are based upon guessing each answer. If the student had information on what the answer should be, the alternatives would not be equally probable.)

939 We will continue to work with the quiz with five questions with four choices for each question. The probability for success for each question is $\frac{1}{4}$; for failure it is $\frac{3}{4}$. Which of the following, if expanded, will have terms each of which is the probability of getting either zero, one, two, three, four, or five of the problems correct (successes) on the quiz?

$$\left(\frac{3}{4}+\frac{1}{4}\right)^5 ; \left(\frac{3}{4}+\frac{1}{4}\right)^4 ; \left(\frac{3}{4}+\frac{1}{4}\right)^{20} ; \left(\frac{4}{5}+\frac{1}{5}\right)^4$$

$$\left(\frac{3}{4}+\frac{1}{4}\right)^5$$

940 Then, if you were given a multiple-choice quiz of five questions with four different choices for each question and you wanted to find various probabilities of answering any number of the questions correctly (or incorrectly), a convenient method of accomplishing this is first to write the following expansion:

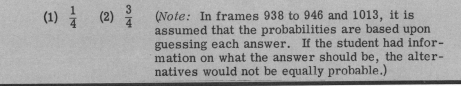

$$\left(\frac{3}{4}+\frac{1}{4}\right)^5 = \binom{5}{0}\left(\frac{3}{4}\right)^5 + \binom{5}{1}\left(\frac{3}{4}\right)^4\left(\frac{1}{4}\right) + \binom{5}{2}\left(\frac{3}{4}\right)^3\left(\frac{1}{4}\right)^2 + \binom{5}{3}\left(\frac{3}{4}\right)^2\left(\frac{1}{4}\right)^3$$
$$+ \binom{5}{4}\left(\frac{3}{4}\right)\left(\frac{1}{4}\right)^4 + \binom{5}{5}\left(\frac{1}{4}\right)^5$$

(1) The second term of the expansion is the probability of getting one question correct (success) and four questions wrong (failure). (Notice the exponents of $\frac{3}{4}$ and $\frac{1}{4}$ in this term.) Compute this probability.

▼

(2) The _____ term of the expansion is the probability of getting three questions correct and two wrong. Compute this probability.

(1) 405/1,024

Solution: $\binom{5}{1} = \frac{5}{1} = 5$

$\left(\frac{3}{4}\right)^4 = \frac{81}{256}$

$\binom{5}{1}\left(\frac{3}{4}\right)^4\left(\frac{1}{4}\right) = \frac{5}{1} \cdot \frac{81}{256} \cdot \frac{1}{4} = 405/1,024$

(2) fourth; $\frac{45}{512}$

Solution: $\binom{5}{3} = \frac{5 \cdot 4 \cdot 3}{3 \cdot 2 \cdot 1} = 10$

$\left(\frac{3}{4}\right)^2 = \frac{9}{16}$

$\left(\frac{1}{4}\right)^3 = \frac{1}{64}$

$\binom{5}{3}\left(\frac{3}{4}\right)^2\left(\frac{1}{4}\right)^3 = \frac{\overset{5}{\cancel{10}}}{1} \cdot \frac{9}{\underset{8}{\cancel{16}}} \cdot \frac{1}{64} = \frac{45}{512}$

---

941 Consider again the five question quiz with four choices for each answer and the related binomial expansion:

$$\left(\frac{3}{4} + \frac{1}{4}\right)^5 = \binom{5}{0}\left(\frac{3}{4}\right)^5 + \binom{5}{1}\left(\frac{3}{4}\right)^4\left(\frac{1}{4}\right) + \binom{5}{2}\left(\frac{3}{4}\right)^3\left(\frac{1}{4}\right)^2 + \binom{5}{3}\left(\frac{3}{4}\right)^2\left(\frac{1}{4}\right)^3$$
$$+ \binom{5}{4}\left(\frac{3}{4}\right)\left(\frac{1}{4}\right)^4 + \binom{5}{5}\left(\frac{1}{4}\right)^5$$

(1) The probability of getting at least four questions wrong is the sum of the first two terms. Compute this probability.
(2) Which terms would you add to find the probability of getting at least four questions correct? Compute this probability.

(1) $\frac{81}{128}$

Solution:

$\binom{5}{0} = 1; \quad \left(\frac{3}{4}\right)^5 = \frac{243}{1,024}; \quad \binom{5}{0}\left(\frac{3}{4}\right)^5 = 1 \cdot \frac{243}{1,024} = \frac{243}{1,024}$

$\binom{5}{1} = 5; \quad \left(\frac{3}{4}\right)^4 = \frac{81}{256}; \quad \binom{5}{1}\left(\frac{3}{4}\right)^4\left(\frac{1}{4}\right) = 5 \cdot \frac{81}{256} \cdot \frac{1}{4} = \frac{405}{1,024}$

$\binom{5}{0}\left(\frac{3}{4}\right)^5 + \binom{5}{1}\left(\frac{3}{4}\right)^4\left(\frac{1}{4}\right) = \frac{243}{1,024} + \frac{405}{1,024} = \frac{648}{1,024} = \frac{81}{128}$

(2) the fifth and sixth terms

$\binom{5}{4}\left(\frac{3}{4}\right)\left(\frac{1}{4}\right)^4 + \binom{5}{5}\left(\frac{1}{4}\right)^5 = \frac{15}{1,024} + \frac{1}{1,024} = \frac{16}{1,024} = \frac{1}{64}$

942 If you were given a multiple-choice quiz of three questions with five possible choices for each question, **(1)** What is the probability of success on each trial (question) if success means you answer the question correctly? **(2)** What is the probability of failure?

(1) $\dfrac{1}{5}$ (2) $\dfrac{4}{5}$

943 If you were given a multiple-choice quiz of three questions with five possible choices for each question, one of which is correct, and you were to find various probabilities of getting so many questions right or wrong, which of the following, if expanded, will have terms which are the various probabilities you are to find?
$$\left(\frac{4}{5}+\frac{1}{5}\right)^2;\ \left(\frac{4}{5}+\frac{1}{5}\right)^3;\ \left(\frac{4}{5}+\frac{1}{5}\right)^{15};\ \left(\frac{1}{3}+\frac{2}{3}\right)^5$$

$$\left(\frac{4}{5}+\frac{1}{5}\right)^3$$

944 Write the binomial expansion you would use to compute various probabilities of getting any number of questions right or wrong out of a total of three questions with five choices for each, only one of which is correct.

$$\left(\frac{4}{5}+\frac{1}{5}\right)^3=\binom{3}{0}\left(\frac{4}{5}\right)^3+\binom{3}{1}\left(\frac{4}{5}\right)^2\left(\frac{1}{5}\right)+\binom{3}{2}\left(\frac{4}{5}\right)\left(\frac{1}{5}\right)^2+\binom{3}{3}\left(\frac{1}{5}\right)^3$$

945 To find the various probabilities of getting any number of questions right or wrong out of three questions, each with five choices, only one of which is correct. You could make use of this binomial expansion:
$$\left(\frac{4}{5}+\frac{1}{5}\right)^3=\underbrace{\binom{3}{0}\left(\frac{4}{5}\right)^3}_{\substack{\text{first}\\\text{term}}}+\underbrace{\binom{3}{1}\left(\frac{4}{5}\right)^2\left(\frac{1}{5}\right)}_{\substack{\text{second}\\\text{term}}}+\underbrace{\binom{3}{2}\left(\frac{4}{5}\right)\left(\frac{1}{5}\right)^2}_{\substack{\text{third}\\\text{term}}}+\underbrace{\binom{3}{3}\left(\frac{1}{5}\right)^3}_{\substack{\text{fourth}\\\text{term}}}$$

(1) Which term is the probability of getting exactly two wrong and one right? Find this probability.

(2) Which terms would you add to find the probability of getting at least two questions right? Find this probability.

(1) the second; $\binom{3}{1}\left(\frac{4}{5}\right)^2\left(\frac{1}{5}\right)=3\cdot\dfrac{16}{25}\cdot\dfrac{1}{5}=\dfrac{48}{125}$

(2) the third and fourth
$$\binom{3}{2}\left(\frac{4}{5}\right)\left(\frac{1}{5}\right)^2+\binom{3}{3}\left(\frac{1}{5}\right)^3=\frac{12}{125}+\frac{1}{125}=\frac{13}{125}$$

●**946** Suppose you took a true-false quiz of 10 questions. Answer the following about the quiz:

(1) Write the binomial expansion you would use to find the probability of getting any number of questions correct on the quiz.

(2) What is the probability of getting exactly six questions correct?

(3) What is the probability of getting at least eight questions correct?

(1) $\left(\frac{1}{2}+\frac{1}{2}\right)^{10} = \binom{10}{0}\left(\frac{1}{2}\right)^{10} + \binom{10}{1}\left(\frac{1}{2}\right)^{9}\left(\frac{1}{2}\right) + \binom{10}{2}\left(\frac{1}{2}\right)^{8}\left(\frac{1}{2}\right)^{2}$

$+ \binom{10}{3}\left(\frac{1}{2}\right)^{7}\left(\frac{1}{2}\right)^{3} + \binom{10}{4}\left(\frac{1}{2}\right)^{6}\left(\frac{1}{2}\right)^{4} \binom{10}{5}\left(\frac{1}{2}\right)^{5}\left(\frac{1}{2}\right)^{5}$

$+ \binom{10}{6}\left(\frac{1}{2}\right)^{4}\left(\frac{1}{2}\right)^{6} + \binom{10}{7}\left(\frac{1}{2}\right)^{3}\left(\frac{1}{2}\right)^{7} + \binom{10}{8}\left(\frac{1}{2}\right)^{2}\left(\frac{1}{2}\right)^{8}$

$+ \binom{10}{9}\left(\frac{1}{2}\right)\left(\frac{1}{2}\right)^{9} + \binom{10}{10}\left(\frac{1}{2}\right)^{10}$

(2) $\frac{105}{512}$

Solution: $\binom{10}{4}\left(\frac{1}{2}\right)^{6}\left(\frac{1}{2}\right)^{4} = \frac{10 \cdot 9 \cdot 8 \cdot 7}{4 \cdot 3 \cdot 2 \cdot 1} \cdot \left(\frac{1}{2}\right)^{10} = \frac{105}{512}$

(3) $\frac{7}{128}$

Solution: $\binom{10}{8}\left(\frac{1}{2}\right)^{2}\left(\frac{1}{2}\right)^{8} + \binom{10}{9}\left(\frac{1}{2}\right)\left(\frac{1}{2}\right)^{9} + \binom{10}{10}\left(\frac{1}{2}\right)^{10}$

$= \frac{10 \cdot 9 \cdot 8 \cdot 7 \cdot 6 \cdot 5 \cdot 4 \cdot 3}{8 \cdot 7 \cdot 6 \cdot 5 \cdot 4 \cdot 3 \cdot 2 \cdot 1} \cdot \frac{1}{1,024}$

$+ \frac{10 \cdot 9 \cdot 8 \cdot 7 \cdot 6 \cdot 5 \cdot 4 \cdot 3 \cdot 2}{9 \cdot 8 \cdot 7 \cdot 6 \cdot 5 \cdot 4 \cdot 3 \cdot 2 \cdot 1}$

$\cdot \frac{1}{1,024} + \frac{10!}{10!} \cdot \frac{1}{1,024} = \frac{45}{1,024} + \frac{10}{1,024} + \frac{1}{1,024} = \frac{56}{1,024}$

$= \frac{7}{128}$

comment

The binomial expansion of $[(1-p) + p]^{n}$ gives, term by term, the binomial distribution: the probability of x successes in n trials each of which has a probability of success equal to p and a probability of failure equal to $1-p$. Note that $[(1-p) + p]^{n} = (1)^{n} = 1$. This shows that the sum of the probabilities is what it should be. We will not do anything more with the binomial distribution, but note that the computational part of it can become tremendous. For example, if $p = \frac{4}{5}$ and $n = 100$, to find the probability of at least 90 successes we would need:

$$\binom{100}{90}\left(\frac{4}{5}\right)^{90}\left(\frac{1}{5}\right)^{10} + \binom{100}{91}\left(\frac{4}{5}\right)^{91}\left(\frac{1}{5}\right)^{9} + \binom{100}{92}\left(\frac{4}{5}\right)^{92}\left(\frac{1}{5}\right)^{8} + \cdots + \binom{100}{100}\left(\frac{4}{5}\right)^{100}$$

and each one of these terms would be difficult to find without some aids to computation. Some of these aids which are available are tables of binomial distributions, logarithms, approximation methods for factorial numbers, computers, and simple statistical techniques which give good approximations for such probabilities.

---

947 Knowing that techniques of evaluation are available, let us work a few more probability problems without doing the arithmetic. For example, in finding $P(10; 13, 0.7)$, carry the work this far:

$$P(10; 13, 0.7) = \binom{13}{10}(0.7)^{10}(0.3)^3 = \frac{13!}{10!3!}(0.7)^{10}(0.3)^9$$

Find $P(38; 50, 0.2)$.

$$P(38; 50, 0.3) = \binom{50}{38}(0.2)^{38}(0.8)^{12}$$

$$= \frac{50!}{38!12!}(0.2)^{38}(0.8)^{12}$$

---

948 If a pair of dice is rolled, find the probability of getting either a 7 or an 11. (*Note:* The sample space is listed on Panel 1.)

$\frac{2}{9}$

Solution: If A is the event of rolling a 7, then $P(A) = \frac{6}{36}$. If B is the event of rolling an 11, then $P(B) = \frac{2}{36}$. To find the probability of A *or* B; note that A and B are mutually exclusive, so:

$$P(A \cup B) = P(A) + P(B) = \frac{6}{36} + \frac{2}{36} = \frac{8}{36} = \frac{2}{9}$$

---

949 If a pair of dice is rolled, the probability of getting a 7 or an 11 is $\frac{2}{9}$. Now, if a pair of dice is rolled three times, find the probability of getting a 7 or an 11 *at least* one time out of the three.

Working the problem directly, we get:

$$P\left(1; 3, \frac{2}{9}\right) + P\left(2; 3, \frac{2}{9}\right) + P\left(3; 3, \frac{2}{9}\right)$$

$$= \binom{3}{1}\left(\frac{2}{9}\right)\left(\frac{7}{9}\right)^2 + \binom{3}{2}\left(\frac{2}{9}\right)^3\left(\frac{7}{9}\right) + \binom{3}{3}\left(\frac{2}{9}\right)^3$$

$$= 3\left(\frac{2}{9}\right)\left(\frac{7}{9}\right)^2 + 3\left(\frac{2}{9}\right)^2\left(\frac{7}{9}\right) + \left(\frac{2}{9}\right)^3$$

A simpler method is to compute 1- the probability of zero successes. We get: $1 - P\left(0; 3, \frac{2}{9}\right) = 1 - \binom{3}{0}\left(\frac{7}{9}\right)^3 = 1 - \left(\frac{7}{9}\right)^3$

The two answers are equal.

950 A hat contains 20 red balls and 10 white balls. If a single ball is drawn from the hat, the probability that the ball is white is $\frac{10}{30} = \frac{1}{3}$. If five balls are drawn with replacement from the hat, find **(1)** the probability that none is white, **(2)** the probability that at least one is white.

(1) $\left(\frac{2}{3}\right)^5$ **(2)** $1-\left(\frac{2}{3}\right)^5$

Self-test VIII

1 **(1)** A permutation is _____ .
(2) Two permutations are the same (equal) if and only if they are _____ .

2 **(1)** The symbol $_5P_3$ represents _____
(2) Find $_5P_3$.

3 **(1)** 5! is read _____ and stands for _____ .
(2) $n!$ is read _____ and stands for _____ .

4 Write each answer in factorial form.
(1) $_6P_6 =$ _____
(2) $_{100}P_{100} \doteq$ _____
(3) $_nP_k =$ _____
(4) $_{25}P_4 =$ _____

5 How many permutations of three elements can be formed from the set $\{a, b, c, d, e, f\}$?

6 From a set of 10 people, two people are to be chosen at random to form a committee. The first person chosen will be chairman and the second person chosen to be a member. How many different committees can be formed?

7 **(1)** A combination is a _____ .
(2) Two combinations are the same if they _____ .

8 **(1)** List the different combinations of three elements which can be formed from the set $\{1, 2, 3, 4\}$.
(2) How many different permutations of three elements can be formed from the same set? (Do not list these permutations.)

9 How many different hands of cards, each hand containing 10 cards, can be dealt at random from a deck of cards? Do not do the arithmetic.

10 The recovery rate from disease Y is 0.8. If we observe 10 people having disease Y, we want to find the probability that exactly eight people recover.
   (1) $n =$ ___
   (2) $x =$ ___
   (3) $p =$ ___
   (4) $P($ _____ $)$ [Copy $P($ _____ $)$ when you answer.]
   (5) Find the probability that exactly eight people recover.

11 If five coins are tossed, find the probability that at least four are heads.

12 (1) What binomial expansion would you write which would give the probability, term by term, of getting x questions correct in a multiple-choice quiz with three choices for an answer, only one of which is correct? (Write the coefficients as combinations.) There are 3 questions in the test
   (2) Write the term which is the probability of getting exactly two questions correct.

part VI REVIEW

This part of the program will be a general review.

---

951 Consider an experiment which can be performed a large number of times under essentially the same conditions. An outcome A should be defined precisely enough that at the end of each trial of the experiment exactly one of the two following statements is true: (1) A has occurred. (2) A has not occurred. If the experiment were performed N times, A would occur a certain number of times. We indicate this number by $n(A)$.
(1) The smallest possible value for $n(A)$ is ___.
(2) The largest possible value for $n(A)$ is ___.

(1) 0   (2) N

---

952 The number of times event A has occurred $n(A)$ is without much significance by itself. For example, consider each shot that Joe Zilch takes in a basketball game to be an experiment and outcome A occurs if he makes a basket. Suppose at the end of the game you are told that $n(A) = 1$. What other information would you want before you decide whether Joe shot well during that game?

N,   the number of shots he took (or the number of trials of the experiment)

---

953 For the experiment in frame 952, case I: $n(A) = 1$ where $N = 2$ conveys a much different meaning than case II: $n(A) = 1$ where $N = 30$. In the first instance, Joe has nothing to be embarrassed about, but in the second instance, you would be charitable if you merely said that Joe had a bad night. Rather than giving both values $n(A)$ and N separately, a single measure which reflects the meaning desired is the relative frequency of A, defined by relative frequency of $A = n(A)/N$.
▼

For the first case listed above, (1) relative frequency of A = ___.
For the second case listed above, (2) relative frequency of A = ___.

(1) $\frac{1}{2}$ (2) $\frac{1}{30}$

954 If N trials of an experiment are performed and $n(A) = 0$, then relative frequency of A = _____.

$\frac{0}{N} = 0$

955 If N trials of an experiment are performed and $n(A) = N$, then relative frequency of A = _____.

$\frac{N}{N} = 1$

956 Since $0 \leq n(A) \leq N$, and the relative frequency of $A = n(A)/N$, then
___ $\leq$ relative frequency of $A \leq$ ___.
(Copy $\leq$ relative frequency of $A \leq$ when you answer.)

$0 \leq$ relative frequency of $A \leq 1$

957 Now note that the relative frequency of A by itself does not give a complete picture of the situation. When you read, "Three out of four dentists recommend Glob for cleaning teeth," you are being told that, if A is the outcome that a dentist, when interviewed, recommended Glob, then relative frequency of $A = \frac{3}{4}$. But $n(A)$ and N have been lost. Possibly, $N = 10,000$ so that (1) $n(A)$ = _____ , but it also is possible that $N = 4$, in which case (2) $n(A)$ = _____ ,

(1) $\frac{3}{4} = \frac{n(A)}{N}$ (2) $\frac{3}{4} = \frac{n(A)}{4}$

$\frac{3}{4} = \frac{n(A)}{10,000}$ $n(A) = 3$

$n(A) = 7,500$

958 We feel more secure with a relative frequency for a large value of N because, intuitively or from past experiences, we have found that, as N becomes large, the relative frequency of A tends to remain relatively fixed. This statement contains the germ of the idea of the probability of outcome A. We will assume that for a given experiment and outcome A there is some constant $P(A)$, called the _____, such that, as N becomes large, the relative frequency of A will ultimately become arbitrarily close to $P(A)$.

probability of A

959 Now, for a given experiment with an outcome A, if we say that $P(A) = \frac{1}{3}$, we *do not* mean that each three times the experiment is performed A must occur once. We mean that, as the experiment is performed a great number of times, we expect the relative frequency of A ultimately to get closer and closer to ___.

$\frac{1}{3}$

comment

The general problem with which we were concerned at this point can be stated as follows: The probabilities of rather simple outcomes of an experiment were given or assumed. We then found probabilities of more complicated outcomes. The manner in which we attacked the problem was to build a theoretical model of an experiment and construct a mathematical structure which was consistent and reasonable when applied to an actual experience.

960 We defined a finite sample space S as a set of elements $\{e_1, e_2, \ldots, e_n\}$. With each $e_i \in S$, $i = 1, 2, \ldots, n$, there is associated a number $P(e_i)$, called the probability of e_i, such that
(1) ___ $\leq P(e_i) \leq$ ___ for $i = 1, 2, \ldots, n$
(2) $P(e_1) + P(e_2) + \cdots + P(e_n) =$ ___
[Copy $\leq P(e_i) \leq$ when you answer (1).]

(1) $0 \leq P(e_i) \leq 1$ (2) 1

961 Let $T = \{f_1, f_2, f_3, f_4, f_5\}$ and $P(f_1) = 0.2$, $P(f_2) = 0$, $P(f_3) = 1$, $P(f_4) = 0.3$, $P(f_5) = 0.1$. Is T a sample space with probabilities satisfying the conditions in frame 960? Why?

no, $P(f_1) + P(f_2) + \cdots + P(f_5) \neq 1$

962 Let $S = \{e_1, e_2, \ldots, e_n\}$ be a sample space. Any subset A of S is called an event in S. Suppose $T = \{f_1, f_2, f_3\}$; List all possible events in T.

$E_1 = \emptyset$ $E_2 = \{f_1\}$
$E_3 = \{f_2\}$ $E_4 = \{f_3\}$
$E_5 = \{f_1, f_2\}$ $E_6 = \{f_1, f_3\}$
$E_7 = \{f_2, f_3\}$ $E_8 = \{f_1, f_2, f_3\}$

963 $S = \{e_1, e_2, \ldots, e_n\}$ is a sample space and $P(e_i)$, $i = 1, 2, \ldots, n$ have been assigned such that
$0 \le P(e_i) \le 1$ and $P(e_1) + P(e_2) + \cdots + P(e_n) = 1$, and let A be any event in S. Then we define $P(A)$, the probability of A to be the sum of the probabilities of the elements of A. If A is empty, that is, if $A = \emptyset$, we define $P(\emptyset) = 0$. Let $T = \{f_1, f_2, f_3\}$ and $P(f_1) = 0.3$, $P(f_2) = 0.2$, $P(f_3) = 0.5$. All the possible events in T are:
$E_1 = \emptyset$ $\qquad\qquad$ $E_2 = \{f_1\}$
$E_3 = \{f_2\}$ $\qquad\qquad$ $E_4 = \{f_3\}$
$E_5 = \{f_1, f_2\}$ $\qquad$ $E_6 = \{f_1, f_3\}$
$E_7 = \{f_2, f_3\}$ $\qquad$ $E_8 = \{f_1, f_2, f_3\}$
Find the probability of each event.

$P(E_1) = 0$, $P(E_2) = 0.3$, $P(E_3) = 0.2$, $P(E_4) = 0.5$,
$P(E_5) = 0.5$, $P(E_6) = 0.8$, $P(E_7) = 0.7$, $P(E_8) = 1$

964 Now, given any experiment, we consider a finite set of outcomes such that each trial of the experiment must result in *exactly one* of these outcomes. For example, let an experiment consist of tossing two coins:

$e_1 \longleftrightarrow$ no heads occur
$e_2 \longleftrightarrow$ exactly one head occurs
$e_3 \longleftrightarrow$ exactly two heads occur

Are these outcomes such that each trial of the experiment will result in one and only one of them?

yes   *(Note:* We do not consider such unexpected results as the coins landing on edge or disappearing.)

965 *Experiment:* Two coins are tossed. Let e_1 be the outcome that no heads occur and e_2 be the outcome that at least one head occurs. Are these outcomes such that any trial of the experiment will result in exactly one of them?

yes

966 The immediate question is how can we assign values to $P(e_i)$, the probability of the outcome e_i. We can never be absolutely sure. At times we assign the values on the basis of a reasonable symmetry in the outcomes. For example, if an honest coin is tossed and e_1 is the outcome of a head and e_2 is the outcome of a tail, then we let $S = \{e_1, e_2\}$, and there is every reason to feel that an assignment of (1) $P(e_1) =$ ___ and (2) $P(e_2) =$ ___ is reasonable.

(1) $\frac{1}{2}$ (2) $\frac{1}{2}$

967 For other experiments, the best we can do is to make a reasonable approximation of $P(e_i)$ on the basis of the _____ of e_i for a large number of trials of the experiment or of similar experiments.

relative frequency

968 For a given experiment, a large number of sample spaces could be constructed. Suppose a single die is rolled. We might let $S = \{e_1, e_2, e_3\}$ where

$e_1 \longleftrightarrow$ an even number turns up
$e_2 \longleftrightarrow$ a 1 turns up
$e_3 \longleftrightarrow$ a 3 or 5 turns up

Or, we might let $T = \{e_1, e_2\}$ where

$e_1 \longleftrightarrow$ an even number turns up
$e_2 \longleftrightarrow$ _____

an odd number turns up (or a 1, 3, or 5 turns up)

969 Since we have a choice of sample spaces for an experiment, the question is how to decide on one. There are two considerations:
1. We are ultimately going to try to find the (1) _____ of some outcome A. Then A must be capable of being described in terms of the outcomes used to set up the sample space.
2. We must ultimately be able to assign reasonable values to the (2) __ for $i = 1, 2, \ldots, n$. The sample space must be such that this can be done.

(1) probability   (2) $P(e_i)$

970 Take an example. *Experiment:* Roll a die. Suppose we want to find the probability of A, where A is the outcome of a number greater than 4 turning up.
Let $S = \{e_1, e_2, e_3, e_4, e_5, e_6\}$ where

$e_1 \longleftrightarrow$ a 1 turns up $e_2 \longleftrightarrow$ a 2 turns up
$e_3 \longleftrightarrow$ a 3 turns up $e_4 \longleftrightarrow$ a 4 turns up
$e_5 \longleftrightarrow$ a 5 turns up $e_6 \longleftrightarrow$ a 6 turns up

It seems reasonable to let $P(e_1) = P(e_2) = \cdots = P(e_6) = \frac{1}{6}$.

Now A occurs whenever e_5 or e_6 occurs. So A is the event $\{e_5, e_6\}$.
$P(A) = \underline{}$.

$\frac{1}{3}$ *Solution:* $P(e_5) + P(e_6) = \frac{1}{6} + \frac{1}{6} = \frac{2}{6}$ or $\frac{1}{3}$

comment

We have been relaxed in our use of the words *outcome* and *event*, using them almost interchangeably. For example, consider again the experiment of rolling a single die and the sample space used to compute A, the probability that a number greater than 4 turns up:

$e_1 \leftrightarrow$ a 1 turns up $e_2 \leftrightarrow$ a 2 turns up
$e_3 \leftrightarrow$ a 3 turns up $e_4 \leftrightarrow$ a 4 turns up
$e_5 \leftrightarrow$ a 5 turns up $e_6 \leftrightarrow$ a 6 turns up

Events involve the e's while *outcomes* involve verbal descriptions identified with the e's. Technically, then, A is the *event* $\{e_5, e_6\}$, but A is the *outcome* a number greater than 4 appears. However, we shall continue to refer to A as both (1) the event (subset) and (2) the outcome.

The concept of event A as a subset of a sample space S and $P(A)$ as the sum of the probabilities of the elements of A is valuable to remember. Even after you have learned various theorems for finding probabilities of compound events, a problem often has more meaning if you look at the event in terms of a subset of a sample space.

---

971 *Experiment:* Toss three coins. Set up a sample space $S = \{e_1, e_2, \ldots, e_8\}$ and save it.

$e_1 \leftrightarrow HHH$ $e_2 \leftrightarrow HHT$ $e_3 \leftrightarrow HTH$ $e_4 \leftrightarrow THH$
$e_5 \leftrightarrow HTT$ $e_6 \leftrightarrow THT$ $e_7 \leftrightarrow TTH$ $e_8 \leftrightarrow TTT$

Of course, your correspondences may be in a different order.

---

972 For $S = \{e_1, e_2, \ldots, e_8\}$, what values would you assign to $P(e_1), P(e_2), \ldots, P(e_8)$?

It seems reasonable to let $P(e_i) = \frac{1}{8}$ for $i = 1, 2, \ldots, 8$.

---

973 For the experiment in frames 971 and 972, suppose A is the event that at least two tails appear.
(1) $A =$ _____ $\therefore$ (2) $P(A) =$ _____ .

(1) $\{e_5, e_6, e_7, e_8\}$ (2) $\frac{1}{8} + \frac{1}{8} + \frac{1}{8} + \frac{1}{8} = \frac{1}{2}$

---

974 Now we recall some of the definitions and theorems which are useful in computing probabilities without recourse to constructing a sample space. If A is an event, then A', the complement of A, is

▼

given by $A' = \{x \mid x \in S \text{ and } x \notin A\}$. Thus, if $S = \{e_1, e_2, e_3, e_4, e_5\}$ and $A = \{e_1, e_3\}$, then $A' = $ _____ .

$\{e_2, e_4, e_5\}$

---

975 If $S = \{e_1, e_2, e_3, e_4, e_5, e_6\}$ is a sample space and $A = \{e_1, e_2, e_3, e_4, e_5, e_6\}$ is an event, then $A' = $ ___.

$\emptyset$

---

976 If $S = \{e_1, e_2, \ldots, e_n\}$ and $A = \emptyset$ is an event, then $A' = $ _____ .

S or $\{e_1, e_2, \ldots, e_n\}$

---

977 *Definition:* Two events A and B are mutually exclusive if and only if $A \cap B = \emptyset$. If $S = \{e_1, e_2, e_3, e_4\}$, $A = \{e_1\}$, $B = \{e_2, e_3\}$, $A \cap B = $ ___. A and B are _____ events.

$\emptyset$,   mutually exclusive

---

978 Let an experiment be that of tossing a die. Let:
A be the event that a number greater than 1 turns up
B be the event that an even number turns up
C be the event that a 3 turns up
Then,
(1) A' is the event that _____
(2) B' is the event that _____
(3) C' is the event that _____
(4) Which of the following pairs of events are mutually exclusive: A and B, A and C, B and C?

---

(1) a 1 turns up
(2) an odd number turns up
(3) a number other than 3 turns up (or a 1, 2, 4, 5, or 6 turns up)
(4) B and C

---

979 Two events are mutually exclusive if they cannot both occur on the same trial of the experiment, that is, if they have no elements in common. Obviously, if A is any event, (1) $A \cap A' = $ ___; so A and A' are (2) _____ events.

---

(1) $\emptyset$ (2) mutually exclusive

980 So, given any event A, we automatically have another event A'.
Now, given two events A and B, another event $A \cup B$ can be formed.
$A \cup B = \{x \mid x \in A \text{ or } x \in B\}$. If $S = \{e_1, e_2, \ldots, e_{10}\}$,
$A = \{e_2, e_3, e_4, e_6\}$, $B = \{e_3, e_6, e_7\}$; then $A \cup B =$ _____ .

$\{e_2, e_3, e_4, e_6, e_7\}$

981 Now, $A \cup B \longleftrightarrow$ event A *or* event B. So, given two events A and B,
if we wish to find the probability that event A or event B occurs,
we want $P(A \cup B)$. If an experiment consists of tossing a die and
A is the event that an even number appears and B is the event that
a number greater than 3 appears, then A or B will occur if a
—, —, —, or — appears.

2, 4, 5,   6

982 We found, if A and B are mutually exclusive, such as shown in this
diagram,

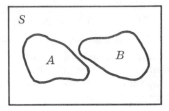

then $P(A \cup B) =$ _____ .

$P(A) + P(B)$

983 For example, let $S = \{e_1, e_2, e_3, e_4, e_5\}$ with $P(e_1) = 0.1$,
$P(e_2) = 0.1$, $P(e_3) = 0.3$, $P(e_4) = 0.2$, $P(e_5) = 0.3$. If $A = \{e_1, e_2, e_4\}$,
(1) $P(A) =$ ___ . If $B = \{e_3\}$, **(2)** $P(B) =$ ___ . Then **(3)** $A \cup B =$
_____ and **(4)** $P(A \cup B) =$ ___ .

(1) 0.4   **(2)** 0.3   **(3)** $\{e_1, e_2, e_3, e_4\}$ **(4)** 0.7

984 Note, if $S = \{e_1, e_2, e_3, e_4, e_5\}$, $P(e_1) = 0.1$, $P(e_2) = 0.1$, $P(e_3) = 0.3$,
$P(e_4) = 0.2$, $P(e_5) = 0.3$, Let $A = \{e_1, e_2, e_4\}$,
(1) $P(A) =$ ___ . Let $B = \{e_2, e_3\}$, **(2)** $P(B) =$ ___ .
(3) $A \cup B =$ _____ and **(4)** $P(A \cup B) =$ ___ . **(5)** Why is it
not true in this case that $P(A \cup B) = P(A) + P(B)$?

(1) 0.4   **(2)** 0.4   **(3)** $\{e_1, e_2, e_3, e_4\}$ **(4)** 0.7
(5) A and B are not mutually exclusive events

985 We found that, if A and B are mutually exclusive events, $P(A \cup B) = P(A) + P(B)$. Suppose an experiment is to draw a single card from a deck of cards. A is the event that the card is a king, B is the event that the card is a 10. Then (1) $P(A) =$ ___, (2) $P(B) =$ ___. Obviously, A and B are mutually exclusive; so (3) $P(A \cup B) =$ _____.

(1) $\frac{4}{52}$ or $\frac{1}{13}$ **(2)** $\frac{4}{52}$ or $\frac{1}{13}$ **(3)** $P(A) + P(B) = \frac{1}{13} + \frac{1}{13} = \frac{2}{13}$

986 If A is any event, A' is its complement, and $A \cap A' =$ ___.

$\emptyset$

987 Since $A \cap A' = \emptyset$, A and A' are mutually exclusive events; so $P(A \cup A') =$ _____.

$P(A) + P(A')$

988 Note also, if $S = \{e_1, e_2, \ldots, e_n\}$ and A is any event, $A \cup A' =$ ___.

S

989 So $A \cup A' = S$, $P(A \cup A') = P(A) + P(A')$. But (1) $P(S) = P(A \cup A') =$ ___. $\therefore$ (2) $P(A) + P(A') =$ ___.

(1) 1   **(2)** 1

990 If the probability that you will catch a cold this year is 0.6, what is the probability you will not catch a cold this year?

1 - 0.6 = 0.4

991 If A and B are events, then $P(B \mid A)$ is the _____.

conditional probability of B, given that A has occurred.

992 To show that $P(B \mid A)$ can be different from $P(B)$, consider this example: A hat contains two red balls and one white ball. Two balls are drawn from the hat in succession without replacement. Let: A be the event that the first ball is white
$\quad\quad$ B be the event that the second ball is white
$\quad\quad$ $S = \{e_1, e_2, e_3, e_4, e_5, e_6\}$ where

$e_1 \longleftrightarrow R_1 R_2$ $e_2 \longleftrightarrow R_1 W$ $e_3 \longleftrightarrow R_2 R_1$
$e_4 \longleftrightarrow R_2 W$ $e_5 \longleftrightarrow W R_1$ $e_6 \longleftrightarrow W R_2$

▼

$P(e_1) = P(e_2) = \cdots = P(e_6) = \frac{1}{6}$
(1) $B = $ _____ ; so (2) $P(B) = $ ___ . But, assuming A has occurred,
(3) $P(B \mid A) = $ _____

(1) $\{e_2, e_4\}$ (2) $\frac{1}{3}$ (3) 0, since, if A has occurred, the white
ball cannot appear as the second ball drawn

993 Two coins are tossed in succession. Let $S = \{e_1, e_2, e_3, e_4\}$ where

$e_1 \leftrightarrow HH, \qquad e_2 \leftrightarrow HT, \qquad e_3 \leftrightarrow TH, \qquad e_4 \leftrightarrow TT.$

$P(e_1) = P(e_2) = P(e_3) = P(e_4) = \frac{1}{4}$. If B is the event that the second
coin tossed is a head, (1) $B = $ _____ and (2) $P(B) = $ ___ .

(1) $\{e_1, e_3\}$ (2) $\frac{1}{2}$

994 Consider again the experiment: Two coins are tossed in succession.
Let A be the event that the first coin is a head and B be the event
that the second coin is a head. We found $P(B) = \frac{1}{2}$. To find $P(B \mid A)$,
we assume A has occurred. Then the sample space consists of
only the points HT and HH, each with a probability of $\frac{1}{2}$. In this
sample space, $P(B \mid A) = $ ___ .

$\frac{1}{2}$

995 If A and B are events, $A \cap B = \{x \mid x \epsilon A$ and $x \epsilon B\}$. For example,
let $S = \{e_1, e_2, e_3, e_4, e_5\}$, $A = \{e_1, e_3, e_4\}$, $B = \{e_3, e_4, e_5\}$,
$A \cap B = $ _____ .

$\{e_3, e_4\}$

996 Given two events A and B, if we wish to find the probability of the
occurrence of both events, that is, of the event A and the event B,
we want $P(A \cap B)$.
Experiment: Toss a die. Let $S = \{e_1, e_2, \ldots, e_6\}$ where $e_1 \leftrightarrow$ a one
turns up, $e_2 \leftrightarrow$ a two turns up, etc., and let $P(e_1) = P(e_2) = \ldots =$
$P(e_6) = \frac{1}{6}$. Let A be the event that an even number turns up, let B
be the event that a number greater than three turns up. Now, find
the probability that an even number greater than three turns up,
that is, that A and B occur. (1) $A = $ _____ , (2) $B = $ _____ ,
(3) $A \cap B = $ _____ . $\therefore$ (4) $P(A \cap B) = $ ___ .

(1) $\{e_2, e_4, e_6\}$ (2) $\{e_4, e_5, e_6\}$
(3) $\{e_4, e_6\}$ (4) $\frac{1}{3}$

997 We found that, if A and B are events, then the probability of the
occurrence of event A and event B is given by
$P(A \cap B) = P(A) \cdot P(B \mid A)$.

▼

Experiment: Two cards are drawn in succession without replacement from a deck of cards. Find the probability that the first is an ace and the second is an ace.

Let A be the event that the first card is an ace and B be the event that the second card is an ace. Then $P(A \cap B) = P(A) \cdot P(B \mid A)$
$$= \frac{4}{52} \cdot \frac{3}{51} = \frac{12}{2,652}$$

998 Two events A and B are independent if and only if $P(B \mid A) = P(B)$. In that case, $P(A \cap B) = $ _____ .

$P(A) \cdot P(B)$

999 If two cards are drawn from a deck of cards *with* replacement, and A is the event the first card is an ace and B is the event the second card is a club, find the probability that event A and event B occur.

Since the first card is replaced, A and B are independent events; so
$$P(A \cap B) = P(A) \cdot P(B) = \frac{4}{52} \cdot \frac{13}{52} = \frac{52}{2,704} = \frac{1}{52}$$

1000 The theorem can be extended to n independent trials. For example, the repeated tosses of a coin are independent events; so if a coin is tossed five times, find the probability of getting five heads.

Let A be the event that the first coin is a head
   B be the event that the second coin is a head
   C be the event that the third coin is a head
   D be the event that the fourth coin is a head
   E be the event that the fifth coin is a head
Then, $P(A \cap B \cap C \cap D \cap E) = P(A) \cdot P(B) \cdot P(C) \cdot P(D) \cdot P(E)$
$$= \frac{1}{2} \cdot \frac{1}{2} \cdot \frac{1}{2} \cdot \frac{1}{2} \cdot \frac{1}{2} = \frac{1}{32}$$

1001 Now, if A and B are *not* mutually exclusive,

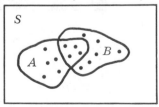

we see that $P(A) + P(B)$ contains the probabilities of elements in $A \cap B$ twice, once in A and once in B. So we see that $P(A \cup B) = P(A) + P(B) - P(A \cap B)$. If a single card is drawn

▼

from a deck of cards, find the probability that it is an ace or a club.

Let A be the event that the card is an ace and B be the event that the card is a club. Then $P(A \cup B) = P(A) + P(B) - P(A \cap B)$
$$= \tfrac{1}{13} + \tfrac{1}{4} - \tfrac{1}{52} = \tfrac{16}{52} = \tfrac{4}{13}$$

1002 If A is the event that you will get a cold next winter, $P(A) = 0.7$. If B is the event that you will get a sore throat next winter, $P(B) = 0.4$. What is wrong with: The probability you will get a cold or get a sore throat next winter is given by $P(A \cup B) = P(A) + P(B)$.

Of course, the answer 1.1 is ridiculous and is the result of using $P(A \cup B) = P(A) + P(B)$ for events which are not mutually exclusive. You need to know $P(A \cap B)$.

1003 If A is the event that you catch a cold next winter and B is the event that you get a sore throat next winter, $P(A) = 0.7$, $P(B) = 0.4$, and $P(B \mid A) = 0.5$. Find the probability that you get a cold or a sore throat next winter. That is, find $P(A) + P(B) - P(A \cap B)$.

First, find $P(A \cap B) = P(A) \cdot P(B \mid A) = (0.7)(0.5) = 0.35$
Then, find $P(A \cup B) = 0.7 + 0.4 - 0.35 = 0.75$

1004 Finally, if an experiment can result only in either a success or a failure and the probability of success is p, then if n independent trials of the experiment are performed, the probability of exactly x successes out of the n trials is given by

$P(x; n, p) = \binom{n}{x} (p)^x (1-p)^{n-x}$. Find the probability of getting exactly three heads in tossing six coins.

Here, $p = \tfrac{1}{2}$, $n = 6$, $x = 3$.
$$P\left(3; 6, \tfrac{1}{2}\right) = \binom{6}{3}\left(\tfrac{1}{2}\right)^3\left(\tfrac{1}{2}\right)^3$$
$$= \frac{6 \cdot 5 \cdot 4}{1 \cdot 2 \cdot 3}\left(\tfrac{1}{2}\right)^6 = \frac{5}{16}$$

1005 Recall: $\binom{n}{k} = \dfrac{n(n-1) \cdots (n-k+1)}{k!}$

or $\binom{n}{k} = \dfrac{n!}{k!\,(n-k)!}$

$\binom{6}{4} =$ _____

$\dfrac{6 \cdot 5 \cdot 4 \cdot 3}{1 \cdot 2 \cdot 3 \cdot 4} = 15$ or $\dfrac{6!}{4!\,2!} = \dfrac{6 \cdot 5 \cdot 4 \cdot 3 \cdot 2 \cdot 1}{4 \cdot 3 \cdot 2 \cdot 1 \cdot 2 \cdot 1} = 15$

1006 Since $\binom{n}{k} = \dfrac{n!}{k!\,(n-k)!}$ and $0! = 1$, then $\binom{n}{n} =$ _____ .

$\dfrac{n!}{n!\,(0)!} = 1$

1007 $\binom{n}{0} =$ _____ .

$\dfrac{n!}{0!\,n!} = 1$

1008 If a pair of dice are tossed, find the probability of getting a seven.

$\dfrac{1}{6}$ (from Panel 1, or any other method)

1009 If a pair of dice are rolled, the probability of getting a seven is $\frac{1}{6}$. If a pair of dice are rolled 10 times in succession, find the probability that a seven appears exactly one time. (You may leave your answer in exponential form.)

Here, $p = \frac{1}{6}$, $n = 10$, $x = 1$.
$$P\left(1;\ 10,\ \tfrac{1}{6}\right) = \binom{10}{1}\left(\tfrac{1}{6}\right)^1 \left(\tfrac{5}{6}\right)^9 = \frac{10.5^9}{6^{10}}$$

1010 A manufacturer of hair restorer claims that 0.6 of the people using the product will grow hair. If this is true, then find the probability that, if five men use the product, fewer than two will succeed in growing hair. We want exactly zero or exactly one success. (You may leave your answer in exponential form.)

$$P(0;\ 5,\ 0.6) + P(1;\ 5,\ 0.6) = \binom{5}{0}(0.4)^5 + \binom{5}{1}(0.6)(0.4)^4$$
$$= (0.4)^5 + 5(0.6)(0.4)^4$$

1011 If 0.6 of the voters favor candidate X, find the probability that *at least* three out of five voters selected at random favor candidate X. (You may leave your answer in exponential form.)

At least three means exactly three *or* exactly four *or* exactly five.
$$P(3;\ 5,\ 0.6) + P(4;\ 5,\ 0.6) + P(5;\ 5,\ 0.6)$$
$$= \binom{5}{3}(0.6)^3(0.4)^2 + \binom{5}{4}(0.6)^4(0.4) + \binom{5}{5}(0.6)^5$$
$$= \frac{5 \cdot 4 \cdot 3}{1 \cdot 2 \cdot 3}(0.6)^3(0.4)^2 + \frac{5 \cdot 4 \cdot 3 \cdot 2}{1 \cdot 2 \cdot 3 \cdot 4}(0.6)^4(0.4) + (0.6)^5$$
$$= 10(0.6)^3(0.4)^2 + 5(0.6)^4(0.4) + (0.6)^5$$

1012 Expand the binomial $\left(\frac{2}{3}+\frac{1}{3}\right)^5$ by writing the coefficient of each term as a combination. (Use the same patterns as established before in this program.)

$$\left(\frac{2}{3}+\frac{1}{3}\right)^5 = \binom{5}{0}\left(\frac{2}{3}\right)^5 + \binom{5}{1}\left(\frac{2}{3}\right)^4\left(\frac{1}{3}\right) + \binom{5}{2}\left(\frac{2}{3}\right)^3\left(\frac{1}{3}\right)^2 + \binom{5}{3}\left(\frac{2}{3}\right)^2\left(\frac{1}{3}\right)^3$$

$$+ \binom{5}{4}\left(\frac{2}{3}\right)\left(\frac{1}{3}\right)^4 + \binom{5}{5}\left(\frac{1}{3}\right)^5$$

1013 Answer the following concerning a multiple-choice test with eight questions, each with three possible answers, only one of which is correct.

(1) What binomial distribution would you write so that each term is the probability of getting some specific number of the eight questions correct? (Write your answer with combinations for coefficients, and use the patterns previously established in this program.)

(2) Write the term which is the probability of getting exactly seven questions correct and one wrong.

(3) What terms would you add to find the probability of getting less than three wrong?

(1) $\left(\frac{2}{3}+\frac{1}{3}\right)^8 = \binom{8}{0}\left(\frac{2}{3}\right)^8 + \binom{8}{1}\left(\frac{2}{3}\right)^7\left(\frac{1}{3}\right) + \binom{8}{2}\left(\frac{2}{3}\right)^6\left(\frac{1}{3}\right)^2$

$+ \binom{8}{3}\left(\frac{2}{3}\right)^5\left(\frac{1}{3}\right)^3 + \binom{8}{4}\left(\frac{2}{3}\right)^4\left(\frac{1}{3}\right)^4 + \binom{8}{5}\left(\frac{2}{3}\right)^3\left(\frac{1}{3}\right)^5$

$+ \binom{8}{6}\left(\frac{2}{3}\right)^2\left(\frac{1}{3}\right)^6 + \binom{8}{7}\left(\frac{2}{3}\right)\left(\frac{1}{3}\right)^7 + \binom{8}{8}\left(\frac{1}{3}\right)^8$

(2) $\binom{8}{7}\left(\frac{2}{3}\right)\left(\frac{1}{3}\right)^7$

(3) $\binom{8}{6}\left(\frac{2}{3}\right)^2\left(\frac{1}{3}\right)^6 + \binom{8}{7}\left(\frac{2}{3}\right)\left(\frac{1}{3}\right)^7 + \binom{8}{8}\left(\frac{1}{3}\right)^8$

1014 If five cards are drawn in succession, with replacement, from a deck of cards, find the probability of getting *at least* two aces. (You may leave your answer in exponential form.)

On a single trial, the probability of getting an ace is $\frac{4}{52}$ or $\frac{1}{13}$; so $p = \frac{1}{13}$, $n = 5$. We want at least two aces; so we want

$$P\left(2; 5, \frac{1}{13}\right) + P\left(3; 5, \frac{1}{13}\right) + P\left(4; 5, \frac{1}{13}\right) + P\left(5; 5, \frac{1}{13}\right)$$

$$= \binom{5}{2}\left(\frac{1}{13}\right)^2\left(\frac{12}{13}\right)^3 + \binom{5}{3}\left(\frac{1}{13}\right)^3\left(\frac{12}{13}\right)^2 + \binom{5}{4}\left(\frac{1}{13}\right)^4\left(\frac{12}{13}\right) + \left(\frac{1}{13}\right)^5$$

$$= \frac{5 \cdot 4}{1 \cdot 2}\left(\frac{1}{13}\right)^2\left(\frac{12}{13}\right)^3 + \frac{5 \cdot 4 \cdot 3}{1 \cdot 2 \cdot 3}\left(\frac{1}{13}\right)^3\left(\frac{12}{13}\right)^2 + \frac{5 \cdot 4 \cdot 3 \cdot 2}{1 \cdot 2 \cdot 3 \cdot 4}\left(\frac{1}{13}\right)^4\left(\frac{12}{13}\right) + \left(\frac{1}{13}\right)^5$$

$$= 10\left(\frac{1}{13}\right)^2\left(\frac{12}{13}\right)^3 + 10\left(\frac{1}{13}\right)^3\left(\frac{12}{13}\right)^2 + 5\left(\frac{1}{13}\right)^4\left(\frac{12}{13}\right) + \left(\frac{1}{13}\right)^5$$

An easier method would be:

$$1 - P\left(0; 5, \frac{1}{13}\right) - P\left(1; 5, \frac{1}{13}\right)$$

$$= 1 - \binom{5}{0}\left(\frac{1}{13}\right)^0\left(\frac{12}{13}\right)^5 - \binom{5}{1}\left(\frac{1}{13}\right)\left(\frac{12}{13}\right)^4$$

$$= 1 - \left(\frac{12}{13}\right)^5 - 5\left(\frac{1}{13}\right)\left(\frac{12}{13}\right)^4$$

1015 Hat 1 contains eight red balls and three white balls.
Hat 2 contains two red balls and five white balls.
Experiment: A coin is tossed. If a head appears, draw a ball from hat 1; if a tail appears, draw a ball from hat 2. Let A be the event of getting a red ball.
Copy this experiment and the event.
Event A could happen by tossing a head and getting a red ball from hat 1 *or* _____ .

tossing a tail and getting a red ball from hat 2.
Have a copy of the experiment and event.

1016 Suppose: B is the event of tossing a head *and* getting a red ball from hat 1. C is the event of tossing a tail *and* getting a red ball from hat 2. Then $A = B \cup C$ and a trial of the experiment consists of one toss of the coin.
(1) $P(B \cap C) =$ ___
(2) In terms of $P(B)$ and $P(C)$, $P(A) =$ _____
[Copy $P(A) =$ when you answer.]

(1) 0   (2) $P(A) = P(B) + P(C)$

1017 To find $P(A)$, you must compute $P(B)$ and $P(C)$ since:
$P(A) = P(B) + P(C)$.
  (1) Compute $P(B)$, that is, the probability of getting a head *and* a red ball from hat 1.
  (2) Compute $P(C)$, that is, the probability of getting a tail *and* a red ball from hat 2.

  (1) $\frac{4}{11}$ *Solution:* $\frac{1}{2} \cdot \frac{8}{11} = \frac{4}{11} = P(B)$
  (2) $\frac{1}{7}$ *Solution:* $\frac{1}{2} \cdot \frac{2}{7} = \frac{1}{7} = P(C)$

1018 Then $P(A) = P(B) + P(C)$ where $P(B) = \frac{4}{11}$ and $P(C) = \frac{1}{7}$. Find $P(A)$.

$\frac{39}{77}$

1019 Hat 1 contains 10 red balls and two white balls. Hat 2 contains one red ball and six white balls.
Experiment: A coin is tossed. If a head appears, draw a ball from hat 1; if a tail appears, draw a ball from hat 2. Let B be the event of getting a white ball. Find $P(B)$.

$\frac{43}{84}$ *Solution:* $P(B) = \frac{1}{2} \cdot \frac{2}{12} + \frac{1}{2} \cdot \frac{6}{7}$

$= \frac{1}{12} + \frac{3}{7}$

$= \frac{7 + 36}{84} = \frac{43}{84}$

appendix a ELEMENTARY SET THEORY

This appendix is provided for reference and review for those who have forgotten some of the elementary results from a study of set theory. It includes only those concepts and results of set theory which are requisite for this program, and it makes no attempt to be rigorous.

1. Sets, Elements, Membership

A collection of objects of any sort will be called a *set*. For example, we may consider the set of former presidents of the United States, or the set of integers from 1 to 10, or the set of solutions of the equation $x^2 + 3x - 2 = 0$. Each of these examples is a *finite set*. The set of all real numbers, the set of all points on a given line, the set of even integers are examples of *infinite sets*.

Each of the objects which make up a given set is called an *element* of that set or a *member* of that set. For example, 4 is an element (or member) of the set of even integers; George Washington is an element of the set of former presidents of the United States; 2 is *not* an element of the set of solutions of the equation $x^2 + 3x - 2 = 0$.

Given any specific set A, it is assumed that, for any given object x, *exactly one* of the following conditions is true:
1. x is an element of the set A.
2. x is not an element of the set A.
This fundamental relationship of *membership* or *belonging* between objects and sets is denoted by the symbol ϵ. If S is a set and x is a member of S, we write $x \in S$ (read, "x is a member of the set S," or "x is an element of the set S," or "x belongs to the set S.")

If x is not an element of the set S, we write $x \notin S$ (read, "x is not an element of the set S," or "x is not a member of the set S," or "*x* does not belong to the set *S*.") For example, let *N* be the set of positive integers (natural numbers). Then, 15 ∊ *N*, π ∉ *N*.

2. Equality of Sets

Two sets are equal if and only if they have the same elements. Thus, if every element of a set *A* is also an element of a set *B* *and* if every element of *B* is also an element of *A*, we say that sets *A* and *B* are equal and write *A* = *B*. Note that, to prove *A* = *B*, we must show that if *x* ∊ *A* then *x* ∊ *B* *and* if *x* ∊ *B* then *x* ∊ *A*. Also, to prove *A* ≠ *B*, we must exhibit an *x* which is an element of one of the sets but is not an element of the other. A set, then, is completely determined by its members.

3. Designating Sets

We will often describe a set by enclosing within braces the names of its members separated by commas. For example, {1, 2, 3} denotes the set whose members are the first three positive integers. Note that, by definition of equality of sets,
$$\{1, \ 2, \ 3\} = \{1, \ 3, \ 2\}$$
since the order in which the members appear is of no importance, and
$$\{1, \ 2, \ 3\} = \{1, \ 2, \ 2, \ 3\}$$
since an object is either an element of a set or it is not, and we do not count a member of a set more than once.

This method of describing a set is called the *roster* notation and is convenient for finite sets having a small number of elements.

For infinite sets or finite sets having a large number of elements, a notation (sometimes called *set-builder* notation), described as follows, is used. A rule is constructed which can be used to determine whether or not any given object is a member of the set or not. For example, a rule determining the set of positive integers might be: "An object is an element of the set if and only if the object is an integer and the object is greater than zero." Then, replacing the words "the object" by some symbol, say *X*, we obtain a formula in *X*, "*X* is an integer and *X* > 0." Now we designate the set by:
$$\{X \mid X \text{ is an integer and } X > 0\}$$
read, "The set of all *X* such that *X* is an integer and *X* > 0." In general, then, given a formula in *X*, denoted by *f(X)*, we denote the set determined by that formula by {*X* | *f(X)*}, read "The set of all *X* such that *f(X)*." (Note that the vertical bar is read, "such that."

Note that the choice of symbol *X* is arbitrary and that for a given formula *f(X)*,

$$\{X \mid f(X)\} = \{Y \mid f(Y)\}$$
and the same set can be defined by more than one formula in X.
For example,
$$\{X \mid 0 < X < 5\} = \{X \mid X > 0 \text{ and } X^2 < 25\}$$
This notation can be used for finite or infinite sets.

Examples:
$\{X \mid X^2 = 4\} = \{2, -2\}$
$\{X \mid X \text{ is an integer and } 5 < X < 10\} = \{6, 7, 8, 9\}$
$\{X \mid X > 0\} = $ the set of positive real numbers
$\{X \mid X \geq 5 \text{ and } X \leq 5\} = \{5\}$
Note that $\{5\}$ *is a set* having exactly one member and is not the
same thing as the member, that is, $\{5\} \neq 5$.
$$\{X \mid X + 2 = 2\} = \{0\}$$

4. The Empty Set

It is evidently possible that, for some formulas in X, the sets so
defined will be found to have no members. For example,
$\{X \mid X > 3 \text{ and } X < 2\}$ obviously has no members. Such a set is
called an empty set. By definition of equality of sets, there is
only one set having no members; so we refer to it as *the* empty
set and denote it by $\emptyset$.

5. Inclusion; Subsets

Let A and B be sets. A is *included* in B, or A is a *subset* of B if
and only if every element of A is an element of B. In this case,
we write $A \subset B$, and read, "A is included in B" or "A is a subset
of B." For example, if $S = \{a, b, c\}$ and $T = \{a, b, c, d, e\}$, then
$S \subset T$ since every element of S is an element of T. We have immediately the following:

1. For any set A, $A \subset A$ since every member of any set is a
   member of itself.
2. For any set A, $\emptyset \subset A$, since every member of the empty set is
   a member of A. (There certainly are no members of $\emptyset$ which
   are not in A.) Hence, the empty set is a subset of any set.
3. If $A \subset B$ and $B \subset C$ then $A \subset C$. For, if every member of A
   is a member of B and every member of B is a member of C,
   then every member of A is a member of C.
4. $A \subset B$ and $B \subset A$ if and only if $A = B$. This is simply a different formulation of the definition of equality of sets.

Examples:

1. Let A be the set of integers and B be the set of even integers.
    Then $B \subset A$.
2. Let A = {1, 2, 3}. There are eight subsets of A:
    {1, 2, 3} {1, 2} {1, 3} {2, 3} {1} {2} {3} and $\emptyset$.

Note: If $S \subset T$ we sometimes say that T includes S or T contains S, and write $T \supset S$. We also call T a *superset* of A. Also if $S \subset T$ and $S \neq T$ we sometimes say that S is a *proper subset* of T or that S is properly contained in T. Thus, in the last example, there are seven proper subsets of A (namely, the last seven listed).

6. Operations on Sets $A \cap B$ $A \cup B$

Let A and B be sets. The *intersection* of A and B, written $A \cap B$ and read "A intersect B," is the set of all objects which are members of both A and of B.
Symbolically:

$$A \cap B = \{X \mid X \in A \text{ and } X \in B\}$$

Examples:

1. Let A = {1, 2, 3, 4} and B = {2, 4, 6, 8}. Then $A \cap B$ = {2, 4}.
2. Let B = {1, 2, 3} and B = {1, 2, 3, 4, 5}. Then $A \cap B$ = {1, 2, 3}.
3. Let A = {1, 2, 3} and B = {5, 10, 15}. Then $A \cap B$ = $\emptyset$.

Two sets S and T are called *mutually exclusive* sets or *disjoint* sets if and only if $S \cap T = \emptyset$.

For example, if A is the set of even integers and B is the set of odd integers, then $A \cap B = \emptyset$; so A and B are disjoint sets.

Let A and B be sets. The *union* of A and B, written $A \cup B$ and read "A union B," is the set of all objects which are members of A or of B (or both). Symbolically,

$$A \cup B = \{X \mid X \in A \text{ or } X \in B\}$$

The word "or" is used here in the inclusive sense, that is, it is used in the sense of "and/or."

Examples:

1. Let A = {1, 2, 3} and B = {2, 4, 6}. Then $A \cup B$ = {1, 2, 3, 4, 6}.
2. Let A = {1, 2, 3} and B = {1, 2, 3, 4, 5}. Then
    $A \cup B$ = {1, 2, 3, 4, 5}.
3. Let A = {1, 2, 3} and B = {5, 10, 15}. Then
    $A \cup B$ = {1, 2, 3, 5, 10, 15}.
4. Let A be the set of even integers and B be the set of odd integers. Then $A \cup B$ is the set of all integers.

In any particular discussion, all sets being considered may be subsets of some set called the universal set U for that discussion. For example, in any problem from elementary algebra, the universal set would probably be the set of real numbers. Then, if A is any set, the *complement* of A, denoted by A' and read "A complement," is the set of all members of the universe which are *not* members of A. Symbolically:

$$A' = \{X \mid X \in U \text{ and } X \notin A\}.$$

that which result in A

Examples:

1. Suppose U is the set of real numbers and $A = \{X \mid X < 3\}$.
   Then $A' = \{X \mid X \geq 3\}$.
2. Suppose $U = \{1, 2, 3, 4, 5, 6, 7, 8, 9, 10\}$ and $A = \{2, 4, 6\}$.
   Then $A' = \{1, 3, 5, 7, 8, 9, 10\}$.

7. Important Properties of Operations on Sets (Without Proofs)

1. $A \cup B = B \cup A$ commutativity of union
2. $A \cap B = B \cap A$ commutativity of intersection
3. $A \cup (B \cup C) = (A \cup B) \cup C$ associativity of union
4. $A \cap (B \cap C) = (A \cap B) \cap C$ associativity of intersection
5. $A \cap (B \cup C) = (A \cap B) \cup (A \cap C)$ distributive law of intersection over union
6. $A \cup (B \cap C) = (A \cup B) \cap (A \cup C)$ distributive law of union over intersection
7. $(A \cup B)' = A' \cap B'$ De Morgan's laws
8. $(A \cap B)' = A' \cup B'$

appendix b ANSWERS TO SELF-TEST QUESTIONS

Self-test I

1 (1) 10   (2) 6   (3) 4

2 (1) 120   (2) 80

3 (1) 0   (2) 0   (3) 100   (4) 1

4 (1) 10   (2) 4   (3) 6   (4) 8   (5) 2

5 (1) $\frac{60}{100}$ or $\frac{3}{5}$ or 0.6   (2) $\frac{250}{500}$ or $\frac{1}{2}$ or 0.5

6 0.53

Self-test II

1 (1) $\frac{15}{100}$ (2) $\frac{29}{100}$ (3) $\frac{10}{100}$ (4) $\frac{25}{100}$ (5) $\frac{13}{100}$ (6) $\frac{8}{100}$ (7) 1

2 $\{e_1,\ e_2,\ e_3,\ e_4,\ e_5,\ e_6\}$

3 (1) outcomes   (2) element   (3) sample space

4 (1) $e_1 \leftrightarrow HHH$ $e_5 \leftrightarrow HTT$
        $e_2 \leftrightarrow HHT$ $e_6 \leftrightarrow THT$
        $e_3 \leftrightarrow HTH$ $e_7 \leftrightarrow TTH$
        $e_4 \leftrightarrow THH$ $e_8 \leftrightarrow TTT$

Your order may be different.

(2) $\{e_1,\ e_2,\ e_3,\ e_4,\ e_5,\ e_6,\ e_7,\ e_8\}$

(3) $\{e_5, e_6, e_7, e_8\}$ Your answer depends upon the order in which you listed the outcomes in (1).

5 (1) $\{e_{18}, e_{23}, e_{24}, e_{28}, e_{29}, e_{30}, e_{33}, e_{34}, e_{35}, e_{36}\}$
(2) $\frac{10}{36}$ or $\frac{5}{18}$

Self-test III

1 (1) $\{e_1, e_2, e_3, e_4, e_5, e_6\}$ (2) $\{e_1, e_2, e_4, e_6\}$ (3) $\{e_3, e_5\}$
(4) 1

2 $1 - P(A')$

3 (1) $P(e_1) + P(e_2) + \cdots + P(e_6)$ must equal 1, but
$P(e_1) + P(e_2) + \cdots \quad P(e_6) = 1.2$. Something is wrong.
(2) Each $P(e_i)$ must be such that $0 \le P(e_i) \le 1$, but $P(e_4) = -0.2$.
Something is wrong.

4 (1) sample space   (2) probabilities   (3) subset
(4) probabilities

5 $S = \{e_1, e_2, e_3, e_4, e_5, e_6, e_7, e_8, e_9, e_{10}, e_{11}, e_{12}\}$ where

$e_1 \longleftrightarrow W_1 W_2$ $e_7 \longleftrightarrow W_3 W_1$
$e_2 \longleftrightarrow W_1 W_3$ $e_8 \longleftrightarrow W_3 W_2$
$e_3 \longleftrightarrow W_1 B$ $e_9 \longleftrightarrow W_3 B$
$e_4 \longleftrightarrow W_2 W_1$ $e_{10} \longleftrightarrow B W_1$
$e_5 \longleftrightarrow W_2 W_3$ $e_{11} \longleftrightarrow B W_2$
$e_6 \longleftrightarrow W_2 B$ $e_{12} \longleftrightarrow B W_3$

It is reasonable to assign $P(e_1) = P(e_2) = \cdots = P(e_{12}) = \frac{1}{12}$
$A = \{e_1, e_2, e_4, e_5, e_7, e_8\}$ $\therefore \ P(A) = \frac{1}{2}$

Self-test IV

1 $\{e_5, e_6\}$

2 (1) $\{e_{30}, e_{35}, e_{36}\}$
(2) $\{e_1, e_8, e_{15}, e_{22}, e_{29}, e_{36}\}$
(3) no, $e_{15} \notin A$ (4) yes, $e_{15} \in B$

3 (1) $\{e_1, e_2, e_3, e_4, e_5, e_6, e_7, e_8, e_9, e_{10}\}$
(2) $\{e_2, e_3, e_6, e_7, e_8\}$
(3) $\{e_6, e_7, e_9, e_{10}\}$
(4) $\{e_6, e_7\}$
(5) $\frac{2}{10}$ or $\frac{1}{5}$

4 (1) $\{e_1, e_2, e_3, e_4, e_5, e_6, e_7, e_8\}$
  (2) $\{e_3, e_4, e_5\}$
  (3) $\{e_7, e_8\}$
  (4) $\emptyset$
  (5) 0
  (6) mutually exclusive or dependent

5 (1) 45 (2) 35 (3) 55 (4) 30
  (5) 45 (6) 55 (7) 60 (8) 40

6 (1) $\frac{45}{100}$ or $\frac{9}{20}$ (2) $\frac{55}{100}$ or $\frac{11}{20}$ (3) $\frac{60}{100}$ or $\frac{3}{5}$ (4) $\frac{40}{100}$ or $\frac{2}{5}$
  (5) $\frac{35}{100}$ or $\frac{7}{20}$ (6) $\frac{10}{100}$ or $\frac{1}{10}$ (7) $\frac{25}{100}$ or $\frac{1}{4}$ (8) $\frac{30}{100}$ or $\frac{3}{10}$

7 (1) $\frac{35}{45}$ or $\frac{7}{9}$ (2) $\frac{25}{55}$ or $\frac{5}{11}$ (3) $\frac{10}{45}$ or $\frac{2}{9}$ (4) $\frac{30}{55}$ or $\frac{6}{11}$

8 $P(A \cap B) = P(A) \cdot P(B \mid A)$

9 $\frac{5}{33}$
  Solution:
  Let A = the event that the first ball is red.
  Let B = the event that the second ball is red.
  $P(A) = \frac{5}{12}$
  $P(B \mid A) = \frac{4}{11}$
  $P(A \cap B) = \frac{5}{\underset{3}{\cancel{12}}} \cdot \frac{\cancel{4}}{11} = \frac{5}{33}$

10 (1) $\{e_1, e_2, e_3, e_5\}$ (2) $\{e_1, e_2, e_4, e_6\}$
  (3) $\{e_1, e_3, e_4, e_7\}$ (4) $\{e_1\}$ (5) $\frac{1}{8}$

Self-test V

1 (1) dependent (2) independent

2 (1) $P(B) = \frac{2}{5}$ (2) $P(B \mid A) = \frac{2}{5}$ (3) independent $P(B) = P(B \mid A)$

3 (1) $P(B) = \frac{2}{5}$ (2) $P(B \mid A) = \frac{1}{2}$ (3) dependent $P(B) \neq P(B \mid A)$

4 (1) No, because if one red ball and one white ball were drawn on a single trial, then none of the outcomes has occurred.
  (2) No. *Any* trial of the experiment results in two events in the sample space. For instance:
  1. 1. If both are red, e_1 and e_3 occur.
     2. If both are white, e_2 and e_4 occur.
     3. If one is white and one is red, e_3 and e_4 occur.

5 $\frac{1}{5,356}$
  Solution:
  Let A be the event that the first card is an ace of hearts.
  Let B be the event that the second card is an ace of hearts.
  $P(A) = \frac{2}{104} = \frac{1}{52}$ $P(B \mid A) = \frac{1}{103}$ $P(A \cap B) = \frac{1}{52} \cdot \frac{1}{103} = \frac{1}{5,356}$

6 $\frac{1}{8}$

Solution:

Let A be the event that the first toss is a head.
Let B be the event that the second toss is a head.
Let C be the event that the third toss is a head.
$P(A \cap B \cap C) = P(A) \cdot P(B) \cdot P(C) = \frac{1}{2} \cdot \frac{1}{2} \cdot \frac{1}{2} = \frac{1}{8}$

7 $\frac{1}{190}$

Solution:

Let A be the event that the first bulb is defective.
Let B be the event that the second bulb is defective.
$P(A \cap B) = P(A) \cdot P(B \mid A) = \frac{2}{20} \cdot \frac{1}{19} = \frac{2}{380} = \frac{1}{190}$

Self-test VI

1 (1) $A \cup B$ (2) $A \cap B$

2 (1) $P(A \cap B) = P(A) \cdot P(B \mid A)$ or $P(A \cap B) = P(B) \cdot P(A \mid B)$
(2) $P(A \cup B) = P(A) + P(B) - P(A \cap B)$
or $P(A \cup B) = P(A) + P(B) - P(A) \cdot P(B \mid A)$
or $P(A \cup B) = P(A) + P(B) - P(B) \cdot P(A \mid B)$

3 (1) $A \cap B = \emptyset$ (2) $P(A \cap B) = 0$ (3) $P(A) + P(B)$

4 (1) $P(A \cap B \cap C \cap D) = P(A) \cdot P(B) \cdot P(C) \cdot P(D)$
(2) $P(A \cup B \cup C \cup D) = P(A) + P(B) + P(C) + P(D)$

5 (1) If we are given two events X and Y, and if we use the "exclusive or," we mean that X may occur, or that Y may occur, but both X and Y may not occur. It excludes the possibility of both X *and* Y.
(2) If we are given two events X and Y, and if we use the "inclusive or," we mean that X may occur, or that Y may occur, or that both X and Y may occur. It includes the possibility of both X *and* Y.
(3) inclusive

6 (1) $P(e_3) + P(e_4) + P(e_5) + P(e_6)$
(2) $P(e_6) + P(e_7) + P(e_{10}) + P(e_{11})$
(3) $P(e_3) + P(e_4) + P(e_5) + P(e_6) + P(e_6) + P(e_7) + P(e_{10}) + P(e_{11})$
(4) $P(e_3) + P(e_4) + P(e_5) + P(e_6) + P(e_7) + P(e_{10}) + P(e_{11})$

7 $\frac{5}{9}$

Solution:

Let A be the event that the ball from hat 1 is red.
Let B be the event that the ball from hat 2 is red.
Let C be the event that at least one ball is red.
Then $C = A \cup B$
$$\begin{aligned} P(C) &= P(A \cup B) \\ &= P(A) + P(B) - P(A \cap B) \\ &= P(A) + P(B) - P(A) \cdot P(B \mid A) \\ &= \tfrac{10}{30} + \tfrac{5}{15} - \tfrac{10}{30} \cdot \tfrac{5}{15} = \tfrac{5}{9} \end{aligned}$$

8 $\frac{9}{20}$

Solution: Suppose

A is the event that the coin turns up heads and a white ball is drawn.

B is the event that the coin turns up tails and a white ball is drawn.

C is the event that a white ball is drawn.

$P(C) = P(A \cup B) = P(A) + P(B) - P(A \cap B)$

$P(C) = \frac{1}{2} \cdot \frac{2}{5} + \frac{1}{2} \cdot \frac{1}{2} = \frac{1}{5} + \frac{1}{4} = \frac{9}{20}$

Self-test VII

1 0.3

2 *SSS   SSF*

   SFS   FSS

   SFF   FSF

   FFS   FFF

3 $P(SSS) = (0.7)^3$ $P(SSF) = (0.7)^2(0.3)$

   $P(SFS) = (0.7)^2(0.3)$ $P(FSS) = (0.7)^2(0.3)$

   $P(SFF) = (0.7)(0.3)^2$ $P(FSF) = (0.7)(0.3)^2$

   $P(FFS) = (0.7)(0.3)^2$ $P(FFF) = (0.3)^3$

4 (1) $(0.7)^3$ or 0.343   (3) $3(0.7)(0.3)^2$ or 0.189

   (2) $3(0.7)^2(0.3)$ or 0.441   (4) $(0.3)^3$ or 0.027

5 $P(1; 3, 0.8)$

6 the probability of getting exactly zero successes in three trials of an experiment where the probability of success on any given trial is p

7 (1) $\left(\frac{1}{6}\right)^3$ or $\frac{1}{216}$ (2) $3\left(\frac{1}{6}\right)^2\left(\frac{5}{6}\right)$ or $\frac{15}{216}$

   (3) $3\left(\frac{1}{6}\right)\left(\frac{5}{6}\right)^2$ or $\frac{75}{216}$ (4) $\left(\frac{5}{6}\right)^3$ or $\frac{125}{216}$

8 $\frac{7}{8}$

Solution:

$$P\left(1; 3, \frac{1}{2}\right) + P\left(2; 3, \frac{1}{2}\right) + P\left(3; 3, \frac{1}{2}\right)$$

$$= 3\left(\frac{1}{2}\right)\left(\frac{1}{2}\right)^2 + 3\left(\frac{1}{2}\right)^2\left(\frac{1}{2}\right) + \left(\frac{1}{2}\right)^3$$

$$= \frac{3}{8} + \frac{3}{8} + \frac{1}{8} = \frac{7}{8}$$

9 $\frac{15}{16}$ *Solution:* $1 - P\left(0; 4, \frac{1}{2}\right) = 1 - \left(\frac{1}{2}\right)^4 = \frac{16}{16} - \frac{1}{16} = \frac{15}{16}$

Self test VIII

1 (1) a set of elements listed in a straight line in a specific order
   (2) identical

2 (1) the number of permutations of three elements chosen from a set of five elements
   (2) $_5P_3 = 5 \cdot 4 \cdot 3 = 60$

3 (1) five factorial, $\quad 5 \cdot 4 \cdot 3 \cdot 2 \cdot 1$
   (2) n factorial, $\quad n(n-1)(n-2) \cdots 3 \cdot 2 \cdot 1$

4 (1) $6 \cdot 5 \cdot 4 \cdot 3 \cdot 2 \cdot 1 = 6!$
   (2) $100 \cdot 99 \cdot 98 \cdots 4 \cdot 3 \cdot 2 \cdot 1 = 100!$
   (3) $\dfrac{n!}{(n-k)!}$
   (4) $\dfrac{25!}{21!}$

5 $_6P_3 = 6 \cdot 5 \cdot 4 = 120 \quad$ or $\quad _6P_3 = \dfrac{6!}{(6-3)!} = \dfrac{6!}{3!}$

6 $_{10}P_2 = 10 \cdot 9 = 90 \quad$ or $\quad _{10}P_2 = \dfrac{10!}{(10-2)!} = \dfrac{10!}{8!}$

7 (1) set of elements listed in a straight line without regard to order
   (2) contain the same elements

8 (1) 123   124   134   234
   These, of course, could be listed in a different order.
   (2) 24

9 $\dbinom{52}{10} = \dfrac{52 \cdot 51 \cdot 50 \cdot 49 \cdot 48 \cdot 47 \cdot 46 \cdot 45 \cdot 44 \cdot 43}{10!}$

  or $\dbinom{52}{10} = \dfrac{52!}{10!\,42!}$

10 (1) 10
    (2) 8
    (3) 0.8
    (4) $P(8; 10, 0.8)$
    (5) $P(8; 10, 0.8) = \dbinom{10}{8}(0.8)^8(0.2)^2 = \dfrac{10!}{8!\,2!}(0.8)^8(0.2)^2$

  or $\quad P(8; 10, 0.8) = \dbinom{10}{8}(0.8)^8(0.2)^2$

$$= \frac{10 \cdot 9 \cdot 8 \cdot 7 \cdot 6 \cdot 5 \cdot 4 \cdot 3}{1 \cdot 2 \cdot 3 \cdot 4 \cdot 5 \cdot 6 \cdot 7 \cdot 8}(0.8)^8(0.2)^2$$

$$= 45(0.8)^8(0.2)^2$$

11 $\frac{3}{16}$ *Solution:* $P\left(4;\ 5,\ \frac{1}{2}\right) + P\left(5;\ 5,\ \frac{1}{2}\right)$

$$= \binom{5}{4}\left(\frac{1}{2}\right)^4\left(\frac{1}{2}\right) + \binom{5}{5}\left(\frac{1}{2}\right)^5$$

$$= \frac{5}{1}\ \frac{4}{2}\ \frac{3}{3}\ \frac{2}{4}\left(\frac{1}{2}\right)^5 + \left(\frac{1}{2}\right)^5$$

$$= 5\left(\frac{1}{2}\right)^5 + \left(\frac{1}{2}\right)^5$$

$$= 6\left(\frac{1}{2}\right)^5 = \frac{3}{16}$$

12 (1) $\left(\frac{2}{3}+\frac{1}{3}\right)^3 = \binom{3}{0}\left(\frac{2}{3}\right)^3 + \binom{3}{1}\left(\frac{2}{3}\right)^2\left(\frac{1}{3}\right) + \binom{3}{2}\left(\frac{2}{3}\right)\left(\frac{1}{3}\right)^2 + \binom{3}{3}\left(\frac{1}{3}\right)^3$

(2) $\binom{3}{2}\left(\frac{2}{3}\right)\left(\frac{1}{3}\right)^2$

Index   *Numbers following entries indicate frames.*

Panels

Panel 1

An experiment consists of tossing a pair of dice. (We might think of one die being red and the other blue for identification.) Then, for example, if the red die turned up 5 and the blue die turned up 2, we will identify this outcome by (5, 2). If the red die turns up 2 and the blue die 5, we will indicate this by (2, 5). Then, S contains 36 elements.

$$
\begin{array}{llllll}
e_1 \leftrightarrow (1,1) & e_2 \leftrightarrow (1,2) & e_3 \leftrightarrow (1,3) & e_4 \leftrightarrow (1,4) & e_5 \leftrightarrow (1,5) \\
e_6 \leftrightarrow (1,6) & e_7 \leftrightarrow (2,1) & e_8 \leftrightarrow (2,2) & e_9 \leftrightarrow (2,3) & e_{10} \leftrightarrow (2,4) \\
e_{11} \leftrightarrow (2,5) & e_{12} \leftrightarrow (2,6) & e_{13} \leftrightarrow (3,1) & e_{14} \leftrightarrow (3,2) & e_{15} \leftrightarrow (3,3) \\
e_{16} \leftrightarrow (3,4) & e_{17} \leftrightarrow (3,5) & e_{18} \leftrightarrow (3,6) & e_{19} \leftrightarrow (4,1) & e_{20} \leftrightarrow (4,2) \\
e_{21} \leftrightarrow (4,3) & e_{22} \leftrightarrow (4,4) & e_{23} \leftrightarrow (4,5) & e_{24} \leftrightarrow (4,6) & e_{25} \leftrightarrow (5,1) \\
e_{26} \leftrightarrow (5,2) & e_{27} \leftrightarrow (5,3) & e_{28} \leftrightarrow (5,4) & e_{29} \leftrightarrow (5,5) & e_{30} \leftrightarrow (5,6) \\
e_{31} \leftrightarrow (6,1) & e_{32} \leftrightarrow (6,2) & e_{33} \leftrightarrow (6,3) & e_{34} \leftrightarrow (6,4) & e_{35} \leftrightarrow (6,5) \\
e_{36} \leftrightarrow (6,6) & & & &
\end{array}
$$

Assuming that the dice are honest and that the toss is honest, it seems reasonable to assign equal probabilities to each element in S. Therefore, we let $P(e_1) = P(e_2) = \cdots = P(e_{36}) = \frac{1}{36}$.

Panel 2

If A and B are events in a sample space S, then

$P(A \cap B) = P(A) \cdot P(B \mid A)$
$P(A \cup B) = P(A) + P(B) - P(A \cap B)$

If A and B are mutually exclusive events, then
$P(A \cup B) = P(A) + P(B)$.

If A and B are independent events, then $P(A \cap B) = P(A) \cdot P(B)$.

(1) $\binom{n}{k} = \frac{{}_{n}P_{k}}{k!}$ (2) $\binom{n}{k} = \frac{n!}{k!(n-k)!}$

(Expressions 1 and 2 are equivalent.)

$P(x; n, p) = \binom{n}{x} (p)^{x} (1-p)^{n-x}$